VIBRATIONAL SPECTROSCOPY
OF PHASE TRANSITIONS

CONTRIBUTORS

W. BÜHRER

V. DVOŘÁK

Z. IQBAL

J. PETZELT

C. H. WANG

E. WEIDEKAMM

VIBRATIONAL SPECTROSCOPY OF PHASE TRANSITIONS

Edited by

ZAFAR IQBAL

Corporate Research Center
Allied Corporation
Morristown, New Jersey

FRANK J. OWENS

Energetic Materials Laboratories
AMCCOM
Dover, New Jersey

1984

ACADEMIC PRESS, INC.

(Harcourt Brace Jovanovich, Publishers)

Orlando   San Diego   New York   London
Toronto   Montreal   Sydney   Tokyo

PHYSICS

5 2 4 4 2 3 8 X

ACADEMIC PRESS, INC.
Orlando, Florida 32887

United Kingdom Edition published by
ACADEMIC PRESS, INC. (LONDON) LTD.
24/28 Oval Road, London NW1 7DX

Library of Congress Cataloging in Publication Data

Main entry under title:

Vibrational spectroscopy of phase transitions.

    Includes index.
    1. Phase transformations (Statistical physics)
2. Solid state physics.   3. Vibrational spectra.
I. Iqbal, Z. (Zafar) II. Owens, Frank J.
QC176.8.P45V53 1984   530.4'1   84-368
ISBN 0-12-373780-X (alk. paper)

PRINTED IN THE UNITED STATES OF AMERICA

84 85 86 87   9 8 7 6 5 4 3 2 1

Contents

1. **Basic Concepts and Recent Developments in the Study of Structural Phase Transitions**

   Z. Iqbal

2. **Infrared Spectroscopy of Structural Phase Transitions in Crystals**

   J. Petzelt and V. Dvořák

3. **Raman and Brillouin Scattering Spectroscopy of Phase Transitions in Solids**

   C. H. Wang

4. **Raman and Infrared Spectroscopy of Phase and Conformational Transitions in Biological Systems**

Z. Iqbal and E. Weidekamm

5. **Neutron Scattering Studies of Structural Phase Transitions**
W. Bührer and Z. Iqbal

List of Contributors

Numbers in parentheses indicate the pages on which the authors' contributions begin.

W. BÜHRER (271), Institut für Reaktortechnik, Swiss Federal Institute of Technology (ETH), Zurich, CH-5303 Würenlingen, Switzerland

V. DVOŘÁK (55), Institute of Physics, Czechoslovak Academy of Science, Na Slovance 2, Czechoslovakia

Z. IQBAL* (1, 209, 271), Institute of Inorganic Chemistry, University of Zurich, 8057 Zurich, Switzerland

J. PETZELT (55), Institute of Physics, Czechoslovak Academy of Science, Na Slovance 2, Czechoslovakia

C. H. WANG (153), Department of Chemistry, University of Utah, Salt Lake City, Utah 84112

E. WEIDEKAMM (209), F. Hoffmann-La Roche & Company Ltd., Biological Pharmaceutical Research Division, CH-4002 Basle, Switzerland

* Present address: Corporate Research Center, Allied Corporation, Morristown, New Jersey 07960.

Preface

Research in structural phase transitions (SPTs) has grown and matured during the past decade. This growth has slowed somewhat, but the process of maturing is by no means over. New areas such as quasi-low-dimensional, disordered, and biological systems, incommensurate phase transitions, and multicritical points have increasingly attracted attention. However, some aspects, such as the understanding of the dynamics of the central peak in the scattering spectrum near the critical point, still remain somewhat incomplete. The study of symmetry properties, the application of the Landau model and static renormalization group theory to critical effects, and the development of powerful experimental techniques to probe the dynamics at both a collective and a local level have been consolidated. A volume, *Magnetic Resonance of Phase Transitions,* co-edited by one of us (FJO), was published in 1979. It consists of seminal reviews of studies which focus on the local dynamics of phase transitions using magnetic resonance techniques. The vibrational spectroscopic techniques of neutron and light scattering and infrared spectroscopy have provided some of the most important and crucial information regarding the collective dynamics of systems undergoing SPTs. The experimental results and the theoretical understanding of these data have reached such a level that it is now appropriate to review the important results and assess the current status of this field.

Toward this end, established workers in this field were invited to write topical reviews involving the use of three major experimental methods of vibrational spectroscopy in the study of SPTs. The present volume, together with the one on magnetic resonance of phase transitions, should facilitate the more-established researchers in obtaining a comprehensive overview of the field and should provide to newer scientists and graduate students the material to solve remaining problems. It is inevitable that in a multiauthor volume, the style and taste will vary among chapters, particularly at the pedagogical level. We hope to compensate for this variability by the expertise reflected by the authors in their respective chapters.

In the introductory chapter the more general aspects of vibrational spectroscopy are considered, together with a discussion of the basic concepts of phase transitions and some selected examples of new developments. The next two chapters deal with infrared and light-scattering (Brillouin and Raman) studies of SPTs. The fourth chapter focuses on studies of phase transitions in biological fluids using Raman and infrared spectroscopic techniques, while the fifth chapter is concerned with recent developments in the study of SPTs using quasi-elastic and inelastic neutron scattering.

Although some aspects of phase transitions in magnetic and fluid systems are referred to — particularly in Chapter 1 and Chapter 4, which deals with transitions in fluids of biological molecules — the bulk of this book is concerned with SPTs in solids. It must be emphasized that the chapters can be read independently since they do not depend on material covered elsewhere in the book.

1

Basic Concepts and Recent Developments in the Study of Structural Phase Transitions

Z. IQBAL*

Institute of Inorganic Chemistry
University of Zürich, Zürich, Switzerland

I. INTRODUCTORY REMARKS

In this book we shall be concerned primarily with structural phase transitions (SPTs) occurring under near-equilibrium thermodynamic condi-

---

* Present address: Corporate Research Center, Allied Corporation, Morristown, New Jersey 07960.

1

tions. Nonequilibrium transitions in biological systems and cooperative conformational transitions in biopolymers and biomolecules have increasingly come under attention and will also be considered, although purely conformational transformations in a linear polymer cannot be regarded as a phase transition in the strict thermodynamic sense.

The change of structure at a phase transition in a solid can occur in two distinct ways. First, the change may be via atomic reconstruction to give a new ordered or disordered structure. An example of such a transition is the microcrystalline-to-amorphous transition in tetrahedrally bonded semiconductors (e.g., silicon), which will be briefly considered in this chapter in view of its increasing technological importance. Second, there are those transitions where a periodic lattice is distorted slightly without in any way disrupting the network linkage. This can occur under two limiting conditions:

(a)   as a result of small *displacements* in the lattice positions of atoms or molecular groupings and

(b)   as a result of *ordering* of atoms or molecular groupings.

In the case of (b), couplings occur in real systems leading to a displacive component. Purely displacive systems are also rare—particularly in the regime of criticality near the transition temperature T_c where the growth of correlations (cf. Section III) drives a cross-over from a displacive to an order–disorder regime. Except for Chapter 5 on biological systems, the bulk of the material covered in the following chapters will be concerned with SPTs of the second kind.

In what follows in this introductory chapter, we will attempt first a classification of SPTs of current interest and then proceed to a discussion of some of the basic concepts of SPTs, including some of the recent ideas via renormalization group theory (Wilson and Kogut, 1974), of critical phenomena in these and related systems. The latter section would essentially involve an updating of a recent discussion (Iqbal, 1979). The following part will be concerned with a short discussion and comparison of the basic principles and techniques of phonon (vibrational) spectroscopy. In the final section, selected new developments in the study of SPTs using vibrational spectroscopic techniques, pointing to new directions of research in this exciting area of physics and chemistry, will be summarized. It should also be mentioned that for pedagogical reasons—particularly in introducing the basic concepts of SPT-related phenomena—we will occasionally refer to the simple cases of phase transitions in fluid and magnetic systems.

II. CLASSIFICATION

Phase transitions, in general, are characterized by a quantity referred to as the order parameter $\eta(T)$, which decreases with increasing temperature and

TABLE I
CLASSIFICATION OF STRUCTURAL PHASE TRANSITIONS

Displacive	Ferrodistortive Antiferrodistortive Thermoelastic	Improper[a] Improper[a] Ferroelastic
Order–Disorder	H-tunneling Molecular reorientation[a]	
Electronic	Jahn–Teller (JT) Charge density wave (CDW)[a]	band JT

[a]Incommensurate or commensurate.

goes to zero at the transition temperature T_c (for further details, cf. Section III). The types of SPTs observed in crystals can be classified in accordance with the nature of the order parameter and the details of its interactions with macroscopic parameters such as strain.

In general, three limiting cases of SPTs are observed, namely; displacive, order–disorder, and electronic (see Table I). Displacive and order–disorder transitions involve order parameters which are primarily atomic, whereas electronically induced transitions involve an electron–lattice coupled order parameter.

The displacive and order–disorder limits can be distinguished in terms of a single-cell potential as shown in Fig. 1 for one spatial coordinate Q with an anharmonic potential of the form

$$V(Q) = aQ^2 + bQ^4 \tag{1.1}$$

with constants $a < 0$ and $b > 0$. Equation (1.1) corresponds to a double well potential with an energy difference ΔE between the two minima and the maximum. When $\Delta E \gg kT_c$ (where T_c is the transition temperature), the

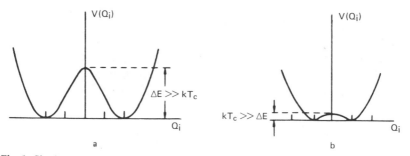

Fig. 1. Single cell potentials in (a) order–disorder and (b) displacive structural phase transition (from Müller, 1981).

phase transition would be associated with a dynamic ordering at one site or orientation, i.e., at one of the potential minima along Q. This would describe transitions in the order–disorder limit. Two types of ordering are usually found, as summarized in Table I:

(a) ordering of the H-atom positions as observed in hydrogen-bonded ferroelectrics, for example, potassium dihydrogen phosphate (KDP) and

(b) ordering of molecular or molecular–ionic orientations such as in sodium nitrite ($NaNO_2$).

In real systems at high temperature, the disordering motions are either large amplitude overdamped motions or *diffusive* relaxational modes, which couple, to first or higher order, with macroscopic parameters such as lattice strain components (cf. Section III.C).

When $\Delta E \ll kT_c$, a cooperative displacement of atoms along Q occurs with decreasing temperature. This describes the limiting case of a displacive type of SPT. Three types of displacive SPTs can occur as listed in Table I:

(a) ferrodistortive, involving displacements corresponding to an optic phonon of long wavelength ($K \sim 0$) and hence leading to a new phase without a change of the number of atoms or formula units in the primitive cell;

(b) antiferrodistortive, involving displacements corresponding to an optic phonon of short wavelength (zone boundary), giving rise to a phase consisting of nZ (where n is an even integer and Z is the number of atoms or formula units per primitive cell in the high-temperature phase) atoms or formula units in the primitive cell;

(c) thermoelastic, involving dislacements corresponding to an acoustic mode of long wavelength that can be represented by a macroscopic strain component.

Both (a) and (c) transition types can give rise to ferroelectric phases (the thermoelastic transitions are then referred to as ferroelastic) which involve the onset of a macroscopic polarization below the transition temperature. Examples of (a) and (b) occur in $BaTiO_3$ and $SrTiO_3$, respectively (see Gränicher and Müller, 1971; see also Iqbal, 1979), whereas the SPT in TeO_2 (Peercy and Fritz, 1974) is an example of a ferroelastic transition.

Molecular and molecular–ionic crystals have sizable order–disorder components even though many transitions in such systems fall in the displacive limit. Examples of such transitions in the displacive limit are observed in NaN_3 (Iqbal and Christoe, 1975; Raich and Hüller, 1979) and sym-triazine (Elliott and Iqbal, 1975; Rae, 1982; Raich and Bernstein, 1980). In these crystals rotational–(or reorientational–) translational coupling has been invoked to explain the nature of the transitions. Crystals such as KCN (Rowe *et al.,* 1978; Michel and Naudts, 1977a,b) are orientationally disordered in the upper temperature phases, but ordering leads to a displacive component via rotational–translational coupling. In such crystal systems, two regimes (one more displacive and the other more order–disorderlike) can be separated depending on the molecular–ionic rotational flipping rate λ. When $\lambda \gg \omega_0$, where ω_0 is the bare phonon frequency, the regime is largely displacive, whereas when $\lambda \ll \omega_0$, a largely order–disorder regime is prevalent (Rowe *et al.*, 1978). In chain-like systems, however, such as biphenyl and terphenyl, the order–disorder component becomes prominent with increasing chain length (Cailleau *et al.*, 1979; Girard *et al.*, 1978).

The third category of SPTs listed in Table I involves a degenerate, low energy electronic state as the primary order parameter. In Jahn–Teller (JT) systems, the phase transitions come about through the coupling of the electronic and the acoustic degrees of freedom. This can occur at a localized level involving, for example, $4f$ electrons in $TbVO_4$ or else at a delocalized level as in Nb_3Sn. The latter transitions are called band JT transitions.

In one- and two-dimensional metallic systems the conduction electron density can exhibit a periodic nonuniformity giving rise to a charge density wave (CDW). Representative examples of one- and two-dimensional systems are the charge transfer tetrathiofulvalene-tetracyanoquinodimethane (TTF-TCNQ) system and the layered transition metal selenide $NbSe_2$, respectively. In one-dimensional systems the interaction of the electrons with the lattice opens a gap at the Fermi-wave vector K_F, giving rise to an insulating state (Peierls, 1955 and Fig. 2).

Many SPTs are known which are characterized by an atomic or ionic displacement of wave vector K which is an irrational fraction of a basic lattice vector in reciprocal space (e.g., $\mathbf{a}^*$). A transition then occurs involving a

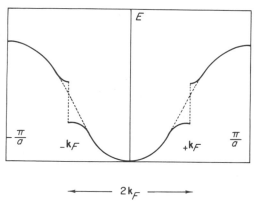

Fig. 2. Schematic representation of a Peierls transition for a half-filled band. An energy gap in E (**K**) opens up at $\pm \mathbf{K}_F$.

modulated wave that is incommensurate with the underlying lattice. Such transitions are referred to as incommensurate phase transitions and will be discussed in more detail in Section III. Incommensurate phases are more prevalent in low-dimensional metallic systems where the formation of a CDW is usually incommensurate with the underlying lattice.

Improper (also sometimes referred to as extrinsic) ferroelectric SPTs are transitions in which the macroscopic polarization is induced in the low temperature phase via higher order coupling with an order parameter whose symmetry differs from that of the polarization. All known examples of improper ferroelectric SPTs involve usually a degenerate (in the high temperature phase) order parameter with displacements corresponding to a zone boundary vibrational mode. A well-studied example of this type of transition is observed in gadolinium molybdate $Gd_2(MoO_4)_3$ (see Pytte, 1970; Dorner et al., 1972).

III. BASIC CONCEPTS AND RECENT THEORETICAL DEVELOPMENTS

In this section we will provide a survey of the basic ideas associated with the study of phase transitions (and in particular SPTs). Starting with the basic thermodynamic foundations, we will proceed to an examination of the microscopic theory and some details of critical phenomena in these systems. Finally, we will discuss the newly emerging ideas in the study of incommensurate phase transitions and in particular the concept of solitons, which is now being applied to various aspects of phase transition-related phenomena (see e.g., Bruce, 1978 and references therein).

A. Response Functions and the Order Parameter

Response functions are thermodynamic parameters that specify phase transition phenomena in the vicinity of the transition temperature T_c. We can start from the Gibbs free energy G, which describes the thermodynamic stability of a given phase and is given by the usual expression

$$G = U - TS + pV, \qquad (1.2)$$

where U, T, S, p, and V represent the internal energy, temperature, entropy, pressure, and volume, respectively, of the thermodynamic ensemble under consideration. The so-called order of a phase transition can be defined in terms of the partial derivative $(\delta G/\delta P)_T$. When $(\delta G/\delta P)_T$ changes continuously through T_c, the transition is second order. However, when $(\delta G/\delta P)_T$ is discontinuous near T_c the transition is first order. It is customary to represent the critical temperature that represents the thermodynamic stability limit of a particular phase by T_0. In the case of second-order phase transitions, therefore, $T_c = T_0$. However, for transitions which have appreciable first-order character, $T_0 > T_c$ and $T_0 - T_c$ represent the temperature range of thermal hysteresis.

The order parameter $\eta(T)$ of a phase transition is the crucial quantitative parameter of a system undergoing a phase transition. Generally, the order parameter is an observable, quantitative property of the system which *responds* to the external thermal (or some other proportional field such as the pH and relative humidity in biological systems, see Chapter 5) gradient and vanishes identically above the transition temperature. In many cases $\eta(T)$ is a relatively simple macroscopic parameter such as the magnetization (M) of a spin system undergoing a magnetic phase transition or the polarization (P) in the case of a ferroelectric phase transition. In the gas–liquid phase transition the order parameter is somewhat less obvious. It is given by the difference in density $\rho_L - \rho_G$ between the liquid (L) and gaseous (G) phases since as T approaches $T_c, \rho_L - \rho_G \rightarrow 0$. In SPTs, $\eta(T)$ measures the extent to which the atomic geometry in the less symmetrical low temperature phase differs from that of the more symmetrical high temperature phase. In SPTs approaching the order–disorder limit, $\eta(T)$ does indeed measure the degree of long-range ordering of atomic, ionic, or molecular entities, whereas in the displacive limit it measures the degree of small amplitude displacements of atoms or molecular groupings. The functional dependence of the order parameter with respect to a field variable such as the temperature (T) also characterizes the order of a phase transition. When $\eta(T)$ varies continuously to zero through $T_0 = T_c$, the transition is second order. However, when a discontinuous drop of $\eta(T)$ to zero at T_0 ($> T_c$) occurs, then the transition is first order (Fig. 3).

Important response functions of the order parameter that diverges at T_0, are the susceptibility (χ), and the constant field specific heat (C_H). The

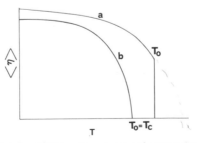

Fig. 3. Temperature behavior of the order parameter near a first- (curve *a*) and second- (curve *b*) order phase transition.

susceptibility for a magnetic transition is given by

$$\chi_M = (\delta M/\delta H)_T, \tag{1.3}$$

where M and H represent the magnetization and the magnetic field, respectively. The corresponding response function of a ferroelectric transition is

$$\chi_F = (\delta P/\delta E)_T, \tag{1.4}$$

where P and E are the macroscopic polarization and the applied electric field gradient, respectively. The susceptibility, therefore, corresponds to the *response* of a critical system variable to its conjugate field. The analogous response function in the fluid-to-gas phase transition is the isothermal compressibility (κ) which is given by

$$\kappa = (-1/V)(\delta V/\delta P)_T. \tag{1.5}$$

The constant field specific heat $C_{H'}$ represents the *response* of the heat content of a system (which is equal to the entropy S) to a temperature gradient and is given by

$$C_{H'} = T(\delta S/\delta T)_{H'}, \tag{1.6}$$

where the subscript H′ here refers to a general field parameter.

B. Landau's Theory of Phase Transitions

The starting point for a microscopic lattice dynamical theory of SPTs is based on Landau's description of second-order phase transitions (Landau and Lifshitz, 1959). Landau's model describes the stringent symmetry conditions under which an SPT occurs, where at every temperature and even at T_c ($= T_0$), only one phase is present. For first-order phase transitions, we recall that the order parameter *responds* discontinuously at T_0 ($> T_c$) and in practice, both phases can coexist around the transition temperature. The four conditions of Landau's theory can be discussed as follows:

Condition I. If a function $\rho_0(r)$ represents the density of electrons in the crystal and assumes the full symmetry of the underlying atomic lattice, then when the lattice changes slightly and continuously (second-order transition), the new density function $\rho(r)$ can be written as

$$\rho(r) = \rho_0(r) + \Delta\rho(r), \tag{1.7}$$

where $\Delta\rho(r)$ is the small change due to the lowered symmetry. Under conditions of Eq (1.7), Landau postulates that the symmetry group of $\rho(r)$ cannot have symmetry operations that do not exist for the symmetry group of $\rho_0(r)$. *Hence, the symmetry group of $\rho(r)$ (low temperature phase) must be a subgroup of that of $\rho_0(r)$ (high temperature phase).*

Condition II. If the function $\rho_0(r)$ can be expanded in terms of the irreducible representations of the symmetry group of the structure under consideration, then one can write

$$\Delta\rho(r) = \sum_{i,j} c_{ij}\phi_{ij}(r),\qquad(1.8)$$

where functions $\phi_{ij}(r)$ are the j-dimensional basis states for the ith irreducible representation. Landau then assumes that in a continuous phase transition, changes corresponding to two different representations will occur only by accident. Thus

$$\Delta\rho(r) = \sum c_{ij}\phi_{ij}(r),\qquad(1.9)$$

where the coefficients C_j are proportional to the order parameter $\eta(t)$. Hence, *a second-order phase transition can only involve a change of symmetry corresponding to a single irreducible representation, of the point group symmetry of the lattice.*

Condition III. Since the order parameter η, which is the amplitude of the distortion in the low temperature phase, is small in the vicinity of T_c, the free energy of the system can be expanded in powers of η as follows:

$$G = G_0 + \tfrac{1}{2}A\eta^2 + \tfrac{1}{3}Bf_3\eta^3 + \tfrac{1}{4}Cf_4\eta^4 + \cdots,\qquad(1.10)$$

where $G_0, A, B, C, \ldots$, are temperature-dependent coefficients and the f_m are homogeneous polynomials of order m in ζ_i which remain invariant under the operations of the high temperature space group. The ζ_i can be defined as

$$C_j = \eta\zeta_i \qquad (\text{with } \sum_i \zeta_i^2 = 1)\qquad(1.11)$$

and according to Eq. (1.9) represents the symmetry properties of the distorted phase. If the symmetry properties of the low temperature (distorted) phase are known, Eq. (1.10) can be written in terms of η only as

$$G = G_0 + \tfrac{1}{2}A\eta^2 + \tfrac{1}{3}B'\eta^3 + \tfrac{1}{4}C'\eta^4.\qquad(1.12)$$

The conditions for the stability of the system — in this instance that of a particular lattice configuration — are

$$\delta G/\delta\eta = 0 \qquad \text{and} \qquad \delta^2 G/\delta\eta^2 > 0.\qquad(1.13)$$

Applying the conditions of Eq. (1.13) to expression (1.12), Landau has shown that a second-order transition would occur at T_c when

(a) $A(T_c) = 0$,
(b) $B'(T_c) = 0$,

and

(c) $C'(T_c) > 0$.

Stipulation (a) simply expresses the fact that the transition is triggered by a change of sign of coefficient A, while (c) guarantees the stability of the distorted phase at finite values of η. Stipulation (b) is more general, stating that *the third-order coefficient in the free energy for a second-order transition vanishes accidentally at* T_c *or identically by symmetry*. The first situation may arise as a result, for example, of applied pressure and corresponds to an isolated point — a tricritical point — in the (p, T) phase diagram. The second situation implies that there are no third-order invariant polynomials [f_3 in Eq. (1.10)] or they vanish for the particular symmetry of the low temperature phase.

Condition IV. For a transition to be second order only such values of the wave vector K, *characterizing the basis functions* ϕ_j *in Eq. (1.9), are allowed which are simple (rational) fractions of a reciprocal lattice vector of the high temperature phase*. This condition obviously makes the transition to a modulated incommensurate phase a special case (cf. discussion in Section III.E).

C. Microscopic Soft-Mode Theory

Landau's model, which has been outlined, is essentially a macroscopic, thermodynamic approach to structural phase transitions in general, which was extended to ferroelectrics by Devonshire (1949). However, a critical new approach from the lattice-dynamical point of view was proposed independently by Cochran (1959) and Anderson (1960). This approach, which was formulated within the framework of harmonic or nearly harmonic lattice dynamics, was tested out in the decade between the late 1960s and 1970s, by the then emerging technique of neutron inelastic scattering and the revitalized (by the laser and electronic technology) techniques of Raman, Brillouin, and infrared spectroscopy. As the experimental results started coming in, and novel, more exotic materials were examined, it became increasingly necessary to modify the original model in terms of anharmonic lattice dynamics (Cowley, 1963 and 1977) and coupled order parameters; and, in the 1970s, SPTs were also brought within the framework of critical phenomena (cf. Section III.D).

1. The Soft-Mode Concept

The basic Cochran–Anderson model follows from Landau's thermodynamic stability conditions stated in terms of Eqs. (1.12) and (1.13). From these equations and Landau's Condition III we can write

$$\delta G/\delta\eta = A\eta + C\eta^3 = 0. \tag{1.14}$$

Then

$$(A + C\eta^2) = 0 \quad \text{or} \quad \eta^2 = -A/C. \tag{1.15}$$

Since coefficient A can be written as

$$A = A_0(T - T_0), \tag{1.16}$$

where $T_0 = T_c$ for a second-order transition, we can write η as

$$\eta = \eta_0(T_0 - T)^{1/2} \tag{1.17}$$

assuming that coefficient C is temperature-independent.

The connection between a phonon frequency ω and the corresponding order parameter η follows from the equation of motion of a simple one-dimensional harmonic oscillator. This can be written as

$$m\omega^2 = \delta^2 G/\delta\eta^2, \tag{1.18}$$

where G is the oscillator potential and η corresponds to a small amplitude displacement. Since from Eq. (1.13) it follows that

$$\delta^2 G/\delta\eta^2 = A, \tag{1.19}$$

then from Eqs. (1.16) and (1.18) we have

$$\omega = \omega_0(T - T_0)^{1/2}. \tag{1.20}$$

Equation (1.20) defines the concept of a soft mode as a mode of vibration which goes to zero frequency at T_0. The low-temperature distorted structure can then be thought of as resulting from the condensation of the soft-mode eigenvector.

The temperature dependences of the order parameter and the soft-mode frequency given by Eqs. (1.17) and (1.20) imply that the particles move in an average or mean field corresponding to the long-range forces implicit in Landau's theory. This assumption is basically incorrect in real systems, where near T_0 fluctuations of the order parameter lead to critical effects (see discussion in Section III.D).

It must also be pointed out that Eq. (1.20) describes the soft mode for purely displacive SPTs. Mode couplings and the onset of diffusive or relaxational modes occur for transitions of mixed character and those approaching the order–disorder limit. These aspects will be considered in the following discussions.

2. Lattice Dynamics of the Simple Soft Mode

Fröhlich (1949) was the first to state the correlation between lattice dynamics and ferroelectric SPTs. He pointed out that an anomaly in the lattice vibrational spectrum of a ferroelectric is implied by the Lyddane–Sachs–Teller (LST) relationship

$$\omega_{LO}^2/\omega_{TO}^2 = \epsilon(0)/\epsilon(\infty), \tag{1.21}$$

where ω_{LO} and ω_{TO} represent, respectively, the transverse and longitudinal optic modes of a cubic diatomic crystal and $\epsilon(0)$ and $\epsilon(\infty)$ are, respectively, the low- and high-frequency dielectric constants. Since $\epsilon(0)$ diverges at T_c for a ferroelectric SPT, it follows from Eq. (1.21) that $\omega_{TO}^2 \to 0$.

It was, however, Cochran (1959) and Anderson (1960) who, as mentioned earlier, formulated the soft-mode concept. Cochran (1959, 1969) then brought this concept within the framework of the harmonic lattice dynamics of dielectric crystals.

Assuming an ionic lattice where all positive and negative ions can be treated as point charges of magnitude $\pm Ze$, and $\epsilon(\infty)$ is taken as unity, ω_{TO} and ω_{LO} can be written as

$$m\omega_{TO}^2 = \beta - (Ze)^2/3V\epsilon(0), \tag{1.22a}$$

$$m\omega_{LO} = \beta + (2Ze)^2/3V\epsilon(0), \tag{1.22b}$$

where β represents the short range (SR) repulsive interaction and V the primitive unit cell volume. From Eqs. (1.22a) and (1.22b) it is evident that a cancellation of ω_{TO} but not of ω_{LO} can occur when the SR term β approaches the long-range (LR) Coulombic term $(Ze)^2/3V\epsilon(0)$ in Eq. (1.22a). Thus a soft TO phonon can exist leading to a phase transition. The eigenvector of such a mode for a ferrodistortive phase transition from a cubic high-temperature to a tetragonal low-temperature phase is shown in Fig. 4.

The soft mode for an antiferrodistortive transition such as that in SrTiO$_3$, involves a zone boundary ($K \frown 0$) phonon. The eigenvector of this mode in SrTiO$_3$ is depicted in Fig. 5 and corresponds to a triply degenerate (in the cubic high-temperature phase) mode corresponding to the R (zone boundary) point of the perovskite Brillouin zone (see Fig. 6). Lattice dynamics calculations for SrTiO$_3$ (Stirling, 1972) indicate a reversal of the signs of the

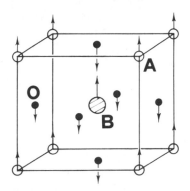

Fig. 4. Eigenvector of the ferrodistortive mode in a cubic ABO_3 lattice.

LR and SR interactions for the boundary compared to the zone center TO mode and hence one can write

$$\omega_s^2(\text{zone boundary}) \propto [\text{LR interaction}] - [\text{SR interaction}]. \quad (1.23)$$

In ideal cases the validity of Eqs. (1.22) and (1.23) can be tested by examining the hydrostatic pressure dependence of the soft-mode frequency and of T_c (Samara *et al.* 1975). With increasing compression the SR interaction terms which vary as $-r^{-n}$ (where r is an interatomic distance and n is a number >10) are more sensitive than the LR interaction terms which vary as $-r^{-3}$. Hence it is observed that T_c decreases and the soft-mode frequency for a particular temperature increases for a $K \rightarrow 0$ soft-mode driven ferrodistortive SPT; whereas the soft-mode frequency decreases and T_c increases for an antiferrodistortive SPT.

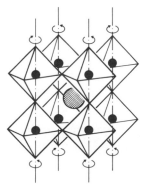

Fig. 5. Antiferrodistortive transition soft-mode eigenvector in ABO_3 perovskites. Oxygen ions are located at the corners of the octahedra (hatched circle represents A atom and filled circles represent the B atoms).

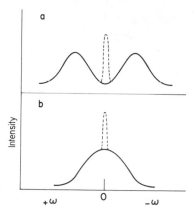

Fig. 6. Inelastic scattering intensity as a function of frequency (full lines) for (a) an underdamped oscillator response and (b) for an overdamped oscillator response. The broken curves show schematically the much narrower central peak (from Iqbal, 1979).

The lattice dynamical model of SPTs outlined above applies to transitions in the displacive limit and to largely ionic, insulating crystals. The microscopic driving force, however, is not specified. The possible existence of a low-frequency quasi-harmonic vibrational mode, which makes the lattice unstable with respect to displacements corresponding to the eigenvector of the low-frequency mode, is specified, however. Within this framework the origin of the temperature dependence of the mode can be obtained by including anharmonic phonon–phonon interactions (Cowley, 1963, 1970). Anharmonicity leads to a broadening of the response (decrease in phonon lifetime) and a shift Δ in frequency. The mode frequency is then given by

$$\omega_s^2 = \omega_{s(h)}^2 + \Delta, \tag{1.24}$$

where $\omega_{s(h)}$ is the so-called *bare* or purely harmonic frequency and Δ is proportional to the density of final states into which the phonon decays. In the case of decay into two phonons

$$\Delta = A(n_1 + n_2 + 1), \tag{1.25}$$

where A is a constant and the n_i's represent Bose factors ($= [\exp(h\omega_i/kT) - 1]^{-1}$). In the high-temperature limit where $kT \gg h\omega_i$, the Bose factors tend to $kT/h\omega_i$ and Eq (1.25) can be approximated as

$$\Delta \simeq A'T/\omega_0 = A'T. \tag{1.26}$$

A quasi-harmonic unstable phonon can be represented by a double well potential of the form given by Eq. (1) and depicted in Fig. 1. In the harmonic approximation, $\omega_{s(h)}^2$ is negative and can be written as

$$\omega_{s(h)}^2 = -a/m = -A'T_0, \tag{1.27}$$

where a is the constant from Eq. (1), m is the particle mass, and $T_0 = T_c$. From Eqs. (1.27) and (1.26), Eq. (1.24) can be written as

$$\omega_s^2 = -A'T_0 = A'T + A'(T - T_0). \tag{1.28}$$

Equation (1.28) is equivalent to Eq. (1.20) which describes the temperature dependence of the soft mode. However, it must now be noted that the soft-mode behavior has been derived from a more microscopic approach. In terms of the anharmonic model, mode softening to zero frequency occurs on approaching T_0, due to a temperature-induced renormalization of the soft-mode frequency. Quantitative calculations for a crystal undergoing a displacive SPT like $SrTiO_3$ show, however, that the contribution of anharmonic interactions are *not* strong (Cowley, 1977). It is the very large degree of cancellation in the harmonic frequencies [cf. Eqs. (1.22) and (1.23)] for particular modes which lead to rather low frequencies and hence make the contribution of the anharmonic interactions rather dramatic.

For SPT systems in the order–disorder limit the anharmonic contributions are large and the atomic displacements are sizable. Soft modes in such systems are not quantized small-amplitude displacement waves (phonons) but can be considered as pseudo-spin excitations by analogy with magnetism (Brout *et al.*, 1966). Two situations occur in such systems:

(i) the tunneling limit such as in potassium dihydrogen phosphate (KDP), where the tunneling probability of the order parameter—the H-atom positions—is large and

(ii) the relaxational mode limit such as in $NaNO_2$ and NH_4Br, where the order parameter fluctuations occur via diffusive Debye-like reorientational modes.

In (i) the pseudo-spin mode is quasi-resonant and appears, for example, in the light scattering spectrum as an overdamped quasi-elastic component. In contrast, the relaxational mode is observed as an $\omega = 0$ (elastic) component in a neutron or light scattering experiment. In such a system as $T \rightarrow T_0$, the relaxation time, which equals $1/\omega$ and is typically $\sim 10^{-9}$ sec, increases and then diverges at T_0 (if the transition is ideally second order).

3. Coupled Soft-Mode Models

a. The Central Peak

Riste *et al.* (1971) were the first to observe, using neutron scattering, that in $SrTiO_3$, the low-frequency response consisted of two components above

T_0. One was the inelastic component corresponding to the soft phonon and the other was a quasi-elastic component whose intensity grew rapidly as $T \rightarrow T_0$ and completely dominated the scattering close to T_0. The latter quasi-elastic component is now commonly referred to in the literature as the central peak and has been observed both in neutron and light scattering experiments in a wide variety of materials. The experiment also indicated that the central peak had a small but measurable width in wavevector but the energy width was extremely narrow—less than 5×10^9 Hz. Three kinds of theoretical models have been developed to explain the phenomenon of the central peak.

The first involves the use of anharmonic perturbation theory and invokes a coupling of the soft-mode to thermal relaxational processes (Cowley *et al.* 1971). At small K and low frequencies the decay processes are governed by thermal relaxations. When the soft-mode frequency ω_s is in the regime where $\omega_s \gg 1/\tau$ (τ is the relaxation time), the soft mode is collision-free (zero sound) and shows no interactive effects. However, when $\omega_s \ll 1/\tau$, the collision-dominated (first sound) regime sets in and the soft-mode transfers intensity to the thermal *bath*, resulting in the evolution of the central peak as $T \rightarrow T_0$ and remains at a finite frequency at T_0. Linear coupling can occur below T_0 when the SPT leads to a ferrodistorted (non-centric) phase. Above T_0 four-phonon coupling can occur when the crystal is centric (Silberglitt, 1972). In the case of noncentric crystals above T_0, coupling can occur to nonthermodynamic fluctuations of the phonon density (Cowley, 1977).

The second model involves an explanation in terms of either impurities (Halperin and Varma, 1976) or a surface effect (Darlington and O'Connor, 1976). In this picture a static central peak arises because of localized distortions into the low-temperature phase in the vicinity of the defects. A peak of dynamic origin can also occur if the impurities are allowed to hop between two equivalent sites—the width of the central peak is then related to the time between the hops.

The third model explains the central peak as an intrinsic phenomenon associated with the formation of clusters of the new phase in the old phase in the temperature region around T_0. Computer simulation studies (Schneider and Stoll, 1973) show that these clusters also occur in three dimensions. The central peak then is due to scattering by the relaxing domain walls or solitons (see Section III.E for more detailed discussion of the soliton concept) of these relatively long-lived clusters.

The experimental situation in a scattering experiment is shown schematically for an underdamped and a damped oscillator in Fig. 6, and the temperature dependence of the intensity of such a peak observed in lead germanate using light scattering is depicted in Fig. 7 (Lockwood *et al.*, 1976). Although the temperature dependence is in agreement qualitatively with anharmonic

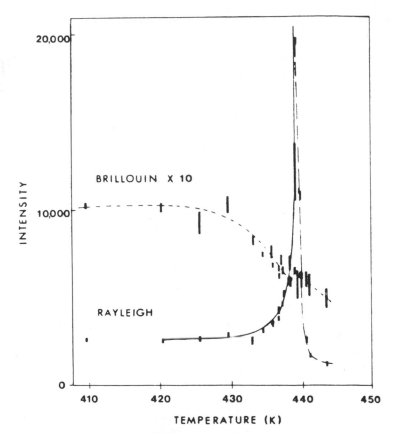

Fig. 7. Light scattering results showing the central (Rayleigh) and acoustic (Brillouin) peak intensities as a function of temperature for lead germanate. The solid line (————) is of the form $(T_c - T)^{-1}$ + const. (from Lockwood *et al.*, 1976).

models, the extremely narrow line-width observed ($< 2 \times 10^7$ Hz, Töpler *et al.*, 1977) is inconsistent with such models. Also the lifetimes of cluster relaxations derived from computer simulations are much shorter than the observed extremely long-lived central peak excitation. Only the dynamic defect model (Halperin and Varma, 1976) gives excitation lifetimes that are consistent with experiment. By now central peaks have been observed in a wide variety of SPTs and in materials ranging from insulators to metals, but a consistent theoretical model of the phenomenon is by no means available. It is also likely that there may not be a unique explanation for all the observed central peaks.

b. Coupling to Secondary Order Parameters

Coupling of the primary order parameter to a secondary order parameter occurs in a large number of materials leading to a rich variety of SPTs as shown in Table I.   Three kinds of coupled systems have been observed and investigated:

(i)   Antiferrodistortive *improper* SPTs (e.g., in $Gd_2(MoO_4)_3$), where the primary order parameter, corresponding to a mode at a zone boundary point, induces a net spontaneous polarization, which is the secondary order parameter (Cochran, 1971).

If η_x and η_y represent the displacements in an idealized two-dimensional diatomic lattice corresonding to the primary order parameter, and η_0 represents the secondary order parameter corresonding to a spontaneous polarization in the z direction, Cochran (1971) has shown, using a Landau-type free energy expansion in terms of the order parameters, that η and η_0 couple indirectly through the presence of two terms involving $\eta_x \eta_y \eta_s$ and $\eta_0 \eta_s$, where η_s is a shear strain (cf. also Pytte, 1970).

(ii)   Thermoelastic and Jahn–Teller transitions, involving the coupling of an optical phonon and/or electronic excitation with an acoustic phonon or strain displacement, which is the primary order parameter.

Three typical examples of such SPTs exist in the literature: paratellurite TeO_2, which undergoes an almost ideal second-order pure strain transition (Peercy and Fritz, 1974); Nb_3Sn, a high temperature superconductor, where the strain is coupled to optic phonon displacements that are in turn induced by electronic excitations (Shirane and Axe, 1971; Anderson and Blount, 1965; Labbé and Friedel, 1966); and $TbVO_4$, where the strain is coupled to a soft electronic excitation spin wave (Harley *et al.,* 1971).   Anderson and Blount (1965) were the first to realize that in terms of Landau's theory the shear strain displacements alone cannot lead to a phase transition because the contribution of pure strain to the free energy is rather small.   Hence the strain displacements must be driven by something else, which is then the secondary order parameter.   The pressure-induced SPT in TeO_2 from a tetragonal to an orthorhombic structure could be ideally strain-induced, but observed discontinuities in $d(ab)/dP$ and $d(a + b)/dP$ (where a and b are the orthorhombic cell dimensions which derive from the a axes of the tetragonal structure), and the anomalously large slope ratio of the measured soft-shear-mode elastic constant in the two phases necessitates the introduction of a secondary order parameter — a totally symmetric atomic displacement — to explain the results.

(iii)   Transitions, both in the displacive and order–disorder limit, observed in purely molecular and molecular-ionic systems involving coupling of the order parameter with molecular reorientational or librational modes.

These couplings are somewhat more complex than the ones we have considered, giving rise to a wide hierachy of SPTs which have increasingly come under scrutiny since the 1970s. The early models for these transitions were proposed for the molecular crystal chloranil by Chihara *et al.* (1973) and were extended to molecular-ionic crystals like NaN_3 by Iqbal and Christoe (1975). Since then more refined models, for transitions extending from the almost ideally distortive SPT in chloranil, to the intermediate order–disorder and displacive cases of NaN_3 and sym-triazine, to the largely order–disorder SPT in the ammonium halides (NH_4Cl and NH_4Br), have been proposed. The order parameter η for the SPT in chloranil can be considered to be a linear combination of molecular rotations about an axis perpendicular to the ring plane and about the $C = 0$ axis. This displacement corresponds to a one-dimensional representation of the space group at the zone boundary point at $(0, 0, \frac{1}{2})$. Probable couplings between the order parameter and the zone center strains can be written in terms of a coupling term $F_{e,\eta}$ as

$$F_{e,\eta} = -\tfrac{1}{2}(Ke_1 + Je_2 + Le_3 + Me_5^2 + Ne_4^2 + Pe_6^2)\eta^2, \qquad (1.29)$$

where e_i ($i = 1, \ldots , 6$) are the long wavelength strains and the quantities K to P are constants. On applying Landau's thermodynamic conditions to this coupling, step function anomalies are predicted in the elastic constants c_{11}, c_{22}, c_{33}, and c_{55}, and continuous changes of the slopes of the constants c_{44} and c_{66} and T_0. These anomalies have indeed been observed (Yoshihara *et al.*, 1983) supporting the view that the transition in chloranil basically involves some strain coupling to the order parameter.

The situation is reversed in sym-triazine, for example, where the order parameter is associated with a soft acoustic mode which couples with librational phonon excitations. Rae (1982) proposed a model based on the initial suggestion of Elliott and Iqbal (1975) and their temperature-dependent lattice-mode Raman data. It was assumed that the potential energy of the crystal could be expressed as a series expansion of the normal mode coordinates of the Raman-active and the soft-acoustic phonon modes, taking into account a coupling between the acoustic and optic modes. From this expansion, expressions for the frequencies of the four Raman-active modes in the low-temperature phase $\omega_I, \omega_{II}, \omega_{IV}$, and ω_V could be expressed as functions of the order parameter θ according to the following series of relations:

$$\begin{aligned}
\omega_I^2 &= \omega_0^2 + \alpha\theta + \beta_1\theta^2, \\
\omega_{II}^2 &= \omega_0^2 - \alpha\theta + \beta_2\theta^2, \\
\omega_{IV}^2 &= \omega_0'^2 + \alpha'\theta + \beta_1'\theta^2, \\
\omega_V^2 &= \omega_0'^2 - \alpha'\theta + \beta_2'\theta^2,
\end{aligned} \qquad (1.30)$$

where ω_0 and ω_0' are the Raman frequencies in the high-temperature phase, which together with the other coefficients α, β_1, β_2, β_1', and β_2' are assumed to be constant. The primary order parameter θ is taken to be the shear strain. The reasonably good fit of expressions of the form given by Eq. (1.30) to the data of Elliott and Iqbal (1975) shown in Figs. 8a and b as functions of θ and T, respectively, support the model of librational-acoustic phonon coupling for the phase transition in sym-triazine (see also Raich and Bernstein, 1980).

In the case of KCN and NH_4Br, however, it has been proposed that diffusive or relaxational reorientational motions of CN^- and NH_4^+ ions couple to elastic strains (Rowe et al., 1978; Michel and Naudts, 1977a,b; Yamada et al., 1974). In KCN, the CN^- ion relaxational flipping frequency, λ is large and $\gg \omega_0$, where ω_0 is the bare acoustic phonon frequency. Under these conditions the coupled mode model and the neutron scattering data indicate a displacive SPT where the acoustic phonon frequency softens and there is *no* scattering at $\hbar\omega = 0$. In NH_4Br (and the mixed crystal system

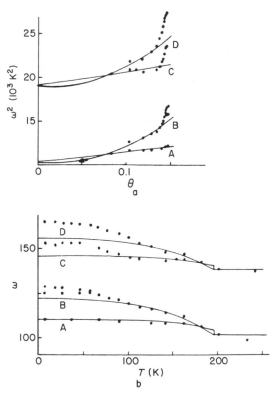

Fig. 8. Experimental ($\cdots$) (in energy units of K, where 1 cm^{-1} = 1.433 K) and theoretical (———) (calculated according to Eq. (1.30)) (a) ω^2 versus θ and (b) ω versus temperature (T) plots. A, B, C, and D correspond to Raman-active librational frequencies ω_I, ω_{II}, ω_{IV}, and ω_V in Eq. (1.29), taken from the data of Elliott and Iqbal (1975) (adapted from Rae, 1982).

$(KCN)_{0.25}$ $(KBr)_{0.75}$), λ is rather slow and $\ll \omega_0$. Here the model and the observed data indicate the absence of phonon softening (and hence an SPT in the order–disorder limit), but the appearance of scattering at $\hbar\omega = 0$. The enhanced scattering at $\hbar\omega = 0$ for relaxational order–disorder SPTs represents, as pointed out earlier (see Section III.C.2), the divergence of the relaxation time near T_0.

D. Critical Behavior and Renormalization Group Theory (RGT)

1. Definitions

Many physical systems undergo phase transitions which are characterized by a *critical point,* usually represented in terms of a temperature or pressure parameter. The critical temperature T_c, which is equal to T_0 for continuous transitions, defines the stability limit of a particular phase. In a fluid system, the vapor pressure curve terminates at a critical point (see Fig. 9a) in $P-T$ space, above which the distinction between gas and liquid disappears. Furthermore, a continuous transition from the liquid to the vapor phase can be achieved by following the dashed curve (---) in Fig. 9a. In a magnetic system the phase diagram terminating at a critical point can be schematically represented as shown in Fig. 9b. In such a system the critical point represents the stability limit of the ordered ferromagnetic (or antiferromagnetic) phase. In a system undergoing a structural phase transition, the critical point clearly represents the stability limit of the two phases concerned. Multicritical† points, such as bicritical and tricritical points, can also be

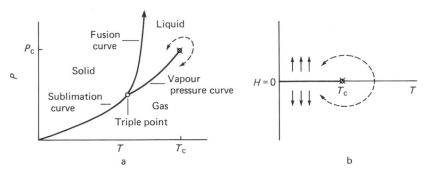

Fig. 9. Projection of the PVT surface in the PT plane of (a) a fluid and (b) the HMT surface in the HT plane of a magnet. See text for more details (from Stanley, 1971).

† The prefixes bi-, tri-, etc., associated with multicritical points represent the *number* of critical lines that meet at a particular point in a phase diagram.

identified in phase transition phenomena. For instance, a bicritical point is predicted in the phase diagram of $SrTiO_3$ with an applied stress in the [100] direction (cf. Fig. 10 and Aharony and Bruce, 1974). With the anisotropic stress $\sigma < 0$, pseudo-spin order is parallel to the [100] direction and one-dimensional Ising exponents (cf. following discussion) are expected. When $\sigma > 0$, pseudo-spin order is orthogonal to [100] and 2-dimensional XY exponents are predicted. The point on the pseudo-spin flop line where the XY and Ising curves meet represents a *bicritical point*. A *tricritical point* represents the point in, for example, temperature–pressure–electric field space (cf. Fig. 11) in KDP, where a line in the phase diagram corresponding to a first-order transition meets lines corresponding to a second-order transition. In other words, in temperature–pressure space the tricritical point is the stability limit of a first-order transition regime, that is, at $P \approx 2$ kbar and $T \approx 114$ K, the SPT in KDP crosses over to a second-order transition regime.

The behavior near the critical point of a system undergoing a phase transition is conveniently described in terms of quantities called *critical exponents*. Critical exponents express the temperaure dependence of macroscopic properties, such as the order parameter (η) and susceptibility (χ), and à critical macroscopic parameter such as the correlation length ξ (see definition), in terms of the extent to which the temperature of the system departs from T_c. The temperature, for convenience, is given in the form of a

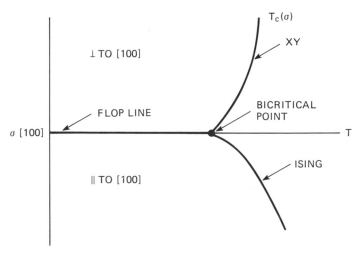

Fig. 10. Phase diagram of a perovskite crystal with stress applied in the [100] direction. For $\sigma < 0$ pseudo-spin order parameter is ∥ to [100] and Ising exponents are predicted. For $\sigma > 0$, the order is ⊥ to [100] and the exponents of the XY model are predicted. The flop line at $T = 0$ corresponds to a first-order transition (from Aharony and Bruce, 1974).

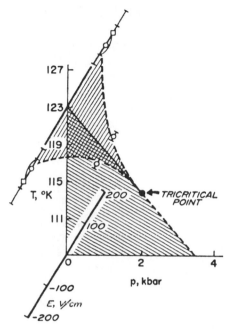

Fig. 11. Portion of the proposed phase diagram for KII_2PO_4 (KDP) showing critical field results. Second-order transition (---); first-order transition (———); first-order, para ↔ ferroelectric (///); and first-order, up domain ↔ down domain (\\\) (from Schmidt *et al.*, 1976).

reduced temperature $t = T-T_c/T_c$. All macroscopic properties are then either measured or calculated as a function of t raised to some power, which is defined to be the critical exponent for that property.

As stated previously critical phenomena occur in the vicinity of $T_c = T_0$ for continuous, second-order transitions. In the critical regime correlated fluctuations of the order parameter occur leading to a breakdown of the long-range, mean-field assumption of Landau's theory. Since the critical fluctuations are correlated, large-scale correlative effects such as anomalous critical scattering of light (the so-called critical opalescence of fluids near T_c), can be observed in this regime and is perhaps one of the most striking harbingers of the critical state. This phenomenon is quantified in terms of the *correlation function G(r)* which defines the extent to which the local particle parameters at a distince r apart are correlated. The range of $G(r)$, which is approximately the range of interaction between two particles of a critical system, is defined as the *correlation length* ξ. The Fourier transform of $G(r)$ defines the structure factor $S(k)$ that governs the scattering power of the medium. Near T_c, the divergence of $S(k)$ for $K \to 0$ gives rise to critical opalescence. Response functions of the order parameter such as the susceptibility also diverge near T_c.

Due to the presence of order parameter fluctuations which extend over large regions and cover very many particles, the details of interparticle interactions become irrelevant in the critical regime and hence a great deal of similarity is found in the critical behavior of widely diverse systems. This concept, which will be discussed in more detail with regard to RGT, has subtle physical, biological, and even philosophical implications, and is referred to as the principle of *universality* (Kadanoff, 1976).

2. Theoretical Models of Critical Behavior

The theoretical problem of describing critical phenomena is to determine the values of the critical exponents in terms of a microscopic model. The earliest model of this type was introduced by van der Waals in 1873 as an explanation of phase transitions in fluids. This was followed by the theory of Weiss for magnetic transitions in 1907 and the general formulation proposed in 1937 by Landau (cf. Section III.B). In all of these theories the state of any selected particle is determined by the average properties of the material as a whole and hence, these theories are referred to as mean-field theories. The values and functional dependences of the critical exponents associated with the order parameter (β), susceptibility (γ), and correlation length (ν) for mean-field theories, are shown in Fig. 12a.

Mean-field theories are qualitatively successful in accounting for important features of phase transitions in systems with long-range forces. However, quantitative predictions are less satisfactory since the importance of short-range interactions, spatial dimensionality, and fluctuations in the regime of criticality are ignored. In 1926, Lenz and Ising constructed the first statistical model of a lattice system with short-range forces. This model, now referred to as the *Ising model,* invokes an array of up and down spins which can be *inserted* in a lattice of any dimensionality. The exact solution of the Ising model in a two-dimensional lattice was achieved by Onsager in 1944 — the values of the exponents β, γ, and ν together with the plots of the corresponding parameters versus the reduced temperature, t, are shown in Fig. 12b, clearly indicating deviations from the mean-field behavior. The three-dimensional Ising model, however, has defied solution until now. Other three-dimensional models — basically involving one-, two-, and three-component spins and referred to as the Ising, *XY,* and Heisenberg models, respectively — have therefore been proposed. Estimates of some of the critical exponents in these models are listed in Table II together with the corresponding mean-field values.

These models clearly show that the critical exponents depend on the range

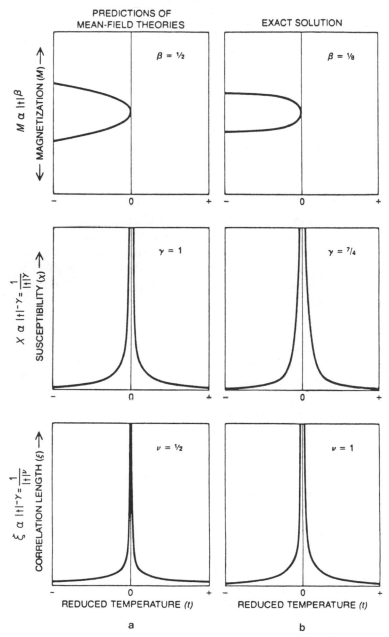

Fig. 12. Order parameter, susceptibility, and correlation length for (a) mean-field and (b) two-dimensional Ising models plotted against the reduced temperature. The critical exponents of these quantities are also indicated (from Wilson, 1979).

TABLE II
CRITICAL EXPONENTS IN FOUR THEORETICAL MODELS

Property	Exponent	Mean-field (any d)	LATTICE ($d = 3$)		
			Ising ($n = 1$)	XY ($n = 2$)	Heisenberg ($n = 3$)
Order parameter	β	0.5	0.325	0.346	0.365
Susceptibility	γ	1.0	1.240	1.316	1.387
Specific heat	α	0	0.110	-0.007	-0.115
Correlation length	ν	0.5	0.630	0.669	0.705

of the forces, the lattice dimensionality d, and the number of spin components or in other words the dimensionality n, of the order parameter. It is important to note that the range of forces determines the temperaure width of the critical regime (Ginzburg, 1960). The temperature width is inversely proportional to the range, and hence, in SPTs, solids such as molecular crystals with short-range forces should display wider critical regions than ionic crystals with long-range forces.

It should be pointed out that each of the last three columns in Table II represents what is called a *universality-class* that is defined only by the dimension of the lattice (d) and of the order parameter (n). The renormalization group theory (RGT) calculations show that parameters such as the structure of the lattice are irrelevant. Experimentally it is indeed found that a great variety of crystal structures in real ferromagnets all yield identical critical behavior, that is, the same values for the critical exponents. Furthermore, widely different systems such as fluids and magnets display similar critical behavior. This is consistent with the thermodynamic calculations of Lee and Yang (1952) which indicate that the ferromagnetic Ising model belonging to the universality class with $d = 3$ and $n = 1$ is ismorphous with the model of the gas–liquid transition.

The space or lattice dimensionality is seldom difficult to determine, but the dimensionality of the order parameter is sometimes less obvious. In the case of a fluid the order parameter is the difference in density between the fluid and vapor phases and is therefore a quantity which has only one magnitude and hence only one component ($n = 1$, therefore). In the case of a self-avoiding *random walk* model, it has been shown that $n = 0$ (Wilson, 1979). A random walk describes, for example, the folding in space of a long-chain polymer.

Near the critical point of a phase transition, fluctuations of the order parameter lead to a situation where events at many scales of length make contributions of *equal* importance. Kadanoff (1966) was the first to treat this problem in an essentially quantitative way. He reasoned that it should be possible to describe a spin system (e.g., the Ising model) on a scale coarser than a lattice spacing without affecting the character of the critical point anomalies. The averaging on a scale of L lattice spacings results in an *equivalent* system of block spins that interacts with the external field and with each other in a way which depends on the value of L. The new block system is, however, at a new effective distance from its critical point. This then leads to relationships between the anomalous free energies of what is effectively the same system at different distances from the critical point. This idea of scale transformations on a near-critical Hamiltonian inspired the development of a new and powerful theory—the RGT which was first applied to phase transitions by Wilson in 1971 (see Wilson's Nobel prize lecture in Wilson, 1983 for historical details and further references).

The RGT strategy is to tackle the problem in steps, one step for each length scale. This integrates out the fluctuations in sequence, starting with fluctations on an atomic scale and then moving to successively larger scales until fluctuations on all scales have been averaged out. The quantity $\mathcal{H}/k_B t$, where $\mathcal{H}$ is the Hamiltonian of the system, is examined after repeated changes of scale in a multi-dimensional parameter space. Critical $\mathcal{H}$'s move along a so-called *critical line* because the correlation length is infinite and hence it will remain unchanged under finite changes of scale. Non-critical $\mathcal{H}$'s, however, move away from the critical line because the correlation length decreases by L each time the length scale is increased by this factor. When continued application of the RG transformation leaves the critical $\mathcal{H}$ unchanged a *fixed point* corresponding to $T_c = T_0$ is reached. The RGT picture of universality is that all systems with critical $\mathcal{H}$ that move to the same fixed point belong to the same universality class, that is, they have the same critical exponents. When only short-range forces are involved, the universality class is solely determined by the dimensionality of the lattice and of the order parameter. In an RGT calculation the critical exponents are determined from the slope of the parameter surface near the fixed point. The slope near the fixed point determines the rate of change of the properties of the system as the temperature (or coupling strength) is varied over some narrow range around T_c. Since the critical exponents define the temperature dependence of particular properties of a critical system, it follows that the slope around T_c determines the critical exponents.

Integral values of the dimensionality parameters d and n have straightforward physical meanings. However, in RGT calculations d and n appear in equations where they can be allowed to vary continuously over some range. Plots of the critical exponents as continuous functions of d and n can therefore be made which indicate that when the spatial dimension d approaches a value of 4, the critical exponents approach the values given by mean-field theory. This brings us to the concept of *marginal* dimensionality (d^*) (see Als-Neilsen and Birgeneau, 1977) which defines the dividing point between mean-field and critical behavior for a system in terms of its spatial dimension. When $d > d^*$, the system exhibits mean-field behavior, whereas critical behavior occurs for $d < d^*$. When $d = d^*$, mean-field theory with only logarithmic correlations is applicable.

The dimensionality of space can be expressed as equal to $4 - \epsilon$, where ϵ is a small number equal to $d^* - d$. When $d = d^*$ the RGT equations are exact and we can make the so-called ϵ expansion (Wilson and Fischer, 1972). The critical exponents can then be determined as the sum of an infinite series of terms that include progressively higher powers of ϵ. The marginal dimensionality d^* can be estimated either from the geometry of the critical fluctuations and applying the Ginzburg criterion (Ginzburg, 1960) or more rigorously from RGT. For four systems:

(a)   a 2-dimensional Ising model represented by K_2CoF_4;
(b)   a 3-dimensional Ising model represented by β-brass;
(c)   a uniaxial, dipolar-coupled ferromagnet represented by $LiTbF_4$; and
(d)   a strain-induced SPT system represented by $PrAlO_3$; the values of d^*
are 4, 4, 3, and 2, respectively.

The squared order parameters of these systems are shown plotted against the reduced temperature t in Fig. 13. It is immediately obvious that when the system dimensionality $d > d^*$, Landau behavior is observed whereas substantial deviations occur when $d < d^*$.

3. Aspects of Critical Behavior in SPTs

RGT calculations suggest that coupling of the primary order parameter to anisotropic strains leads to a first-order transition (Bergman and Halperin, 1976). This situation may be applicable to most SPT systems and hence most SPTs probably have at least some first-order character. The experimental study of critical effects will therefore be dominated by the search for systems where couplings to strain are sufficiently small, so that second-order characteristics can be studied before the system is driven into the discontinuous first-order regime. Two such systems belonging to the ionic and molecular-type crystal types, which have been investigated extensively, are $SrTiO_3$ and $C_6Cl_4O_2$ (chloranil), respectively.

In $SrTiO_3$ the SPT at 108 K clearly shows a deviation of the critical exponent β from the mean-field value. Electron paramagnetic resonance (EPR) studies (Müller and Berlinger, 1971) of the static order parameter $\eta(T)$ give a value of the exponent $\beta = 0.33$ in the reduced temperature t

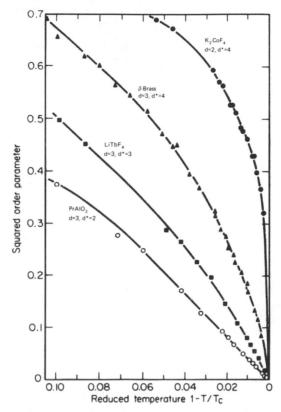

Fig. 13. Squared order parameter determined by neutron scattering for the four examples discussed in the text. When the marginal dimensionality $d^* \leqq d$, Landau behavior (with logarithmic corrections for $d = d^*$) is observed; for $d^* > d$, clear deviations from Landau mean-field behavior is observed (from Als-Nielsen and Birgeneau, 1977).

range between 0.06 and 0.002, which corresponds to that of the Ising model with $d = 3$ and $n = 1$ (see Table II). Other static parameters such as the correlation length show behavior consistent with that of the order parameter. Interestingly, however, the dynamic parameter ω_s, the Raman-active soft-mode frequency, gives an exponent equal to 0.33 in the critical regime as displayed together with the data of Müller and Berlinger (1971) in Fig. 14. In the mean-field limit, ω_s is known to follow the relation (Thomas and Müller, 1968)

$$\omega_s(T) \propto \langle \eta(T) \rangle \qquad \text{for} \qquad T < T_c, \qquad (1.31)$$

where from Landau's theory and the LST relationship (Eq. 1.21) ω_s is pro-

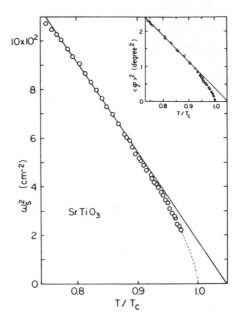

Fig. 14. Square of the A_{1g} soft-mode frequency in $SrTiO_3$ versus the reduced temperature. The plot of the square of the corresponding static order parameter versus the reduced temperature, from the EPR measurements of Müller and Berlinger (1971), is shown in the inset; (O) Fe^{3+}, (●) $Fe^{3+}-V_0$ (Steigmeier and Auderset, 1977).

portional to the (staggered) susceptibility χ^{-1}. Equation (1.31) is not necessarily applicable in the critical regime but its apparent applicability in the case of $SrTiO_3$ needs further investigation particularly with regard to the relationship between static and dynamic quantities in a phase transition. In the case of chloranil, neutron scattering studies (Ellenson and Kjems, 1977) also give a value of $\beta = 0.33 \pm 0.02$, but unlike $SrTiO_3$, ω_s evolves with a mean-field exponent.

For transitions which have an acoustic mode instability, RGT predicts that the critical behavior is always that described by mean-field theory (Cowley, 1976). Experimental results, particularly for sym-triazine (Rae, 1982), support this prediction. A symmetry nonbreaking type zero transition, according to Cowley (1976), can occur when one of the three independent elastic degrees of freedom that is not related to the acoustic modes, becomes critical. The critical region in such an SPT involves no microscopic critical fluctuations, and has been observed in KDP in the presence of an electric field in a Brillouin scattering experiment (Courtens *et al.*, 1979 and see Section V.A).

An interesting manifestation of criticality was recently revealed in an EPR experiment on monodomain transforming $SrTiO_3$ by Bruce *et al.* (1979). It was shown that with the onset of criticality, the growth of correlations drives a cross-over from a weakly anharmonic displacive regime to a strongly anharmonic *cluster-induced* order–disorder regime. In the order–disorder regime the ordering variable (e.g., a cluster-coordinate) diverges at T_0 to give the new phase.

E. Theory of Incommensurate Phases

Incommensurate SPTs are associated with a primary order parameter or distortion which corresponds to a wavevector that cannot be expressed as a (simple) rational fraction of a reciprocal lattice vector. The resulting incommensurate (INC) phase thus does not have strict translational symmetry and is hence not exactly crystalline. Typically, at sufficiently high temperatures the crystals are in a (dynamically) disordered phase. At a temperature T_i, a transition (which is usually second-order) to an INC phase occurs involving a soft mode of wavevector $\mathbf{K}_i$ (corresponding to an irrational fraction of the reciprocal lattice). Unlike usual commensurate phase transitions the frozen-in wave η_i varies smoothly with temperature starting from $\mathbf{K}_i(T_i) = \mathbf{K}_0$ and locks in at some rational fraction $\mathbf{K}_c$ of the reciprocal lattice to give a new commensurate phase.

A schematic phase diagram of such a system is shown in Fig. 15, where c represents a field potential parameter of the system. c may be thought of as controlling the location of the minimum in the dispersion curve of the soft mode. For example, when c is positive the minimum is at a special point in

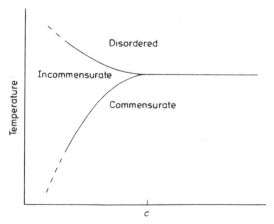

Fig. 15. Schematic phase diagram for a system undergoing an incommensurate phase transition (from Cowley and Bruce, 1978).

the Brillouin zone (say, the zone center) and hence transitions can only take place to a commensurate phase. However, when c is negative, a transition to an INC phase must occur first with decreasing temperature. The point dividing these two parts of the phase diagram is referred to as the *Lifshitz point*.

There are two regimes in the INC phase. Near T_i the distortion η_i has a sinusoidal profile as indicated by Fig. 16. Farther below and in the vicinity of T_c, higher harmonics with wavevectors $\pm n\mathbf{K}_i(T)$ evolve which sizably change the profile of η_i. In this regime nearly commensurate sinusoidal regions separated by narrow regions emerge where the phase of η_i rapidly changes with respect to the phase in the sinusoidal regions. The latter regions create domain walls or discommensurations (McMillan, 1976) and are a typical example of *phase solitons* (the term soliton being derived from *solitary traveling waves*). Further modulation via an inhomogeneous tensor quantity $\xi(\mathbf{K})$ (and the derivative $d\xi(\mathbf{K})/dx$, where x is the modulation

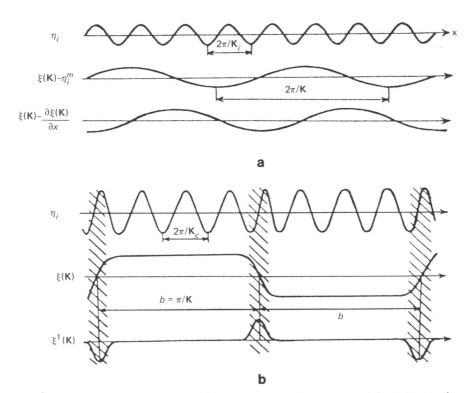

Fig. 16. Schematic representation of the spontaneous order parameter (η_i), tensor quantity $\xi(K)$ (discussed in the text), and $\delta\xi(\mathbf{K})/\delta X$, (a) near T_i and (b) near T_c (from Petzelt, 1981).

direction) which is proportional to η_i^m, also occurs as indicated in Fig. 16. The lattice dynamics situation in such a phase transition is displayed by the schematic sequence as a function of temperature and wavevector in Fig. 17. Of particular interest is the situation in the INC phase represented by Fig. 17c which shows the disperson curve splitting into an upper branch with ordinary soft-mode behavior and a lower branch whose frequency vanishes at K_c at all temperatures in the INC phase.   The former corresponds to a dynamic amplitude distortion in the order parameter, the *amplitudon,* while the latter describes a phase distortion and is referred to as the *phason.*

Quasi-one- and two-dimensional charge density wave (CDW) systems represent special cases involving a modulation of the electron charge density at the Fermi wavevector $K = 2K_F$ to form in most cases an incommensurate

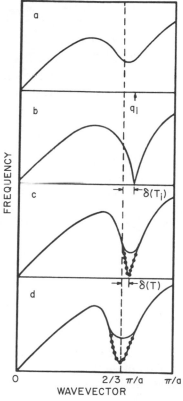

Fig. 17. Schematic behavior of the soft-mode branch (a) above $(T > T_i)$, (b) at $(T = T_i)$, and below the transition temperature T_i to the INC phase, (c) $T_{com} < T < T_i$ and (d) $T < T_{com}$. The amplitudon and phason components are indicated by the full curve and the filled circles, respectively (from Fleury and Lyons, 1981).

CDW, which couples with the lattice to produce a periodic distortion at the same wavevector. For one-dimensional systems this corresponds to a displacive Peierls transition to a CDW modulated INC or commensurate phase where gaps at the Fermi wavevectors $\pm K_F$ open up (cf. Fig 2) to produce an insulating state.

IV. BASIC CONCEPTS OF VIBRATIONAL SPECTROSCOPY

Three main experimental methods have been used over the past years to investigate the atomic dynamics of SPTs and related transitions, via a direct study of the atomic vibrational excitations or phonons and their anharmonic interactions and coupling to relaxational and electronic excitations. These spectroscopic methods are

   (i)   inelastic light scattering,
   (ii) inelastic neutron scattering, and
   (iii) infrared absorption and reflection.

Historically, the techniques of infrared and light scattering spectroscopy were developed in the 1930s, but it was during the last ten years that the use of the laser led to a renaissance in light scattering, while the ready availability of computers and recent developments in optical techniques stimulated the increasing application of Fourier transform methods in infrared spectroscopy. For obvious reasons inelastic neutron scattering came of age only in the early 1960s with new developments arising as a result of increasingly sophisticated electronic instrumentation, and more recently, with the use of pulsed neutron sources.

Traditionally, elastic scattering methods do not fall within the realm of the so-called vibrational spectroscopic techniques. However, in SPT research, elastic, and in particular quasi-elastic scattering experiments involving both neutrons and photons, have revealed new phenomena associated with phonon interactions in the critical regime and will, therefore, be referred to quite often in this book.

The experimental techniques will be treated in some detail in the various chapters. In this introductory chapter, however, we will attempt only a brief overview of each of the techniques and provide a comparison of the methods, to set the experimental aspect of the field in perspective for the researcher entering this area of SPT research. Instrumental details will not be considered — the reader is referred to the extensive literature in this field. The following books and articles provide details of the instrumental aspects: light scattering (Hayes and Loudon, 1978 and references therein), neutron scattering (Dorner and Comes, 1977), and infrared spectroscopy (Möller and Rothschild, 1971).

A. Light Scattering

In a idealized light-scattering experiment an incident-parallel beam of light from a laser source passes through a volume V of the solid—it is then scattered in all directions from the illuminated part of the sample and a detection system can be set up to examine this scattered radiation. The light scattering spectrum consists of three components:

(i) the Rayleigh or elastic scattering component from the essentially zero-frequency excitations in the solid;

(ii) the Brillouin scattering component, resulting from scattering by sound waves and occurring close to the frequency of the incident photons, with typical shifts ranging from ~ 1 cm^{-1} to smaller values; and

(iii) the Raman scattering component that is a result of scattering by the lattice and internal vibrations in crystals which range in frequency shift from 10 cm^{-1} to values as high as ~ 4000 cm^{-1}.

The basic mechanisms of Brillouin and Raman scattering are the same, as will be discussed. However, because the resolution requirements are different for the two components, spectral dispersion is performed via a double (or triple) grating monochromator for the Raman components, whereas the higher spectral dispersivity of an interferometer—usually a Fabry–Perot interferometer—is necessary for resolving the Brillouin spectrum. The inelastic Brillouin and Raman spectra are further subdived into Stokes (energy-loss) and anti-Stokes (energy-gain) components associated with the creation and annihilation of the excitation quanta.

The Rayleigh component in the scattering spectrum is the result of *nonpropagating* entropy fluctuations in the fluid state. These fluctuations propagate in the super-fluid and solid He phase to give rise to what is called second sound. In crystals undergoing SPTs the largest contribution to the Rayleigh scattering intensity can come from effects like the central peak discussed in Section III.C.3 and other parts of this book. The Brillouin–Stokes and anti-Stokes doublet symmetrically located about the unshifted line occurs as a result of the modulation due the compressional sound wave propagating through a fluid and Bragg-type reflection by propagating sound waves in a solid. Crystals are less optically perfect than fluids and studies of Rayleigh and Brillouin scattering are therefore limited by the occurrence of relatively strong scattering at the position of the Rayleigh peak from static crystallographic defects. The use of an I_2-vapor absorption filter coupled with single-moded laser excitation has been used extensively in recent years to overcome this problem.

In the solid state, the condition of Bragg-like scattering is given by

$$\lambda_1 = 2\Lambda \sin \phi/2, \tag{1.32}$$

where λ_1 is the wavelength of the light in the medium, Λ is the wavelength of the propagating sound wave, and ϕ is the scattering angle. Brillouin scattering components are then a result of a Doppler shift $\Delta\omega_B$ caused by the movement of the atomic grating via sound wave propagation. $\Delta\omega_B$ is then given by

$$\Delta\omega_B = \pm 2vn_1\mathbf{K}_0 \sin \phi/2, \tag{1.33}$$

where v is the phase velocity of the sound waves, n_1 is the refractive index of the medium, and $\mathbf{K}_0$ is the incident light wavevector. Combining Eqs. (1.32) and (1.33) indicates that

$$\Delta\omega = \pm\omega, \tag{1.34}$$

where ω is the angular frequency of the sound wave causing the scattering. Two Doppler-shifted Brillouin components of *equal* intensity therefore occur (this is in contrast to the Stokes and anti-Stokes–Raman components; see discussion below), where ω corresponds to $\mathbf{K} = 0$ acoustic phonons when the incident wavelength corresponds to a few 10^3 Å (typically 5×10^3 Å) which is three orders of magnitude greater than the unit spacing of the atomic grating (typically a few angstroms). The $\mathbf{K} = 0$ acoustic phonons have zero frequencies, behave like sound waves in a continuous medium, and their symmetries are the same as the three components of a polar tensor.

In a Brillouin experiment the sound velocities are measured assuming the refractive index to be known and the elastic constants are then calculated. In piezoelectric crystals like KDP the electric polarization associated with long-wavelength acoustic vibrations have to be taken into account. Further details are beyond the scope of this chapter and the reader is referred to Hayes and Loudon (1978) for detailed considerations via elasticity theory.

Raman scattering is associated with inelastic scattering involving the creation or annihilation of optical phonons (and related excitations) in a solid. If the electronic polarizability α_{ij} can be expanded in normal modes of the crystal, one can write

$$\alpha_{ij} = \alpha_{ij}(0) + \sum_\lambda (\alpha_{ij,\lambda})Q_\lambda + \ldots, \tag{1.35}$$

where Q_λ is a mode of standing wave form. When the polarizability modulation by Q_λ given by the second term in Eq. (1.33) is nonzero, scattered components at frequencies $\omega_0 \pm \omega_\lambda$ and propagation vectors $\mathbf{K}_0 \pm \mathbf{K}$ are observed, where ω_0 and $\mathbf{K}_0$ correspond to the frequency and wavevector of the incident wave. Since the incident wavelength in a normal Raman experiment using laser excitation in the visible and near ultraviolet (UV) region, is three orders of magnitude greater than the atomic spacing, only long-wavelength or $\mathbf{K} = 0$ optical vibrations are excited in first-order Raman scattering.

The intensity of the scattered light I is proportional to the polarization P and the relations can be written as (Placzek, 1934)

$$I_j \propto P_j^2 \propto E_i^2 |\alpha_{ij,\lambda}|^2 Q_\lambda^{02}, \tag{1.36}$$

where E_i is the electric field associated with the incident light wave and Q_λ^0 is the phonon amplitude given by

$$m_\lambda \omega_\lambda^2 Q_\lambda^{02} = \hbar \omega_\lambda (\bar{n} + 1) \tag{1.37}$$

for Stokes scattering. Here m_λ is the effective mass of the phonon and $\bar{n}$ is the Bose–Einstein factor $(=[\exp(\hbar\omega_\lambda/k_B T) - 1]^{-1})$. For anti-Stokes scattering

$$2m_\lambda \omega_\lambda^2 Q_\lambda^{02} = \hbar \omega_\lambda \cdot \bar{n}. \tag{1.38}$$

Hence the ratio of the intensities of Stokes to anti-Stokes scattering are *unequal* and is given by $\exp(-\hbar\omega_\lambda/k_B T)$: the Boltzman factor.

Generally α_{ij} is a tensor and hence, in a Raman scattering experiment using an oriented single crystal, different elements of the tensors from the different symmetry modes can be measured (cf. Loudon, 1964 for details and tables). Raman line-shapes are usually Lorentzian in the under-damped and weakly damped regimes. However, near SPTs the phonon may become over-damped and when $\Gamma \gg \omega_\lambda$ (where Γ is the damping rate and equal to the inverse lifetime of the oscillator), the Raman response approaches that of a relaxational process.

The model applies when the excitation frequency ω_0 is well removed in energy from that of the lowest lying ground electronic state of the crystal. When ω_0 approaches the energy of an electronic state, however, the Raman cross section is enhanced via resonance interaction with the electronic state — the process is then referred to as resonance Raman scattering (RRS). An interesting giant enhancement of the Raman cross section (of the order of $10^5 - 10^6$) occurs for surface layers of organic molecules deposited on *roughened* surfaces of metals like silver and gold. It is now referred to in the literature as surface enhanced Raman scattering (SERS). A complete understanding of the effect has not been achieved but recent experiments have suggested that long-range electromagnetic effects (possibly involving the plasmon excitations of the substrate metal) are responsible for the surface enhancement (see Burstein *et al.*, 1979). SERS has potential applications in the study of surfaces and, therefore, two-dimensional phase transitions in thin layers can, in principle, be studied by this method. However, SERS has been applied till now in SPT research, only to the study of biological fluids (cf. Iqbal and Weidekamm, Chapter 4). RRS has found widespread application in the study of conformational transitions in biological fluids (see Chapter 4) and electronically induced transitions in polymers like the polydiacetylenes (see Iqbal *et al.*, 1977).

B. Infrared Absorption and Reflection

A normal mode of vibration (of long-wavelength and hence $\mathbf{K} = 0$) in a crystal gives rise to resonance absorption of radiation in the infrared spectral range if the mode displacements generate a finite dipole fluctuation. In crystalline solids the absorption of IR radiation is so strong that it is usually difficult to obtain sufficiently thin samples to make quantitative measurements. It is therefore mostly necessary to measure the samples in reflection.

In a reflection experiment the dielectric constant ϵ^* is described in terms of a real and an imaginary component $\epsilon_1 + i\epsilon_2$, describing the amplitude and phase of the reflected light. The real and imaginary parts of ϵ^* are related via the Kramer–Kronig (K–K) relationship and we obtain, in principle, the same information from a K–K analysis of the reflection spectrum, as from an absorption measurement. However, severe approximations have to be made since the K–K analysis requires the measurement to extend over the *entire* range of frequencies, which of course is not experimentally feasible. These approximations include the extrapolation of the low frequency portion of the data and the assumption of a negligible contribution from the high frequency portion of the data. The former approximation is particularly severe in SPT systems where extremely low frequency soft modes are involved.

The development of Fourier transform (FT) interferometric spectroscopy — particularly the development which allows *dispersive* FT spectroscopy (cf. Griffiths, 1975)—provided a more direct and quantitative method of analyzing reflection spectra. Dispersive FT spectroscopy involves the use of a Michelson interferometer with the stationary mirror replaced by the reflecting sample. Because the technique is interferometric, the phase information is not lost and is contained in the phase of the Fourier transform (for further details see Griffiths, 1975).

FT interferometric spectroscopy is now also used in absorption studies, but apart from the speed of measurement and signal-to-noise improvement — particularly in the far infrared region — the FT method has no remarkable advantage over the more conventional dispersion by means of gratings. It must also be pointed out that absorption measurements are more direct and simple when the samples are available only as powders (using the alkali halide disk technique) or as thin films.

C. Neutron Scattering

Neutron scattering involves the interaction of neutrons directly with the nuclei of the atoms. The wavelength and energy of thermal neutrons with $\lambda = 1.8$ Å and $\hbar\nu = 25$ meV are comparable with atomic distances and phonon energies in solids and thus neutron inelastic scattering is a unique tool for studying phonon correlations in both energy and momentum space. Most experimental results have been obtained using three-axis spectrometers consisting of a monochromator, analyzer, and detector sequence (see Currat and Pynn, 1979).

The monoenergetic neutron beam from the monochromatizing single crystal hits the single crystal sample and then the intensity of the scattered neutrons is recorded as a function of the sample orientation angle ϕ, scattering angle ψ (defined as the angle between the propagating vector of the incident beam and the axis of the analyzer), and the scattered neutron energy. In the case of *coherent* neutron inelastic scattering, momentum is explicitly conserved, that is, the total momentum imparted to the crystal $\hbar K'$ equals the phonon momentum, $\hbar K$, plus a reciprocal lattice vector $2\pi G$. The power of the technique lies in the fact that with a single crystal K', K, and G can be so aligned that a resonance in the cross section represents a measurement of $\omega_j(K)$ and K simultaneously. However, if the scattering nucleus possesses a nonzero spin, the neutron–nucleus interaction is dependent on the relative orientation of the neutron and nucleus spins in the course of the scattering process and the scattering is *incoherent*. Hydrogen is the most important example of an incoherently scattering nucleus — most other nuclei of interest are coherent scatters. Incoherent neutron scattering does not contain a momentum conservation term and therefore is of limited interest in the more classical SPT studies. However, the incoherent structure factor (from quasi-elastic scattering data) is important in the determination of molecular reorientational rates in molecular-type crystals (Dorner, 1981).

The measured scattered intensity is a folding of the scattering function $S(K,\omega)$ with the resolution or transmission function of the spectrometer. Diffuse scattering around a Bragg reflection allows measurements of effects such as the central peak (cf. Section III.C) to be made. Furthermore, intensities of an evolving Bragg reflection can be used as a direct measure of the order parameter.

An additional feature of neutron scattering is that the neutron *sees,* in addition to the geometrical distribution of the nuclei, the distribution of the electronic magnetization of a lattice. Thus magnetic phase transitions — only referred to occasionally in this book — can also be studied in great detail by neutron scattering techniques.

D. Comparison of Techniques

The three major techniques of vibrational spectroscopy previously discussed and subsequently considered in the following chapters of this book are essentially complementary. The most versatile from the point of view of pure phonon spectroscopy is, of course, neutron inelastic scattering, particularly because it samples the complete frequency-wavevector space, whereas the optical techniques of infrared, Raman, and Brillouin scattering are restricted primarily to long-wavelength ($K = 0$) excitations. However, second-order processes in both infrared and Raman scattering spectroscopy can give rise to overtone and combination bands, where pairs of phonons at $K \neq 0$ wavevectors can be involved. Second-order optical vibrational spectroscopy may be particularly important in studies of low-dimensional CDW systems where combination bands involving phonons at the Fermi wavevector $2K_F$ are observed with relatively high intensities in Raman scattering experiments (cf. Steigmeier *et al.,* 1979).

From the experimental point of view the primary disadvantages of neutron inelastic scattering are

(i)   the relatively large sample volume in relation to optical spectroscopy using lasers as light sources,

(ii)   the long measurement times required to collect good data,

(iii)   the rather poor spectral resolution as compared with optical techniques, and

(iv)   the low sensitivity of neutron scattering in the detection and study of vibrational modes of frequencies $\gtrsim 200 \text{ cm}^{-1}$.

Recent improvements in technique are overcoming some of these problems but optical methods provide a cheaper, higher resolution alternative when $K = 0$ phonons are to be measured.

The primary disadvantages of the optical phonon spectroscopic techniques are

(i)   the necessity of using defect-free crystals, particularly in quasi-elastic and low frequency-shifted spectroscopy and

(ii)   the space symmetry-restrictive selection rules of Raman and infrared spectroscopy compared to neutron inelastic scattering techniques, where all modes are, in principle, observable.

For centrosymmetric crystals infrared and Raman spectroscopic selection rules are mutually exclusive. Another important selection rule of importance for SPT studies is that at least one component of the soft mode in the *low* temperature (distorted or ordered) phase is *totally* symmetric, that is, of A_g, A_{1g}, or A_1 symmetry and hence by group theory *always* Raman-active (see Worlock, 1971 for a simple derivation of this argument).

V. SELECTED RECENT DEVELOPMENTS IN THE VIBRATIONAL SPECTROSCOPY OF PHASE TRANSITIONS

In this section we have selected for brief discussion some recent examples from three areas of phase transition research using the experimental techniques of neutron and light scattering and infrared spectroscopy, which we hope will point to future activity in this field. The selected areas are

(i)   studies in the critical regime using novel external fields;

(ii)   studies of soft and vibronic modes and gap excitations occurring in the CDW and superconducting regimes of systems of low dimensionality, and

(iii)   experimental trends in *first*-order transitions such as the microcrystalline-to-amorphous transition in tetrahedral semiconductors and the semiconductor-to-metal transition in conjugated polymers such as polyacetylene.

A. Studies in the Critical Regime

An intriguing aspect of critical phenomena is the competition between order and disorder in physical systems. Various consequences of static and dynamic disorder as related to SPTs are considered in different sections of this book. However, it is only very recently that the somewhat dramatic effects of random external fields that drive a phase transition have been investigated experimentally. Although at first sight such a field appears experimentally unrealizable, it has been shown (Fishman and Aharony, 1979) that a randomly diluted *anti*ferromagnet subjected to a uniform external magnetic field behaves like an Ising system exposed to a random field. Studies using neutron scattering (Birgeneau *et al.*, 1983) in the diluted, *site-random,* two-dimensional 2D-antiferromagnet, $Rb_2Co_{0.7}Mg_{0.3}F_4$, and also in related three-dimensional systems, as a function of temperature and the applied external field, show some interesting effects with deep implications regarding the role of dimensionality in phase-transition phenomena. In the absence of a magnetic field, $Rb_2Co_{0.7}Mg_{0.3}F_4$ undergoes an ordering transition corresponding to a $2D$-Ising system at percolation, at low temperature. The lower critical dimensionality d_l, of such a system is 2, where d_l represents the lower dimensionality limit for sustaining long-range order in a physical system. The quasi-elastic neutron scattering about the antiferromagnetic Bragg reflection from the data of Birgeneau *et al.* (1983), shown in Fig. 18 as a function of the magnetic field, clearly indicates an increase in peak width with increasing field. Since the reciprocal of the intrinsic width is proportional to the correlation length of magnetic ordering, the data in Fig.

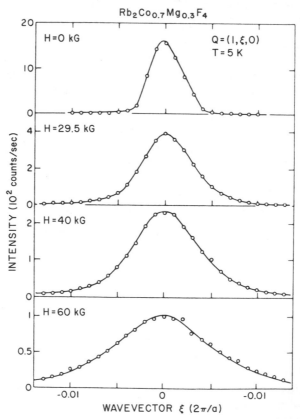

Fig. 18. Quasi-elastic neutron scattering at 5 K for four different magnetic fields in $Rb_2Co_{0.7}Mo_{0.3}F_4$. The scans are in the transverse direction as indicated in the figure and the solid lines are guides to the eye (from Birgeneau *et al.*, 1983).

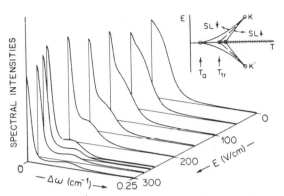

Fig. 19. Half free-spectral range of Fabry–Perot analyzed light scattering spectra showing the Rayleigh and Brillouin components for KDP, taken at a temperature close to T_K. Inset illustrates the phase diagram discussed in the text. The thermodynamic transition line (---) and stability limits for the up (SL ↑) and down (SL ↓) transitions are indicated. The crystal is orthorhombic (2 mm) in the whole plane, except along the hatched line where it is tetragonal (42 mm) (from Courtens *et al.*, 1979).

18 point to the destruction of long-range order in this system (and hence an *increase* in the critical dimensionality parameter d_l) due to the random field. Furthermore, studies as a function of temperature at a constant magnetic field of 40 kG show a distinct change of scattering line-shape below 40 K, from pure Lorentzian to Lorentzian squared. This indicates, as suggested by Kogon and Wallace (1981), a change in the effective dimensionality of the system by a factor of 2.

Another interesting effect (Courtens *et al.*, 1979) observed in the critical regime is for potassium dihydrogen phosphate (KDP), which undergoes a weakly discontinuous paraelectric (PE) to ferroelectric (FE) transition at T_{tr} (note that we use here the notations of Courtens *et al.*) ≈ 122.0 K. Since the PE phase in KDP is noncentrosymmetric, it has a nonzero piezoelectric constant (h_{63}) which couples the polarization to the shear strain e_6, thus producing a soft acoustic mode branch which goes to zero at the extrapolated Curie temperature T_a. The soft acoustic mode couples piezoelectrically to the ferroelectric mode (which involves a coupled proton tunneling and translational mode) that goes to zero at the extrapolated clamped Curie temperature T_c. The difference $T_a - T_c$ is usually of the order of 4.5 K. The somewhat complicated elastic transition described above generates an orthorhombic FE phase. When T is maintained in the neighborhood of the critical temperature and an external electric field applied parallel to the c axis, a polarization P is induced in the crystal and via h_{63} an orthorhombic distortion of the crystal results (Schmidt *et al.*, 1976). The PE-to-FE transition is now *symmetry nonbreaking*. With increasing E the transition becomes continuous and an ordinary critical point (T_K, E_K), where the coexistence curve terminates (cf. inset of Fig. 19), is achieved. Combined Rayleigh and Brillouin scattering data obtained by Courtens et al. (1979) displayed in Fig. 19, however, show a remarkable effect. The data taken near T_K and with increasing field show a shift of the acoustic phonon component to higher frequency but most remarkably there is a sizable *decrease* in the integrated scattering intensity clearly pointing to the absence of critical fluctuations. This observation can be rationalized by suggesting that since the transition is symmetry nonbreaking, fluctuations are *quenched* in the critical regime and the transition is *ideally* Landau-like (Cowley, 1976).

B. Soft Modes in CDW Systems

Two-dimensional transition metal dichalcogenides and quasi-one-dimensional charge transfer salts like $(TMTSF)_2ReO_4$ (TMTSF = tetramethyltetraselenafulvalene) undergo phase transitions involving a CDW (see Section III.E). Some of these materials also undergo transitions to the superconducting state, which in the case of quasi-one-dimensional salts shows interesting properties (cf. Jérome and Bechgaard, 1983).

In the case of the transition metal dichalcogenide, $2H\text{-}TaS_2$, interesting details of the incommensurate CDW phase excitations were revealed via Raman scattering (Sooryakumar et al., 1979). $2H\text{-}TaSe_2$ enters a 3-component CDW-modulated INC phase at $T_i = 122$ K which then locks into a commensurate phase at $T_c = 90$ K. The transition at T_i is second order whereas that at T_c is largely first order. As discussed in Section III.E the incommensurate modulation leads to a splitting of the soft phonon branch into amplitudon and phason components. Under ideal conditions the phason excitation should have zero frequency in the INC phase, but *pinning* at impurity sites is expected to raise its frequency to a finite value.

The A_{1g} and E_{2g} Raman spectra of $2H\text{-}TaSe_2$ in the temperature range of the INC phase, displayed in Fig. 20 (Sooryakumar et al., 1979) show two features in each of the spectra (line at ~ 35 cm^{-1} and shoulder at ~ 55 cm^{-1} in the 91 K A_{1g} spectrum and the lines at ~ 45 and 65 cm^{-1} in the E_{2g} spectrum at 76 K) that can be assigned to a finite phason component and the expected amplitudon mode. As T_i is approached from below the components merge and then soften together. The softening, however, is incomplete. A more detailed study is prevented by the growth of a central component in the E_{2g} spectra and a dramatic increase of damping near T_i.

In $2H\text{-}NbSe_2$, a CDW phase sets in at $T_i = 33$ K and persists into a superconducting state occurring at 7 K. The A_{1g} and E_{2g} Raman spectra of $2H\text{-}NbSe_2$ in the superconducting state are shown in Fig. 21 (Sooryakumar et al., 1979). Sharp lines at 19 cm^{-1} in the A_{1g} spectrum and at 15.5 cm^{-1} in

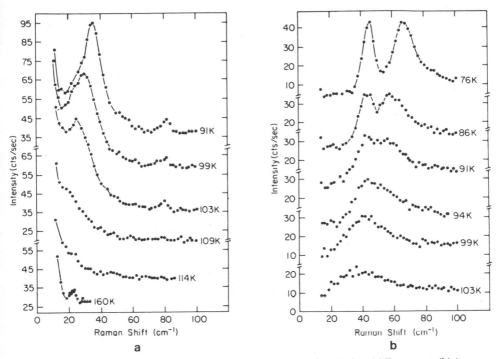

Fig. 20. Raman scattering in the incommensurate phase of 2H-TaSe$_2$; (a) E$_{2g}$ spectra, (b) A$_{1g}$ spectra (from Sooryakumar *et al.*, 1979).

the E_{2g} spectrum appear in the superconducting phase, while the higher frequency lines are associated with the incommensuate CDW as discussed above for 2H-TaSe$_2$. Studies of the E_{2g} spectrum in the superconducting phase as a function of magnetic field applied parallel to the atomic layers of the crystal, show a sizable softening indicating that the sharp feature is associated with excitations across the superconducting gap. This is the first observation of such excitations by Raman scattering, paving the way for exciting new studies in the critical regime, where both the CDW and super-conducting gap excitations can be monitored.

Quasi-one-dimensional charge transfer salts are difficult to investigate by Raman scattering because of laser-induced chemical interaction. However, infrared spectroscopy provides an interesting and direct monitor of the CDW state via electron–phonon coupling activated infrared absorptions in the CDW state. An example of such a study is by Bozio *et al.* (1982) on one of the recently discovered organic superconductors (TMTSF)$_2$ReO$_4$. In the absence of high pressure (TMTSF)$_2$ReO$_4$ undergoes a metal-insulator (MI) transition at 180 K driven by the ordering of the ReO$_4^-$ ion sublattice and the

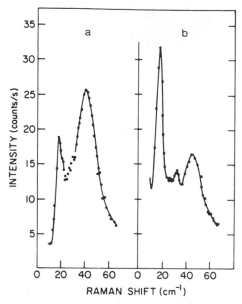

Fig. 21. Raman scattering in the superconducting phase of 2H-NbSe$_2$, $T = 2K$; (a) A$_{1g}$, (b) E$_{2g}$ (from Sooryakumar *et al.*, 1979).

formation of a commensurate CDW along the TMTSF chains. The infrared spectra around this phase transition in the 200–300 cm^{-1} frequency region shown in Fig. 22a (Bozio *et al.*, 1982) indicates the growth of an apparently CDW-modulated mode whose intensity versus temperature profile (cf. Fig. 22b) clearly matches the onset of the MI transition. Interestingly, however, the intensity versus temperature profile of the CDW-modulated mode is reminiscent of the temperature profile of an evolving order parameter (cf. Section III). Careful measurements along these lines should thus provide new and interesting information regarding the critical dynamics of CDW-induced MI transitions.

C. Studies of Unconventional First-Order Transitions

Two first-order transitions with potential technological implications are

(i) the transition from the microcrystalline to the amorphous phase observed in plasma-activated deposition of thin films or laser annealing of amorphous films of tetrahedrally bonded semiconductors and

(ii) the charged soliton-induced semiconductor-to-metal transition in the organic conjugated polymer, polyacetylene (CH)$_x$.

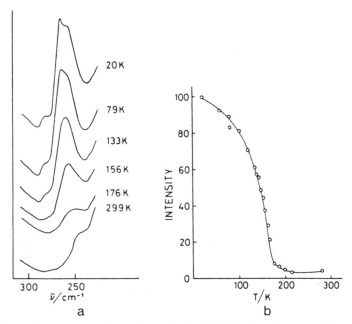

Fig. 22. (a) Temperature dependence of the CDW activated infrared absorption in (TMTSF)$_2$ReO$_4$ powders at 264 cm^{-1}. (b) Normalized integrated intensity of the 264 cm^{-1} mode versus temperature plot (from Bozio *et al.,* 1982).

The microcrystalline-to-amorphous transition observed in silicon and germanium is induced by the decreasing size of the crystallites and accompanying expansion of the intrinsic diamond structure lattice (see Iqbal and Veprek, 1982 and references therein). The resulting evolving elastic energy is the external field (like temperature) which induces the transition. Because of the extremely large first order character of the transition a discontinuous jump to the amorphous phase occurs below a critical crystallite dimension [~ 30 Å for Si (Veprek *et al.,* 1982) and ~ 100 Å for Ge (Hayashi *et al.,* 1982)]. In the amorphous phase the six-membered ring symmetry of the diamond lattice is lost, and nondiamond-like clusters and/or a continuous random network prevails.

Raman scattering data on both silicon (Iqbal and Veprek, 1982) and germanium (Hayashi *et al.,* 1982) displayed in Fig. 23 as a function of deposition temperature or crystallite size, clearly show the softening of the $\Gamma_{25'}$ phonon with decreasing deposition temperature or crystallite size and the evolution of a second component associated with the increasing contribution of the surface or grain boundaries of the crystallites. The detailed $\Gamma_{25'}$ mode frequency versus size profile in the case of silicon, shown in Fig. 24,

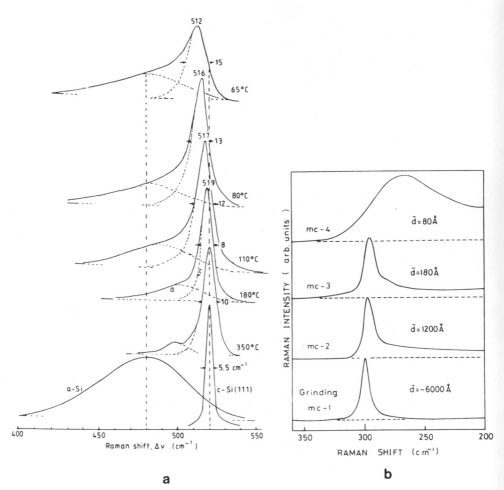

Fig. 23. (a) $\Gamma_{25'}$ phonon Raman spectra of microcrystalline silicon films as a function of decreasing plasma-activated deposition temperature. At a deposition temperature of 65°C the mean crystallite size is ~ 35Å and at 350°C it is near ~ 150Å. Below a critical limit of ~ 30Å the transition to a-Si occurs (from Iqbal and Vepřek, 1982). (b) $\Gamma_{25'}$ phonon Raman spectra of microcrystalline germanium particles; $\bar{d}$ represents the average crystallite size. The spectrum of sample with $\bar{d} = 80$ Å corresponds to that of a-Ge (from Hayashi *et al.* 1982).

approximately follows that of the dispersion surface of the mode. Although the exact microscopic mechanism of the softening still remains a matter of controversy, we can speculate in the context of this chapter that manifestations of dynamic interactions with the approach towards the strongly disordered state are being observed in these materials.

In $(CH)_x$ which is a dimerized Peierls-semiconductor in the *trans*-confor-

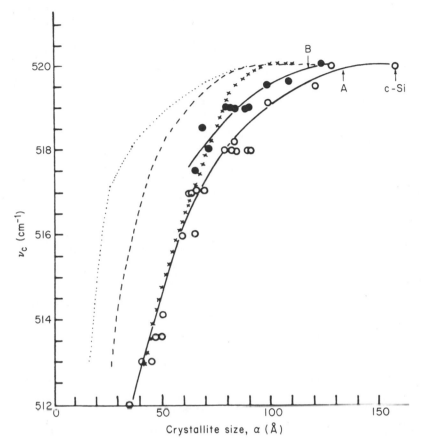

Fig. 24. $\Gamma_{25'}$ phonon frequency versus mean crystallite size plot for microcrystalline silicon (O. ●, ———). Dispersion surface ($\cdots$) for $\Gamma_{25'}$ phonon normalized by assuming the wave-vector to be π/a. The calculated dependence of the phonon frequency ($\ldots$, ---) of two-dimensional slabs of varying thicknesses corresponding to the average crystallite sizes in the polycrystalline matrix (from Iqbal and Vepřek, 1982).

mation, charged solitons can be created both by acceptor or donor doping. The charged soliton is a mobile carrier-like defect localized in the polymer backbone across which the sign of the bond alternation down the chain is reversed (see Fig. 25a). In $(CH)_x$ such a soliton is stable because the electronic states of the two resonance forms of opposite sign are degenerate (Su *et al.*, 1979). With the onset of the semiconductor-to-metal transition on doping, two strong and somewhat asymmetric infrared bands with an anti-resonance-like dip in between evolve that are assignable to charged solitons in $(CH)_x$. This is evident in the spectra shown in Fig. 25b from the work of

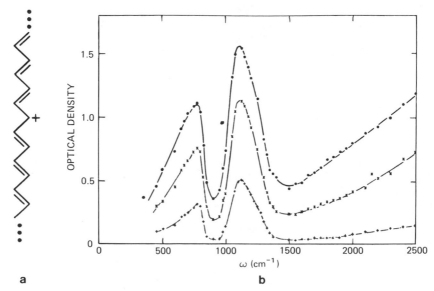

a   **b**

Fig. 25. (a) Schematic model of the charged soliton in trans-polyacetylene, $(CH)_x$. (b) Infrared spectra of $(CD)_x$ with increasing levels of acceptor doping (from Etemaad *et al.*, 1981).

Etemaad *et al.* 1981) for $(CD)_x$, where the increasing oscillator strength of the lines with increasing doping level, is clearly seen. The interaction of the soliton modes in $(CD)_x$ suggested by the antiresonance lineshape is interesting and may provide a spectroscopic probe of the dynamics in the critical regime of the semiconductor-to-metal transition.

VI. CONCLUSIONS AND NEW DIRECTIONS

In this chapter it is hoped that we have introduced the reader to topics ranging from the classification of SPTs and the basic theoretical concepts of such transitions, to some basic ideas of the techniques of vibrational spectroscopy and a summary of a few selected recent experiments pointing (in our opinion) to new directions in this field.

Landau theory and many aspects of the microscopic theory of soft modes are now essentially complete. Exciting new lines of investigation in the critical regime of SPTs using Wilson's powerful calculational technique of renormalization group theory, have been opened up; while much remains to be done in developing theories of incommensurate phases, largely first-order transitions and the soliton dynamics in the conducting phase of polymers like $(CH)_x$. Increasing attention is likely to be paid to two dimensional transitions at surfaces and techniques for this purpose, such as surface enhanced Raman scattering, need further development and understanding. Another area of excitement may lie in the study of biological and nonlinear transitions, from both theoretical and experimental points of view; while the search and study of new forms of superconductive phases should provide new challenges, and the possibility of high temperature superconducting transitions, is likely to lead to one of the great adventures in the physics and chemistry of the next decades.

ACKNOWLEDGMENTS

I would like to thank many of my colleagues over the years at the Cavendish Laboratory, the Energetic Materials Laboratory, the University of Zürich and the ETH, and the Allied Corporation, for stimulation and collaboration in many aspects of solid state and phase transition research. Furthermore, I want to thank Ms. Maria Blanda for her patience and diligence in typing the final manuscript and would like to acknowledge the support of Stan Vepřek of the University of Zürich and the Swiss National Energy Research Foundation.

REFERENCES

Aharony, A., and Bruce, A. D. (1974). *Phys. Rev. Lett.* **33**, 427.
Als-Nielsen, J., and Birgeneau, R. J. (1977). *Am. J. Phys.* **45**, 554.
Anderson, P. W. (1960). *In* "Fizika Dielekrikov" (G. I. Skanavi, ed.), p. 290. Acad. Nauk SSSR, Moscow.
Anderson, P. W., and Blount, E. I. (1965). *Phys. Rev. Lett.* **14**, 217.
Bergman, D. J., and Halperin, B. I. (1976). *Phys. Rev.* **B13**, 2145.
Birgeneau, R. J., Yoshizawa, H., Cowley, R. A., Shirane, G., and Ikeda, H. (1983). *Phys. Rev.* **B28**, 1438.
Bozio, R., Pecile, C., Bechgaard, K., Wudl, F., and Nalewajek, D. (1982). *Solid State Commun.* **41**, 905.
Brout, R., Müller, K. A., and Thomas, H. (1966). *Solid State Commun.* **4**, 507.
Bruce, A. D. (1978). *In* "Solitons and Condensed Matter Physics" (A. R. Bishop and T. Schneider, eds.), p. 116. Springer-Verlag, Berlin and New York.
Bruce, A. D., Müller, K. A., and Berlinger, W. (1979). *Phys. Rev. Lett.* **42**, 185.
Burstein, E., Chen, C. Y., and Lundquist, S. (1979). *In* "Light Scattering in Solids" (J. Birman, H. Cummins, and K. K. Rebane, eds.), p. 479. Plenum, New York.
Cailleau, H., Heidemann, A., and Zeyen, C. M. E. (1979). *J. Phys. C.: Solid State Phys.* **12**, L411.
Chihara, H., Nakamura, N., and Tachiki, M. (1973). *J. Chem. Phys.* **59**, 5387.
Cochran, W. (1959). *Phys. Rev. Lett.* **3**, 412.
Cochran, W. (1969). *Adv. Phys.* **18**, 157.
Cochran, W. (1971). *In* "Structural Phase Transitions and Soft Modes" (E. J. Samuelsen, E. Andersen, and J. Feder, eds.), p. 1, Universitetsforlaget, Oslo.
Courtens, E., Gammon, R., and Alexander, S. (1979). *Phys. Rev. Lett.* **43**, 1026.
Cowley, R. A. (1963). *Adv. Phys.* **12**, 421.
Cowley, R. A. (1970). *J. Phys. Soc. Jpn. Suppl.* **28**, 239.
Cowley, R. A. (1976). *Phys. Rev.* **B13**, 4877.

Cowley, R. A. (1977). *In* "Proceedings of the International Conference on Lattice Dynamics" (M. Balkanski, ed.), p. 625. Flammarion, Paris.

Cowley, R. A., and Bruce, A. D. (1978). *J. Phys. C.: Solid State Phys.* **11**, 3577.

Cowley, R. A., Coombs, G. J., Katiyar, R. S., Ryan, J. F., and Scott, J. F. (1971). *J. Phys. C.: Solid State Phys.* **4**, 2203.

Currat, R., and Pynn, R. (1979). *In* "Neutron Scattering in Materials Science" (G. Kostorz, ed.), p. 131. Academic Press, New York.

Darlington, C. N. W., and O'Connor, D A. (1976). *J. Phys. C.: Solid State Phys.* **9**, 3561.

Devonshire, A. F. (1949). *Philos. Mag.* **40**, 1040.

Dorner, B. (1981). *In* "Structural Phase Transitions I" (K. A. Müller and H. Thomas, eds.), p. 93. Springer-Verlag, Berlin.

Dorner, B., and Comes, R. (1977). *In* "Dynamics of Solids and Liquids by Neutron Scattering" (S. W. Lovesy and T. Springer, eds.), Springer-Verlag, New York and Berlin.

Dorner, B., Axe, J. D., and Shirane, G. (1972). *Phys. Rev.* **B5**, 1950.

Ellenson, W. D., and Kjems, J. K. (1977). *J. Chem. Phys.* **67**, 3619.

Elliott, G. R., and Iqbal, Z. (1975). *J. Chem. Phys.* **63**, 1914.

Etemaad, S. *et al.* (1981). *Phys. Rev.* **23**, 5137.

Fishman, S., and Aharony, A. (1979). *J. Phys. C.: Solid State Phys.* **12**, L729.

Fleury, P. A., and Lyons, K. (1981). *In* "Structural Phase Transitions I" (K. A. Müller and H. Thomas, eds.), p. 9. Springer, Berlin and New York.

Fröhlich, H. (1949). "Theory of Dielectrics." Oxford Univ. Press (Clarendon), London and New York.

Ginzberg, V. L. (1960). *Sov. Phys. Solid State* **2**, 1824.

Girard, A., Cailleau, H., Marqueton, Y., and Ecolivet, C. (1978). *Chem. Phys. Lett.* **54**, 479.

Gränicher, H., and Müller, K. A. (1971). *Mater. Res. Bull.* **6**, 977.

Griffiths, P. R. (1975). "Chemical Infrared Fourier Transform Spectroscopy." Wiley, New York.

Halperin, B. I., and Varma, C. M. (1976). *Phys. Rev.* **B14**, 4030.

Harley, R. T., Hayes, W., and Smith, S. R. P. (1971). *In* "Light Scattering in Solids" (M. Balkanski, ed.), p. 40. Flammarion, Paris.

Hayashi, S., Ito, M., and Kanamori, H. (1982). *Solid State Commun.* **44**, 75.

Hayes, W., and Loudon, R. (1978). "Scattering of Light by Crystals." John Wiley, New York.

Iqbal, Z. (1979). *In* "Magnetic Resonance of Phase Transitions" (F. J. Owens, C. P. Poole, and H. A. Farach, eds.) p. 1. Academic Press, New York.

Iqbal, Z., and Christoe, C. W. (1975). *Solid State Commun.* **17**, 71.

Iqbal, Z., and Vepřek, S. (1982). *J. Phys. C.: Solid State Phys.* **15**, 377.

Iqbal, Z., Chance, R. R., and Baughman, R. H. (1977). *J. Chem. Phys.* **66**, 5520.

Jérome, D., and Bechgaard, K. (1983). *Europhys. News* **14**, No. 5, p. 7.

Kadanoff, L. P. (1966). *Physics* **2**, 263.

Kadanoff, L. P. (1976). *In* "Phase Transitions and Critical Phenomena" (C. Domb and M. S. Green, eds.), Vol. 5A, p. 1. Academic Press, New York.

Kadanoff, L. P. *et al.* (1967). *Rev. Mod. Phys.* **39**, 395.

Kogon, H. S, and Wallace, D. J. (1981). *J. Phys. A.: Math, Nucl. and Gen.* **14**, L527.

Labbé, J., and Friedel, J. (1966). *J. Phys. Radium* **27**, 153, 303.

Landau, L. D., and Lifshitz, E. M. (1959). "Statistical Physics." Pergamon, Oxford.

Lee, T. D., and Yang, C. N. (1952). *Phys. Rev.* **87**, 410.

Lockwood, D. J., Arthur, J. W., Taylor, W., and Hosea, T. J. (1976). *Solid State Commun.* **20**, 703.

Loudon, R. (1964). *Adv. Phys.* **13**, 423.

McMillan, W. L. (1976). *Phys. Rev.* **B14**, 1496.

Michel, K. H., and Naudts, J. (1977a). *Phys. Rev. Lett.* **39**, 212.

Michel, K. H., and Naudts, J. (1977b). *J. Chem. Phys.* **67**, 547.

Möller, K. D., and Rothschild, W. G. (1971). "Far Infrared Spectroscopy." Wiley (Interscience), New York and London.

Müller, K. A. (1981). *In* "Structural Phase Transitions I" (K. A. Müller and H. Thomas, eds.), p. 1. Springer-Verlag, Berlin and New York.

Müller, K. A., and Berlinger, W. (1971). *Phys. Rev. Lett.* **26**, 13.

Peercy, P. S., and Fritz, I. J. (1974). *Phys. Rev. Lett.* **32**, 46.

Peierls, R. E. (1955). "Quantum Theory of Solids." Oxford Univ. Press (Clarendon), London and New York.

Petzelt, J. (1981). *Phase Transitions* **2**, 155.

Placzek, G. (1934). "Handbuch der Radiologie," Vol. VI(2), p. 205, Akademische-Verlag, Leipzig.

Pytte, E. (1970). *Solid State Commun.* **8**, 2101.

Rae, A. I. M. (1982). *J. Phys. C.: Solid State Phys.* **15**, 1883.

Raich, J. C., and Bernstein, E. R. (1980). *J. Chem. Phys.* **73**, 1955.

Raich, J. C., and Hüller, A. (1979). *J. Chem. Phys.* **70**, 3669.

Riste, T., Samuelsen, E. J., Otnes, K., and Feder, J. (1971). *Solid State Commun.* **9**, 1455.

Rowe, J. M., Rush, J. J., Chesser, N. J., Michel, K. H., and Naudts, J. (1978). *Phys. Rev. Lett.* **40**, 455.

Samara, G. A., Sakudo, T., and Yoshimitsu, K. (1975). *Phys. Rev. Lett.* **35**, 1767.

Schmidt, V. H., Western, A. B., and Baker, A. G. (1976). *Phys. Rev. Lett.* **37**, 839.

Schneider, T., and Stoll, E. (1973). *Phys. Rev. Lett.* **36**, 1501.

Shirane, G., and Axe, J. D. (1971). *Phys. Rev.* **B4**, 2957.

Silberglitt, R. (1972). *Solid State Commun.* **11**, 247.

Sooryakumar, R., Bruns, D. G., and Klein, M. V. (1979). *In* "Light Scattering in Solids" (J. L. Birman, H. Z. Cummins, and K. K. Rebane, eds.) p. 347. Plenum, New York.

Stanley, H. E. (1971). "Introduction to Phase Transitions and Critical Phenomena." Oxford Univ. Press, London and New York.

Steigmeier, E. F., and Auderset, E. F. (1973). *Solid State Commun.* **12**, 565.

Steigmeier, E. F., Baeriswyl, D., Auderset, H., and Williams, J. M. (1979). *In* "Proc. Int. Conf. Quasi–One-Dimensional Conductors, Dubrovnik," Vol. 96, Lecture Notes in Physics, p. 229. Springer-Verlag, Berlin and New York.

Stirling, W. G. (1972). *J. Phys. C.: Solid State Phys.* **5**, 2711.

Su, W. P., Schrieffer, J. R., and Heeger, A. J. (1979). *Phys. Rev. Lett.* **42**, 1698.

Thomas, H., and Müller, K. A. (1968). *Phys. Rev. Lett.* **21**, 1256.

Töpler, J., Alefeld, B., and Heidman, A. (1977). *J. Phys. C.: Solid State Phys.* **10**, 635.

Vepřek, S., Iqbal, Z., and Sarott, F. -A. (1982). *Phil. Mag.* **45**, 137.

Wilson, K. G. (1979). *Sci. Am.* **241**, 158.

Wilson, K. G. (1983). *Rev. Mod. Phys.* **55**, 583.

Wilson, K. G., and Fisher, M. E. (1972). *Phys. Rev. Lett.* **28**, 240.

Wilson, K. G., and Kogut, J. (1974). *Phys. Rep.* **12C**, 75.

Worlock, J. M. (1971). *In* "Structural Phase Transitions and Soft Modes" (E. J. Samuelsen, E. Andersen, and J. Feder, eds.), p. 329. Universitetsforlaget, Oslo.

Yamada, Y., Noda, Y., Axe, J. D., and Shirane, G. (1974). *Phys. Rev.* **B9**, 4429.

Yoshihara, A., Bernstein, E. R., and Raich, J. C. (1983). *J. Chem. Phys.* **79**, 445.

2

Infrared Spectroscopy of Structural Phase Transitions in Crystals

J. PETZELT and V. DVOŘÁK

Institute of Physics
Czechoslovak Academy of Science
Prague, Czechoslovakia

I. INTRODUCTION

Structural phase transitions (SPTs) in crystals between high-symmetry or disordered (parent) and low-symmetry or ordered (distorted) phases have attracted the attention of both experimentalists and theoreticians for many years. (An elementary introduction to the problems of SPTs can be found in the review by Scott, 1974.) Different anomalies of static and dynamical properties are observed at SPTs and explained within the framework of more or less sophisticated phase-transition theories. Typical static properties of interest are the temperature dependence of the specific heat, static dielectric and elastic constants, etc. Anomalous dynamical properties (e.g., light scattering or ultrasonic attenuation, the investigation of which provides deeper insight into the microscopic origin of SPTs) reflect anomalies in the spectrum of elementary energy excitations of crystals near the temperature of SPTs. One method to study phase transitions is infrared (IR) spectroscopy which can be looked upon as a complementary technique to Raman and neutron scattering spectroscopy. Although IR spectroscopy only detects long wavelength polar excitations, it still provides fundamental information about an SPT as will be shown in this review. In the first part we give a brief account of the classical theory of IR absorption and summarize some useful formulae; then we discuss general aspects connected with the spectroscopy of SPTs, namely soft-mode and hard-mode spectroscopy. The third part is devoted to the experimental techniques of IR spectroscopy. In the fourth part properties of particular materials representing various types of SPTs are discussed. The list of chosen substances and SPTs as well as the list of quoted IR spectroscopic papers are by no means complete. We chose examples of which, in our opinion, IR spectroscopy gave some new results of comparable or greater importance than other spectroscopic methods such as Raman and neutron scattering. We have not included in our considerations either magnetic and superconductive transitions or reconstructive SPTs and melting.

II. THEORETICAL CONSIDERATIONS

A. Absorption and Reflection of IR Radiation

It is well known that a crystal interacting with IR electromagnetic radiation can be treated macroscopically, i.e., as a continuum. This is due to the fact that the wavelength $\lambda \sim 10^{-4}$ cm, of IR radiation corresponding to the characteristic angular frequency $\omega \sim 10^{13}$ s^{-1} (the order of magnitude of the maximum phonon frequency) of lattice excitations coupled with the IR radiation, is much larger than the lattice constant a ($\sim 10^{-8}$ cm). An IR electromagnetic wave propagating in the crystal must satisfy Maxwell's equations (we always put the magnetic permeability $\mu = 1$, which is usually satisfied in the IR region)

$$\text{div } \mathbf{H} = 0, \qquad\qquad \text{div } \mathbf{D} = 0,$$

$$\text{rot } \mathbf{E} = -\frac{1}{c}\frac{\partial \mathbf{H}}{\partial t}, \qquad \text{rot } \mathbf{H} = \frac{1}{c}\frac{\partial \mathbf{D}}{\partial t} + \frac{4\pi}{c}\mathbf{j}, \qquad (2.1)$$

where $\mathbf{j}$ is the conduction current density. It is assumed that no charges are externally introduced into the medium. The properties of the continuum are hidden in the constitutive relation between the displacement $\mathbf{D}$ and the macroscopic electric field $\mathbf{E}$ which is linear for weak fields. Thus for harmonic fields with the time dependence $e^{i\omega t}$, we have

$$\mathbf{D} = \bar{\epsilon}(\omega)\mathbf{E}. \qquad (2.2)$$

Since the conduction current may be related to the macroscopic field by

$$\mathbf{j} = \bar{\sigma}(\omega)\mathbf{E} \qquad (2.3)$$

we can combine the effects of the displacement and conduction currents as sources of the magnetic field introducing

$$\epsilon(\omega) = \bar{\epsilon}(\omega) - i4\pi\frac{\bar{\sigma}(\omega)}{\omega} \qquad (2.4)$$

so that

$$\text{rot } \mathbf{H} = \frac{1}{c}\epsilon(\omega)\frac{\partial \mathbf{E}}{\partial t}. \qquad (2.5)$$

For an anisotropic medium the permittivity ϵ is a symmetrical second-rank tensor. The permittivity is a complex quantity given by

$$\epsilon(\omega) = \epsilon'(\omega) - i\epsilon''(\omega)$$

$$= \bar{\epsilon}' - 4\pi\frac{\bar{\sigma}''}{\omega} - i\left(\bar{\epsilon}'' + 4\pi\frac{\bar{\sigma}'}{\omega}\right). \qquad (2.6)$$

Its imaginary part can be written in the form

$$\epsilon''(\omega) \equiv 4\pi\frac{\sigma(\omega)}{\omega}, \qquad (2.7)$$

where the real function $\sigma(\omega)$ represents the generalized frequency dependent conductivity. We recall that σ accounts for both conduction and dielectric losses and only at frequencies $\omega \to 0$ when the latter tends to zero, σ may be identified with the static conductivity, $\bar{\sigma}(0)$. On the other hand, at low frequencies in general $4\pi\bar{\sigma}''/\omega$ need not be negligible in comparison with $\bar{\epsilon}'$ (in metals, e.g.) and therefore both the conduction mechanism and dielectric polarization contribute to ϵ'.

The real and imaginary parts satisfy the Kramers–Kronig dispersion relations (Landau and Lifshitz, 1960)

$$\epsilon'(\omega) - 1 = \frac{1}{\pi} P \int_{-\infty}^{+\infty} \frac{\epsilon''(\omega')}{\omega' - \omega} \, d\omega' = 8P \int_0^\infty \frac{\sigma(\omega')}{\omega'^2 - \omega^2} \, d\omega',$$

$$\sigma(\omega) = \sigma(0) - \frac{\omega^2}{2\pi^2} P \int_0^\infty \frac{\epsilon'(\omega')}{\omega'^2 - \omega^2} \, d\omega'. \tag{2.8}$$

Taking into account that a harmonic oscillator of charge e, mass m, and eigenfrequency ω_0 contributes to ϵ' by

$$\epsilon'(\omega) - 1 = \frac{4\pi e^2}{m} \frac{1}{\omega_0^2 - \omega^2}, \tag{2.9}$$

we can formally express $\epsilon'(\omega)$ in the form

$$\epsilon'(\omega) - 1 = \frac{4\pi e^2}{m} P \int_0^\infty \frac{n(\omega') d\omega'}{\omega'^2 - \omega^2}, \tag{2.10}$$

where $n(\omega)$ represents the number of harmonic oscillators with dispersion frequencies in the unit frequency range around ω. Comparing Eqs. (2.8) and (2.10) we have

$$n(\omega) = \frac{2m}{\pi e^2} \sigma(\omega). \tag{2.11}$$

In the high-frequency limit when charges (e.g., electrons) in a solid can be considered as free, we get from Eq. (2.9)

$$\epsilon'(\omega) - 1 = -\frac{4\pi e^2}{m} \frac{N}{\omega^2}, \tag{2.12}$$

where N is the number of charges per unit volume. On the other hand, the high-frequency limit of Eq. (2.8) together with Eq. (2.11) gives

$$\epsilon'(\omega) - 1 = -\frac{8}{\omega^2} \int_0^\infty \sigma(\omega') d\omega' = -\frac{4\pi e^2}{m\omega^2} \int_0^\infty n(\omega') \, d\omega'. \tag{2.13}$$

By comparison of Eqs. (2.12) and (2.13) we get the sum rule (Landau and Lifshitz, 1960)

$$\int_0^\infty n(\omega) \, d\omega = N. \tag{2.14}$$

Combining Eqs. (2.13) and (2.14) we get the sum rule in the form

$$\int_0^\infty \sigma(\omega)\, d\omega = \frac{\pi e^2 N}{2m}. \tag{2.15}$$

Equation (2.15) is of practical use in SPT spectroscopy because the right-hand side is expected to be temperature independent throughout an SPT even for some reasonably limited spectral range of integration. For instance, if an SPT is connected with a large change of the static conductivity (e.g., in a metal-insulator transition), we can expect changes also in the IR and/or the visible and ultraviolet (UV) regions which compensate the low-frequency changes; or if some new strong lattice mode appears in the distorted phase, the strength of some other modes active already in the parent phase should decrease.

Basic information about long-wavelength polar phonons is contained in $\epsilon(\omega)$ which can be determined in the IR region by means of reflection and/or transmission spectral measurements. Reflection and propagation of an electromagentic wave in crystalline media, which are both anisotropic and absorbing, is a complex problem. However, until now the most thoroughly investigated SPTs take place in crystals which are at least of orthorhombic symmetry. In such crystals the principal axes of the real and imaginary parts of ϵ_{ik} coincide in direction and are fixed by the crystallographic axes. Consequently, in such crystals a plane wave falling perpendicularly to the crystal surface along a principal axis propagates through the crystal as a homogeneous (i.e., planes of constant phase and amplitude are identical) purely transverse wave. Only this case of normal incidence will be considered further.

A harmonic transverse plane wave, $\sim \exp\left[-i(k_z z - \omega t)\right]$, satisfies Maxwell equations (2.1) provided

$$|\mathbf{k}|^2 = \epsilon(\omega)\frac{\omega^2}{c^2} \equiv (n - i\kappa)^2 \frac{\omega^2}{c^2}. \tag{2.16}$$

(Since we consider a wave propagating along a principal axis z of ϵ, its tensor indices are omitted.) This condition determines in an implicit form the dispersion $\omega(\mathbf{k})$ of the wave. In an absorbing medium the wavevector $\mathbf{k} \equiv \mathbf{k}' - i\mathbf{k}''$ is complex ($\mathbf{k}' \parallel \mathbf{k}''$ for a homogeneous plane wave considered here); as it follows from Eq. (2.16) the real and imaginary parts of $\mathbf{k}$ are related to the refractive index n and the absorption index (extinction coefficient) κ, respectively,

$$|\mathbf{k}'| = n\frac{\omega}{c}, \qquad |\mathbf{k}''| = \kappa\frac{\omega}{c}, \qquad n > 0, \quad \kappa \geq 0. \tag{2.17}$$

The time-averaged electromagnetic energy flow connected with the wave is attenuated by a factor $e^{-\alpha z}$, where the absorption coefficient,

$$\alpha = 2|\mathbf{k}''| = 2\kappa\omega/c \geq 0. \tag{2.18}$$

By measuring $n(\omega)$ and $\alpha(\omega)$ the permittivity $\epsilon(\omega) \equiv \epsilon'(\omega) - i\epsilon''(\omega)$ is determined from Eq. (2.16) as

$$\epsilon' = n^2 - \kappa^2, \qquad \epsilon'' = 2n\kappa \geq 0. \tag{2.19}$$

At normal incidence of light from vacuum the amplitude reflection coefficient r for the magnetic field is given by

$$r \equiv R^{1/2}e^{-i\theta} = \frac{n - i\kappa - 1}{n - i\kappa + 1}. \tag{2.20}$$

(We recall that the amplitude reflection coefficient for the electric field differs only by the sign which is related to the fact that while the electric field changes the phase by 180° on reflection from a lossless dielectric, the phase of the magnetic field remains unchanged.) From Eq. (2.20) we find the formula for the reflectivity (power reflection coefficient) R, which in most cases is directly measured, as

$$R = r\,r^* = \frac{(n-1)^2 + \kappa^2}{(n+1)^2 + \kappa^2}. \tag{2.21}$$

The phase shift θ of the reflected wave can be determined from the dispersion relation (see, e.g., Stern, 1963)

$$\theta(\omega) = \frac{\omega}{\pi} P \int_0^\infty \frac{\ln R(\omega')}{\omega^2 - \omega'^2}\, d\omega'. \tag{2.22}$$

Knowing R and θ and using Eqs. (2.20) and (2.19), we can determine ϵ from the relation

$$\epsilon = \left(\frac{1+r}{1-r}\right)^2 \tag{2.23}$$

and the optical constants from relations

$$n = \frac{1-R}{1+R-2\sqrt{R}\cos\theta}, \qquad \kappa = \frac{2\sqrt{R}\sin\theta}{1+R-2\sqrt{R}\cos\theta}. \tag{2.24}$$

Since κ is nonnegative, the phase θ of r in Eq. (2.20) is restricted to the range $0 \leq \theta \leq \pi$.

It should be noted that we are neglecting the space dispersion of ϵ, i.e., its dependence on the wavevector $\mathbf{k}$. This effect is proportional to a/λ and therefore for IR radiation this approximation is well justified. The space dispersion of ϵ might become experimentally significant if some ordering develops in the crystal with a translational period much greater than a (e.g., in crystals with incommensurate phases, Golovko and Levanyuk, 1979, or in chiral liquid crystals, Korte and Schrader, 1981), where effects like optical activity (gyration) and related phenomena are commonly observed.

B. Theory of the Dielectric Spectrum

To extract some information from experimentally measured $\epsilon(\omega)$, we have to develop a theory of phonon (sometimes also electron) contribution to $\epsilon(\omega)$. We have to clarify initially which phonons are coupled to the electromagnetic radiation. An incident harmonic electromagnetic plane wave creates a macroscopic electric field $\mathbf{E} = \mathbf{E}_k \exp[-i(kz - \omega t)]$ in a crystal. We recall that for the calculation of the dielectric susceptibility, $\chi^{\alpha\beta} \equiv (dP_\alpha/dE_\beta)_{E=0}$, of the crystal it is useful to work with the field $\mathbf{E}$ rather than with an external applied field $\mathscr{E}$. $\mathbf{E}$ is the sum of $\mathscr{E}$ due to the radiation and macroscopic field produced by the polarized crystal. The latter carries the long-range part of the Coulomb interaction between ions and depend on the crystal surface conditions (Born and Huang, 1954). (The remaining part of the Coulomb interaction creates the so-called Lorentz field which is completely determined by local conditions in the crystal.) Writing the energy of the crystal in the form

$$H = H_0 + H \equiv H_0 - \int \mathbf{P}(\mathbf{r}) \cdot \mathbf{E}(\mathbf{r}) \, dV, \qquad (2.25)$$

where $\mathbf{P}$ is the electric polarization of the crystal, we have to keep in mind that the part of the energy containing the macroscopic field rather than the perturbation due to external field is separated from the total crystal energy H. Assuming periodic boundary conditions we can write

$$\mathbf{P}(\mathbf{r}) = \sum_q \mathbf{P}_q \, e^{i\mathbf{q}\cdot\mathbf{r}} \qquad (2.26)$$

so that

$$H' = -V\Delta(\mathbf{q} - \mathbf{k}) \, \mathbf{P}_q \cdot \mathbf{E}_k \, e^{i\omega t}, \qquad (2.27)$$

where $\Delta(\mathbf{q} - \mathbf{k}) = 1$ if $\mathbf{q} - \mathbf{k}$ is a reciprocal lattice vector and is zero otherwise. Since the wavevector $\mathbf{k}$ of IR radiation may to a good approximation be put equal to zero, only long-wavelength optical phonons with $\mathbf{q} \to 0$ giving rise to polarization P_0 should be considered. The harmonic part of the internal energy U corresponding to Eq. (2.25) can be expanded into the form (Born and Huang, 1954)

$$U = \tfrac{1}{2} \sum_j \omega_j^2 Q_j^2 + \sqrt{V/4\pi} \sum_{j\alpha} f_{j\alpha}^{1/2} Q_j E_\alpha - \tfrac{1}{2} V \sum_{\alpha\beta} \chi_\infty^{\alpha\beta} E_\alpha E_\beta, \quad (2.28)$$

where V is the volume of the crystal and the strength f_j of the Q_j mode is defined in terms of its effective charge $e_{j\alpha}$ and mass m_j, respectively, as

$$f_{j\alpha} = \frac{4\pi}{V} \frac{e_{j\alpha}^2}{m_j}. \quad (2.29)$$

The $\chi_\infty^{\alpha\beta}$ is the high-frequency dielectric susceptibility at frequencies $\omega \gg \omega_j$. The normal coordinates Q_j diagonalize that part of U which does not contain the macroscopic field $\mathbf{E}$; therefore the Q_j describe phonons which are not associated with a macroscopic electric field. The polarization component P_α is given by

$$P_\alpha = -\frac{1}{V} \frac{\partial U}{\partial E_\alpha} = -(1/\sqrt{4\pi V}) \sum_j f_{j\alpha}^{1/2} Q_j + \sum_\beta \chi_\infty^{\alpha\beta} E_\beta. \quad (2.30)$$

The effective charge $e_{j\alpha}$ contains the eigenvector of the normal coordinate Q_j. Obviously, $e_{j\alpha}$ is nonzero only if the corresponding eigenvector transforms like the polarization, i.e., as a polar vector. In other words, polar optic phonons (with $\mathbf{q} \to 0$) only can couple with the IR radiation. Such phonons are IR-active and their number is determined by the symmetry of a particular crystal lattice and can be obtained most readily using group theory (factor-group analysis) (Birman, 1974). Since the IR wave propagates along a principal axis of ϵ_{ik} and consequently it is purely transverse, from Eq. (2.27) it follows that the dipole-moment wave associated with the IR-active phonon must also be transverse. To simplify the interpretation of experiments usually an IR wave polarized along a principal axis perpendicular to the direction of propagation is used. Choosing the coordinate axes parallel to the principal axes we dispense with tensor indices since in this case $\mathbf{P}$ and $\mathbf{E}$ have only one nonzero component.

Adding to U the kinetic energy $\tfrac{1}{2} \Sigma_j \dot{Q}_j^2$ and introducing phenomenologically the dissipation function $R = \tfrac{1}{2} \Sigma_j \gamma_j \dot{Q}_j^2$, the equation of motion for Q_j reads as

$$\ddot{Q}_j = -\frac{\partial U}{\partial Q_j} - \frac{\partial R}{\partial \dot{Q}_j} = -\omega_j^2 Q_j - \gamma_j \dot{Q}_j - \sqrt{V/4\pi} f_j^{1/2} E. \quad (2.31)$$

Looking for the solution in the form $Q_j, E \propto e^{i\omega t}$, we find

$$Q_j = -\sqrt{V} f_j^{1/2} E / [\sqrt{4\pi}(\omega_j^2 - \omega^2 + i\omega\gamma_j)] \quad (2.32)$$

and the susceptibility $\chi(\omega)$ is given by

$$\chi(\omega) = \frac{1}{4\pi} \sum_j \frac{f_j}{\omega_j^2 - \omega^2 + i\omega\gamma_j} + \chi. \quad (2.33)$$

The dielectric permittivity is

$$\epsilon(\omega) = \sum_j \frac{f_j}{\omega_j^2 - \omega^2 + i\omega\gamma_j} + \epsilon_\infty. \tag{2.34}$$

Introducing complex dispersion frequencies $\overline{\omega}_j = (\omega_j^2 - \gamma_j^2/4)^{1/2} + i\gamma_j/2$, Eq. (2.34) can be written in the form

$$\epsilon(\omega) = \sum_j \frac{f_j}{(\overline{\omega}_j - \omega)(\overline{\omega}_j^* + \omega)} + \epsilon_\infty. \tag{2.35}$$

Note that for an underdamped oscillator ($\gamma_j/2 < \omega_j$) the modulus of $\overline{\omega}_j$ merely equals that of ω_j. Taking the imaginary part of $\epsilon(\omega)$ from Eq. (2.34) and using Eqs. (2.7) and (2.29) we find that

$$\int_0^\infty \sigma(\omega)\, d\omega = \frac{1}{8}\sum_j f_j = \frac{\pi}{2V}\sum_j \frac{e_j^2}{m_j}. \tag{2.36}$$

This result, based on the rigid ion approximation, is in agreement with the general sum rule (2.15). In a more rigorous treatment of normal mode damping the damping constant γ_j is, in general, frequency dependent. Actually, using the general formula (Kubo, 1957)

$$\chi(\omega) = \chi_0\left[1 - i\omega \int_0^\infty \vartheta(t)\, e^{-i\omega t}\, dt\right], \tag{2.37}$$

where χ_0 is the static susceptibility and $\vartheta(t)$ is the polarization relaxation function defined as (Mori, 1965)

$$\vartheta(t) = \frac{\langle P(t)\, P(0)\rangle}{\langle P^2\rangle} \tag{2.38}$$

(the angular brackets denote the thermal average) and assuming for simplicity that just one Q_j contributes to P we get

$$\chi(\omega) = \chi_0 \frac{\omega_j^2}{\omega_j^2 - \omega^2 + i\omega\gamma(i\omega)}, \tag{2.39}$$

where

$$\gamma(i\omega) = \frac{1}{\langle P^2\rangle\omega_j^2}\int_0^\infty \langle f(t)f(0)\rangle e^{-i\omega t}\, dt. \tag{2.40}$$

The random force $f(t)$ acting on P expresses the interaction of P with *the bath* of all other degrees of freedom of the system. The damping γ would be frequency independent provided the random force would have an infinitely short memory, i.e., $\langle f(t)f(0)\rangle \propto \delta(t)$; such an approximation is reasonable only at low frequencies.

As we have already pointed out, the dispersion frequencies ω_j are the frequencies of polar optic modes which are free of the macroscopic electric field. Do such modes really exist in the phonon spectrum? To find normal modes we have to solve the equation of motion for Q_j together with Maxwell's equations (2.1) (with $j = 0$). The equation of motion is accounted for by writing $\mathbf{D} = \epsilon \mathbf{E}$ and taking ϵ in the form of Eq. (2.35). Then eliminating $\mathbf{H}$ from Maxwell's equations we get for a harmonic plane wave

$$-|\mathbf{k}|^2 \, \mathbf{E} + \mathbf{k} \, (\mathbf{k} \cdot \mathbf{E}) + \frac{\omega^2}{c^2} \, \epsilon(\omega) \, \mathbf{E} = 0. \tag{2.41}$$

This equation determines in an implicit form the dispersion of normal modes. Again we are interested in modes with $\mathbf{k}$ along one of the principal axes. There are two types of solutions of Eq. (2.41):

(1) Longitudinal (LO) modes ($\mathbf{k} \| \mathbf{E}$) the frequencies of which are determined by the condition $\epsilon_{\|}(\omega_{Lj}) = 0$ and which are $\mathbf{k}$-independent when the space dispersion of $\epsilon_{\|}$ is neglected ($\epsilon_{\|}$ and $\epsilon_{\perp}$ denote the principal values of the permittivity along the principal axis parallel and perpendicular to $\mathbf{k}$, respectively).

(2) Two transverse (TO) modes ($\mathbf{k} \perp \mathbf{E}$) the frequencies of which are determined by the condition

$$\frac{c^2 k^2}{\omega^2} = \epsilon_{\perp}(\omega). \tag{2.42}$$

It is well known that these transverse normal modes are a mixture of phonons and electromagnetic radiation (Born and Huang, 1954), and are referred to as polaritons. In the electrostatic approximation ($c \to \infty$), Eq. (2.41) for transverse modes reduces to the condition $\mathbf{E} = 0$. Therefore the dispersion frequencies ω_j are, in fact, frequencies ω_{Tj} of transverse polar optic phonons in the electrostatic approximation. These phonons represent purely mechanical lattice vibrations where the electromagnetic radiation produced by them is neglected.

The dielectric function $\epsilon(\omega)$ (see Eq. (2.35)) can be expressed in terms of the (generally complex) frequencies $\overline{\omega}_{Lj}$ and $\overline{\omega}_{Tj}$. For simplicity we first consider a crystal with two atoms per unit cell which has one IR active mode. In this case using the condition $\epsilon(\overline{\omega}_L) = 0$, Eq. (2.35) can be put into the form

$$\frac{\epsilon(\omega)}{\epsilon_{\infty}} = \frac{(\overline{\omega}_L - \omega)(\omega_L^* + \omega)}{(\overline{\omega}_T - \omega)(\omega_T^* + \omega)} = \frac{|\overline{\omega}_L|^2 - \omega^2 + i\omega\gamma_L}{|\overline{\omega}_T|^2 - \omega^2 + i\omega\gamma_T} \tag{2.43}$$

from which the well-known Lyddane–Sachs–Teller relation immediately follows in the static ($\omega = 0$) limit. This formula is valid both for $\epsilon_{\|}$ and $\epsilon_{\perp}$; however, we have to keep in mind that in the formula for $\epsilon_{\|}$, for example, the frequencies $\bar{\omega}_L$ and $\bar{\omega}_T$ correspond to longitudinal and transverse modes, respectively, which are both polarized along the chosen principal axis (i.e., that $\mathbf{k}$ ($\to 0$) of the longitudinal mode is parallel to this axis but $\mathbf{k}$ ($\to 0$) of the transverse mode is perpendicular to it). Comparing Eq. (2.43) with Eq. (2.34) (for $j = 1$) we can express the damping $\gamma(\omega)$ in the dispersion formula in terms of the damping γ_T and γ_L of the transverse and longitudinal mode, respectively (neglecting terms of the order of γ^2) (Gervais and Piriou, 1974), as

$$\gamma(\omega) = \gamma_T - \frac{\gamma_L - \gamma_T}{\omega_L^2 - \omega_T^2}(\omega_T^2 - \omega^2). \tag{2.44}$$

Equation (2.43) can be generalized for n optical phonon branches (Kurosawa, 1961; Lowndes, 1970) as

$$\frac{\epsilon(\omega)}{\epsilon_\infty} = \prod_{j=1}^{n} \frac{(\bar{\omega}_{Lj} - \omega)(\bar{\omega}_{Lj}^* + \omega)}{(\bar{\omega}_{Tj} - \omega)(\bar{\omega}_{Tj}^* + \omega)} = \prod_{j=1}^{n} \frac{|\bar{\omega}_{Lj}|^2 - \omega^2 + i\omega\gamma_{Lj}}{|\bar{\omega}_{Tj}|^2 - \omega^2 + i\omega\gamma_{Tj}}. \tag{2.45}$$

This expression clearly shows that the complex frequencies $\bar{\omega}_{Lj}$ and $\bar{\omega}_{Tj}$ are zeros and poles, respectively, of the dielectric function $\epsilon(\omega)$; the resonance frequencies are the moduli $|\bar{\omega}_{Ti}|$ of complex poles $\bar{\omega}_{Ti}$.

The microscopic origin of the damping introduced into Eq. (2.33) for χ phenomenologically lies in the anharmonic phonon interaction. A quite general expression can be derived using the linear response theory and the Green function technique. The susceptibility is given by (Cowley, 1963)

$$\chi^{\alpha\beta}(\omega) = \chi_\infty^{\alpha\beta} + \frac{V}{kT} G\,(P_\alpha P_\beta\,,\,\omega - i\delta), \qquad \delta \to 0_+, \tag{2.46}$$

where G is the analytically continued Fourier transform of the time-dependent Green's function defined as

$$G(P_\alpha P_\beta, t) = \langle P_\alpha(t) P_\beta(0) \rangle \qquad \text{for} \quad t > 0$$
$$= \langle P_\beta(0) P_\alpha(t) \rangle \qquad \text{for} \quad t < 0. \tag{2.47}$$

Looking for the one-phonon contribution to χ we take P_α from Eq. (2.30) and then neglecting the mixing of different optic modes (with $\mathbf{q} \to 0$), χ can be expressed in terms of one-phonon Green's functions as (Cowley, 1963)

$$\chi^{\alpha\beta}(\omega) = \chi_\infty^{\alpha\beta} + \frac{1}{4\pi kT}\sum_j (f_{j\alpha}f_{j\beta})^{1/2} G(Q_jQ_j, \omega - i\delta)$$
$$= \chi_\infty^{\alpha\beta} + \frac{1}{4\pi}\sum_j \frac{(f_{j\alpha}f_{j\beta})^{1/2}}{\omega_j^2 - \omega^2 + 2\,\omega_j\,[\Delta(j,\omega) + i\Gamma(j,\omega)]} \tag{2.48}$$

Δ and Γ are the real and imaginary parts, respectively, of the anharmonic self-energies of the normal modes. The former determines the change of frequency and the latter the damping of the phonon due to anharmonic interactions with other phonons. If the frequency shift Δ and damping Γ are small and nearly frequency independent, then the equations $\omega^2 = \omega_j^2 + 2\omega_j\,\Delta(j,\omega)$ determine the quasi-harmonic frequencies $\omega_j(T)$ at which the imaginary part $\chi''(\omega)$ of Eq. (2.48) has local maxima; $2\Gamma(j,\omega_j(T))$ gives the full width at half maximum of $\chi''(\omega)$. The dispersion formula (Eq. (2.48)) is equivalent to the classical harmonic oscillator formula for χ (Eq. (2.33)) if we identify $\omega_j(T)$ and $2\omega_j\Gamma(j,\omega)$ with ω_j and $\omega\gamma_j$ of the formula (Eq. (2.33)), respectively.

Such a picture corresponds to a weakly anharmonic crystal in which the individual phonons, describing small coherent displacements of atoms from their equilibrium positions, have sufficiently long lifetime—the so-called displacive regime (Bruce, 1982). On the other hand, in a strongly anharmonic crystal each atom is localized near two (or more) minima of its strongly anharmonic potential. In this case, besides relatively fast atomic oscillations about the potential minima which represent a displacive regime in a quasi-statically disordered crystal, there exists a new dynamical degree of freedom, i.e., the hopping of atoms between the potential minima—the so-called order–disorder regime. The polarization connected by these hopping processes satisfies (in the molecular field approximation) the equation of motion

$$\dot{P} + \frac{1}{\tau}P = 0 \tag{2.49}$$

which, when using Eq. (2.37), leads to the Debye relaxation-type formula

$$\chi(\omega) = \frac{\chi_0}{1 + i\omega\tau}. \tag{2.50}$$

This formula expresses the contribution of the "inertialess" polarization coupled with the bath of much faster variables. At low frequencies it is reasonable to approximate the random force correlation function by $\delta(t)$ and hence the relaxation time is frequency independent in such a frequency range. The maximum of the imaginary part $\chi''(\omega)$ of Eq. (2.50) at $\omega = \tau^{-1}$ is equal to $\chi''(\tau^{-1}) = \chi_0/2$. Obviously, at high frequencies the inertia of P cannot be neglected and the formula (Eq. (2.50)) overestimates the dielectric response of a system; consequently the integral of $\omega\chi''(\omega)$ over ω diverges, i.e., it does not satisfy the sum rule (2.15). Even at low frequencies the Debye formula is satisfied only exceptionally—in systems in which the dielectric response is dominated by a single low-frequency polarization mode. This is the case of order–disorder ferroelectric SPTs. More general formulae describing the low-frequency dielectric relaxation have been recently discussed by Ngai (1979).

C. Soft Mode in the Dielectric Spectrum

1. Generalized Susceptibility of the Soft Mode

From a phenomenological point of view an SPT results from the loss of stability of the parent phase. The stability of the crystal is restored by a distortion of the parent phase and in this way a distorted (ordered) phase is created. The distortion is described by a nonzero averaged value of the order parameter η defined in the Landau theory of phase transitions (Cochran, 1971). In general, the stability of a phase with respect to a change $\delta\eta$ of η (we recall that η is zero in the parent phase and nonzero in the distorted phase) can be expressed in terms of the static value $\chi_\eta(0)$ of the generalized susceptibility $\chi_\eta(\omega)$ defined as $\delta\eta = \mathrm{Re}\{\chi_\eta(\omega)F_\eta e^{i\omega t}\}$, where F_η is the amplitude of the force conjugate to η. A phase is stable as far as $\chi_\eta(0)$ is positive and finite. At T_c the stability limit is reached, which means that $\chi_\eta(0)$ becomes infinite; indeed under such circumstances η changes spontaneously even without an applied F_η to the crystal and a distorted phase occurs. We can give a dynamical interpretation of the divergence of $\chi_\eta(0)$: the pole of $\chi_\eta(\omega)$ in the lower half-plane of complex ω represents a collective mode of the crystal. Since at T_c, $\chi_\eta(\omega \to 0) \to \infty$ the frequency of this so-called soft mode goes to zero. The relation of the divergence of $\chi_\eta(0)$ to anomalies in the excitation spectrum of η follows from general arguments (Schneider et al., 1972): it is well known that the space–time Fourier transform of the order-parameter correlation function — the dynamical structure factor $S_\eta(\omega)$ — determines the density of states excited by F_η. $S_\eta(\omega)$ is related to $\chi_\eta''(\omega)$ through the famous fluctuation–dissipation theorem (Kubo, 1957), which for low-lying excitations is given by

$$S_\eta(\omega) \simeq k_B T \frac{\chi_\eta''(\omega)}{\omega}. \tag{2.51}$$

Using the Kramers–Kronig relation (Eq. (2.8)) we conclude that at T_c

$$P \int_{-\infty}^{+\infty} \frac{\chi_\eta''(\omega)}{\omega} d\omega \to \infty. \tag{2.52}$$

On the other hand, it can be shown (Schneider et al., 1972) that the first moment of $\chi_\eta''(\omega)$, i.e., $\int_{-\infty}^{+\infty} \omega\chi_\eta''(\omega)d\omega$, remains finite; in the case of dielectric susceptibility, this is a consequence of the sum rule (Eq. 2.15). Since the area under $\chi_\eta''(\omega)/\omega$ diverges but the area under $\omega^2\chi_\eta''(\omega)/\omega$ is finite, $\chi_\eta''(\omega)/\omega$ must be peaked for small ω. The divergence of $\chi_\eta(0)$ thus implies the existence of a peak at zero frequency of the density of states excited by F_η.

Consequently, the mean-square frequency ω_{av}^2 of excited modes tends to zero at T_c

$$\omega_{av}^2 = \int_0^\infty \omega^2 \frac{\chi_\eta''(\omega)}{\omega} d\omega \Big/ P \int_{-\infty}^{+\infty} \frac{\chi_\eta''(\omega)}{\omega} d\omega \to 0. \qquad (2.53)$$

These general considerations can be directly applied to the most interesting case for IR spectroscopy, i.e., when the soft mode is IR-active in the parent phase. The soft mode then carries the main part of the polarization which can be taken as the order parameter of the so-called proper ferroelectric phase transition (Dvořák, 1983).

In the case of a displacive ferroelectric SPT the soft mode is a transverse optic phonon and its contribution to $\chi(\omega)$ can be modeled by an oscillator formula as Eq. (2.33) (with j = 1). The Curie–Weiss law for the static permittivity at (proper) ferroelectric phase transitions and the Lyddane–Sachs–Teller relation suggest that the soft-mode frequency ω_T is strongly temperature dependent, within the Landau theory as $\omega_T^2 \sim (T - T_c)$. Not too close to T_c, ω_T lies typically in the 10–100 cm^{-1} region.† The temperature dependence of ω_T can be accounted for by considering anharmonic phonon interactions. As it follows from Eq. (2.48), for small damping $(\gamma_T \ll \omega_T)$ the frequency ω_T in Eq. (2.33) should be replaced by the temperature dependent quasi-harmonic frequency $\omega_T(T)$ at which $\chi''(\omega)$ is peaked.

In the case of an order–disorder ferroelectric SPT the soft mode is a relaxation mode of the hopping processes. The dynamics of this polarization mode is governed by the basic equation of irreversible thermodynamics (Landau and Khalatnikov, 1965)

$$\dot{P} = -\lambda \frac{\partial F(P,T,V)}{\partial P}, \qquad (2.54)$$

where F is the free energy of the crystal describing the ferroelectric phase transition and λ is the kinetic coefficient which is assumed to be temperature independent. Linearizing this equation with respect to P and comparing it with Eq. (2.49) we conclude that $\tau = \lambda^{-1}\chi(0)$, that is, the relaxation time τ is temperature dependent and diverges at T_c as the static susceptibility does. This phenomenon is referred to as the *critical slowing down* of the relaxation

---

† When comparing with experiments, we shall use the more convenient IR spectroscopic unit cm^{-1} for ω instead of s^{-1}. Note that 1 cm$^{-1} = 2\pi c$ s$^{-1} \simeq 1.88 \times 10^{11}$ s$^{-1} = 3 \times 10^{10}$ Hz. Here cm^{-1} is a unit for the wavenumber $\nu = \lambda^{-1}$, Hz for the frequency $f = cv$, and s^{-1} for angular frequency $\omega = 2\pi f$. As all three quantities are mutually proportional, we can use any of these units for each of these quantities.

mode. Typical values of τ^{-1} (not too close to T_c) at which the maximum of $\chi''(\omega)$ occurs, lie in the 0.1–1 cm^{-1} region.

In a real crystal we usually do not observe a purely displacive or order–disorder regime. Actually in many cases the $\chi''(\omega)$ spectrum consists of two peaks, at least in the vicinity of T_c, one which is typical for the displacive behavior and one for the order–disorder behavior. Far from T_c the higher frequency peak predominates in the spectrum and softens, but near T_c its frequency remains finite and the softening is taken over by the lower frequency peak which then prevails in the spectrum. The latter dispersion appears as a central peak in the dynamical structure factor $S(\omega)$ in a scattering experiment and is frequently called the central peak or central mode. The simplest model dispersion which contains all features of the picture described above is (Feder, 1976)

$$\chi(\omega,T) \sim \left[\omega_T^2(T) - \omega^2 + i\omega\gamma_T - \frac{\delta^2}{1 + i\omega\tau} \right]^{-1} \tag{2.55}$$

or equivalently (Bruce and Cowley, 1980)

$$\chi(\omega,T) \sim \left[\tilde{\omega}_T^2(T) - \omega^2 + i\omega\gamma_T + \frac{i\omega\tau\delta^2}{1 + i\omega\tau} \right]^{-1}, \tag{2.56}$$

where $\tilde{\omega}_T^2 = \omega_T^2(T) - \delta^2$ is the renormalized eigenfrequency in the low-frequency limit. Here δ is the real bilinear coupling constant between the soft oscillator with the bare eigenfrequency $\omega_T(T) = a(T - T_0)^\beta$ ($\beta = 0.5$ in the mean-field approximation) and a Debye relaxation with the relaxation time τ. For high frequency $\omega\tau \gg 1$, $\omega\tau \gg \delta(\tau/\gamma_T)^{1/2}$, the response is given by the bare oscillator

$$\chi(\omega) \sim (\omega_T^2(T) - \omega^2 + i\omega\gamma_T)^{-1}. \tag{2.57}$$

On the other hand, the low-frequency response for $\omega\tau \ll 1$, $\omega\tau \ll \tilde{\omega}_T/(\delta^2 - \tau^{-2})^{-1/2}$ is given by the renormalized Debye relaxation

$$\chi(\omega) \sim \tilde{\omega}_T^{-2} (1 + i\omega\tilde{\tau})^{-1} \tag{2.58}$$

with a new relaxation time $\tilde{\tau} = (\gamma_T + \delta^2\tau)/\tilde{\omega}_T^2$. The static susceptibility diverges at the new critical temperature

$$T_c = T_0 + \left(\frac{\delta}{a} \right)^{1/\beta} \tag{2.59}$$

at which $\tilde{\omega}_T(T_c) = 0$ and $1/\tilde{\tau}(T_c) = 0$. Therefore, near T_c the $\chi''(\omega)$ spectrum is dominated by the low-frequency relaxation with critical slowing-down of τ which describes the central-peak phenomenon.

Several mechanisms can be responsible for the occurrence of the central peak in general (Bruce and Cowley, 1980). Of them, phonon density fluctuations and most impurity relaxations are expected to appear in the very low-frequency dielectric spectrum. The ferroelectric domain wall dispersion appears typically in the $10^4 - 10^7$ Hz region. We shall not discuss these low-frequency processes further, but take into account only dispersion processes above $\sim 10^8$ Hz. If the central peak occurs in this higher frequency region it is most probably caused by some intrinsic effect due to lattice anharmonicity. In this case a crystal displaying displacive characteristics far from T_c, exhibits in the critical region near T_c a crossover to order–disorder behavior (Bruce, 1982). As a result far from T_c the dynamical structure factor $S(\omega) \sim \chi''(\omega)/\omega$ should contain a peak at the temperature dependent quasi-harmonic frequency $\omega_T(T)$ due to a softening phonon. Experimentally the frequency $\omega_T(T)$ can be determined from the maximum of dielectric losses $\chi''(\omega)$ provided the damping γ_T is sufficiently small. Near T_c, $S(\omega)$ should contain two qualitatively different peaks reflecting the dynamics of a strongly anharmonic crystal:

(1)   a peak corresponding to a phonon of a quasi-statically disordered crystal which is practically temperature independent and

(2)   a central peak due to a diffuse motion of walls between locally ordered clusters which is a collective manifestation of hopping processes.

The critical slowing down of this motion causes narrowing and growing in intensity of this intrinsic central peak as it follows from Eq. (2.50)

$$\chi''(\omega)/\omega = \frac{\chi_0 \tau}{1 + \omega^2 \tau^2}. \qquad (2.60)$$

The quantity τ can be determined experimentally from the lower frequency maximum of $\chi''(\omega)$. In the crossover regime when the soft mode becomes heavily damped, the basic characteristics of the mode, i.e., the real and imaginary parts of the pole of $\chi(\omega)$ cannot be unambiguously determined independently by fitting to a damped harmonic oscillator formula (Eq. (2.33)). In such a case it is useful to characterize the critical mode by the modulus of the lowest complex pole of $\chi(\omega)$ which for an overdamped oscillator approximately equals ω_T^2/γ_T (Takagi and Shigenari, 1979).

2. Selection Rules for the Soft-Mode Absorption in the IR Spectrum and the Static Dielectric Anomaly

We shall now discuss the kind of SPTs in which the soft mode is active in the first-order absorption spectra. As we have already pointed out (see Eq. (2.30)) a mode is IR active if its effective charge is nonzero, that is, if its eigenvector transforms like a polar vector. Infrared activity of soft modes was discussed in detail by Petzelt (1974). A soft mode is IR-active in the parent phase in the case of proper ferroelectric transitions only. In the distorted phase the situation is more complicated. We have to realize that the degeneracy of a soft mode in the parent phase, if any, is always lifted in the distorted phase, at least partially, due to the reduction of symmetry. One of the soft-mode components is always totally symmetric, i.e., it is invariant with respect to all symmetry elements of the distorted phase. This totally symmetric component is IR-active provided the distorted phase belongs to a polar crystal class. This is the case of proper and improper ferroelectric SPTs and moreover of nonferroelectric SPTs with a polar parent phase. We recall that the order parameter of an improper ferroelectric transition is not any of the components of the polarization P_i; the spontaneous polarization occurs as a secondary effect due to the coupling of P_i to the order parameter η (Dvořák, 1974). There are no general rules for the activity of the non-totally symmetric components. For instance, the order parameter for the phase transition in $CsCuCl_3$ from the parent phase D_{6h}^4 ($Z = 2$) into D_6^2 ($Z = 6$) has four components and one of the non-totally symmetric soft-mode components below T_c is IR-active even if the distorted phase is nonpolar (Petzelt *et al.*, 1981).

The IR-active soft modes also determine the main features of the static dielectric anomaly around the transition. In proper ferroelectrics the soft mode is active both in the parent and distorted phases and consequently its effective charge is practically temperature-independent. The corresponding component of the static permittivity fulfills the Curie–Weiss law

$$\epsilon_0 = \frac{C}{T - T_c} + \epsilon_\infty, \qquad (2.61)$$

where the temperature dependent term represents, in fact, the soft-mode contribution and ϵ_∞ represents accordingly the total contribution of all hard modes, i.e., all other modes which are not directly involved in the phase transition.

In the case of improper ferroelectrics the soft mode is active only below T_c and therefore it does not contribute to ϵ_0 above T_c. Obviously, the strength f of the soft mode should be temperature-dependent below T_c since it must vanish above T_c. Actually, the temperature dependence of f can be found from the coupling of the polarization with the order parameter η, i.e., with the soft-mode amplitude Q. In improper ferroelectrics the schematic form of this coupling is $\eta^n P$ (the index n is sometimes referred to as the faintness index (Aizu, 1972)). Linearizing this term and comparing it to Eq. (2.30) we find that $f \propto \eta_s^{(n-1)/2}$. In the framework of Landau theory both the spontaneous value of the order parameter η_s and the soft-mode frequency ω_s are proportional to $(T_c - T)^{1/2}$. Therefore the soft-mode contribution $\Delta\epsilon_s$ to ϵ_0 is

$$\Delta\epsilon_s = \frac{f}{\omega_s^2} \propto (T_c - T)^{n-2}. \tag{2.62}$$

For many improper ferroelectrics $n = 2$ so that $\Delta\epsilon_s$ is temperature-independent and exhibits at T_c a positive stepwise anomaly. For $n \geq 3$ the dielectric anomaly would be generally small and $\Delta\epsilon_s$ would change continuously. We note that these considerations hold only for continuous (second-order) SPTs, whereas most real improper ferroelectric SPTs are strongly discontinuous. In this case any type of discontinuity in $\Delta\epsilon_s$ may occur (Dvořák, 1973).

Concerning the dielectric anomaly caused by the soft mode, there are two further classes of SPTs which deserve special attention: antiferroelectrics and incommensurate ferroelectric SPTs.

3. Dielectric Anomaly at Antiferroelectric Transitions

Antiferroelectricity played an important role in the early stage of investigation of SPTs. By analogy with antiferromagnetic transitions it was assumed that an antiferroelectric structure contains two or an even number of spontaneously polarized sublattices which pairwise compensate each other. However, unlike the magnetic case, the sublattice polarization in an ionic crystal has a well-defined meaning only with respect to some reference undistorted structure. This is because each ion has a well-defined magnetic dipole moment (spin) but only an electric charge rather than an electric dipole moment. (Here we do not consider molecular crystals in which, with a molecule on a particular lattice site, a definite dipole moment could be associated.) Therefore, an antiferroelectric structure has no absolute meaning but depends on the reference structure which in the case of an SPT is provided by the undistorted parent phase. Antiferroelectricity due to an order–disorder SPT can still be well defined in the same way as in antiferromagnets since a definite dipole moment can be attributed to an ion hopping between two (or more) potential minima with respect to its average position in the parent phase. A useful definition of a displacive antiferroelectric SPT based on symmetry arguments was given by Roos et al. (1976). The definition uses the concept of symmetry coordinates of lattice vibrations and differs for ferrodistortive (equitranslational, i.e., without a change of number of atoms in the primitive unit cell or zone center) and antiferrodistortive (nonequitranslational or zone boundary) transitions. This is illustrated by two simple examples shown in Fig. 1. In the ferrodistortive case the antiferro-electric structure is created by the condensation of a zone-center soft mode whereas in the antiferrodistortive case it is created by condensation of

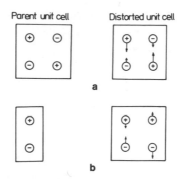

Fig. 1. Schematic illustration of antiferroelectric ordering in ionic crystals: (a) ferrodistortive case, (b) antiferrodistortive case. The arrows indicate ion displacements in the distorted phase.

a zone-boundary soft mode.   Most of the known antiferroelectrics belong to the latter category.   The dielectric anomaly observed at an antiferrodistortive antiferroelectric transition is explained by partial softening of the particular zone-center polar mode which belongs to the same phonon branch as the zone-boundary soft mode.   This feature of the soft branch reflects a small energy difference between antiferroelectric and ferroelectric states.

We would like to note that during the last decade the concept of antiferroelectricity nearly disappeared from the literature.   The reason is that no macroscopic physical property can be found which would unambiguously characterize the antiferroelectric state (contrary to proper and improper ferroelectricity and ferroelasticity).

4. Soft Modes and the Dielectric Anomaly in Incommensurate Ferroelectrics

Many SPTs are known giving rise to incommensurate phases characterized by a frozen-in soft mode, the wavevector $\mathbf{k}$ of which is an irrational fraction of a basic vector $\mathbf{a}^*$ in the reciprocal space of the parent lattice. (More details about incommensurate phases can be found, e.g., in the review by Dvořák, 1980.)   As a result an ordering develops at a temperature T_i which is incommensurate with the underlying lattice.   Since $\mathbf{k}_i$ is usually located near a special point $\mathbf{k}_c$ of the Brillouin zone (e.g., $\mathbf{k}_c = 0, \frac{1}{2}\mathbf{a}^*, \frac{1}{3}\mathbf{a}^*$) an incommensurate phase can be looked on as a modulated commensurate phase which would be induced by a frozen-in soft mode with $\mathbf{k}_c$.   As a rule the incommensurate phase usually exists in some limited temperature region within which the shape of the incommensurate structure gradually changes: Near below T_i the crystal is modulated sinusoidally.   With decreasing temperature, domains of the nearly commensurate phase develop in the incommensurate phase, separated by domain walls (discommensurations), the density of which decreases. Finally at a temperature T_c the incommensurate phase changes (as a rule discontinuously) into a homogeneous commensurate phase. Accordingly, $\mathbf{k}_i$ changes with the temperature and at T_c locks in a commensurate value $\mathbf{k}_c$. If the order parameter of an incommensurate phase is a polarization wave $P(\mathbf{k}_i)$ and $\mathbf{k}_i$ locks in at $\mathbf{k}_c = 0$, then the incommensurate phase can be classified as an incommensurate proper ferroelectric since the low-temperature commensurate phase is in this case a proper ferroelectric. Similarly, if the order parameter of an incommensurate phase is of a nonpolar nature, its only n-th harmonic is coupled to $P(\mathbf{K})$, where $\mathbf{K} = n\mathbf{k}_i$ plus a reciprocal lattice vector, and $\mathbf{K}$ locks in at the Brillouin zone center, then the incommensurate phase is called an incommensurate improper ferroelectric since the commensurate phase is in this case an improper ferroelectric (with the faintness index n). Obviously, only incommensurate proper and improper ferroelectrics are of greatest interest for IR studies.

The soft mode $\eta(\mathbf{k}_i)$ responsible for an incommensurate transition is at least doubly degenerate: $\eta(\mathbf{k}_i)$, $\eta(-\mathbf{k}_i)$. Below T_i this degeneracy is lifted and at least two soft-mode branches $A(\mathbf{q})$ and $\varphi(\mathbf{q})$ appear. Near T_i they are given for small $|\mathbf{q}|$ by

$$A(\mathbf{q}) = (1/\sqrt{2})\,[\eta(\mathbf{k}_i + \mathbf{q}) + \eta(-\mathbf{k}_i + \mathbf{q})],$$
$$\varphi(\mathbf{q}) = (1/\sqrt{2})\,[\eta(\mathbf{k}_i + \mathbf{q}) - \eta(-\mathbf{k}_i + \mathbf{q})]. \tag{2.63}$$

The $A(\mathbf{q})$ modes are called amplitudons since they represent fluctuations of the amplitude of the frozen-in wave $\eta(\mathbf{k}_i) + \eta(-\mathbf{k}_i)$. The $\varphi(\mathbf{q})$ modes represent fluctuations of the phase of this wave and hence are called phasons. Amplitudons behave like normal soft modes below T_i. The amplitudon branch has a temperature dependent gap which disappears at T_i. On the other hand, the phason branch is always gapless reflecting the fact that the energy of the frozen-in incommensurate wave does not depend on its position in an ideal lattice. As for an acoustic branch, the dispersion of phasons for small $|\mathbf{q}|$ is $\omega_\varphi(\mathbf{q}) \sim |\mathbf{q}|$. Unlike acoustic modes, phasons are overdamped for sufficiently small $|\mathbf{q}|$ as normal soft modes near the phase transition temperature. The gapless phason branch represents a qualitatively new feature of lattice vibrations specific for ideal incommensurate phases. It should be pointed out that pinning of the incommensurate wave by crystal imperfections may introduce a gap into the phason spectrum.

It is of great interest to observe phasons (and amplitudons) directly in a light scattering or absorption experiment. The selection rules for IR activity of these excitations in an incommensurate phase were derived by Dvořák and Petzelt (1978). As usual with SPTs some modes which were IR inactive in the parent phase (e.g., modes with nonzero wavevectors) become active in the distorted phase. It can be shown that in the case of an incommensurate phase, phasons and amplitudons with the same wavevector $\mathbf{K}$ as the frozen-in polarization wave $P(\mathbf{K})$ give rise to homogeneous polarization and therefore are IR active. The incommensurate structure consists, however, of many higher polarization frozen-in harmonics induced by anharmonic interaction of P with the soft mode η. Therefore, unlike a commensurate phase, a series of modes from phason and amplitudon branches the wavevectors of which are equal to wavevectors of frozen-in polarization harmonics, are IR active in an incommensurate phase. It should be pointed out that the effective electric charges of these higher harmonics are extremely small and thus the corresponding absorption lines will be extremely weak. The IR activity of nearly homogeneous phasons $\varphi(\mathbf{q} \simeq 0)$ deserves special investigation. It turns out that, as in the case of acoustic modes, such phasons can appear in the dielectric spectrum provided the incommensurate phase originates from a piezoelectric parent phase (Golovko and Levanyuk, 1981; Petzelt, 1981). If the phason branch is really gapless (as in an ideal infinite crystal), it manifests itself as a low-frequency relaxation whose dispersion frequency is determined by the sample geometry as in the case of piezoelectric resonances.

The IR-active amplitudon $A(\mathbf{K})$ and especially the phason $\varphi(\mathbf{K})$ are responsible for specific and pronounced static dielectric anomalies near T_c of the incommensurate ferroelectric phases. With decreasing temperature, the $\mathbf{K}$ of the frozen-in polarization wave tends to zero (remember that the C phase is ferroelectric) so that the IR-active phason $\varphi(\mathbf{K})$ of frequency $\omega_\varphi \sim |\mathbf{K}|$ gradually softens giving rise to an increase of the permittivity ϵ_0. Near T_c, when the incommensurate structure acquires a domain-like character, modes of the phason branch represent coherent oscillations of domain walls. The IR active mode is represented by anti-phase motion of domain walls separating domains with opposite polarization. The frequency of this mode is essentially determined by the repulsion of neighboring domain walls and at T_c goes to zero since the domain-wall separation becomes infinite. In this way we can qualitatively understand the divergence of ϵ_0 approaching T_c from higher temperatures (Nattermann, 1982). On the other hand, in a single-domain commensurate phase below T_c the active phason disappears and a sudden decrease of ϵ_0 is observed. This one-sided divergence of ϵ_0 at a second-order transition point T_c (incommensurate–commensurate phase transitions are usually weakly first order) is a significant feature of incommensurate ferroelectrics. Especially in improper ferroelectrics, where the dielectric anomaly is small in the absence of an incommensurate phase, the occurrence of a sharp peak in ϵ_0 at T_c is clear evidence for an intermediate incommensurate phase. (All problems discussed in this section are more thoroughly treated in the recent review by Petzelt, 1981).

D. Hard-Mode Spectroscopy

The existence of soft modes is doubtless the most interesting manifestation of SPTs which can be revealed in IR or Raman spectra. But it is by no means the most striking change induced by SPTs. As a rule, the most striking spectral changes occur for some hard modes (i.e., modes other than soft modes). They consist in either activation of silent modes and/or the splitting of degenerate modes below the transition temperature T_c.

A general Landau-type thermodynamic theory expressing the changes of mode frequencies and strengths in terms of the spontaneous value of the order parameter η_s was worked out by Petzelt and Dvořák (1976a). The basic idea is as follows: Let us assume an experimental arrangement such that in each spectrum modes of only one particular symmetry (i.e., belonging to a particular irreducible representation of the parent symmetry group) are active. In IR reflection or transmission experiments this can be achieved simply by choosing the E vector of the incident IR radiation along one of the crystallographic axes. Let us discuss such a spectrum. In the parent phase it consists of peaks corresponding to active normal modes of a particular symmetry. Due to the symmetry change of the distorted phase these modes are, in general, no longer normal, i.e., they are bilinearly coupled each to the other and possibly also to some modes of another symmetry in the parent phase. Obviously, all bilinearly coupled modes must be in the distorted phase of the same symmetry. Neglecting interactions with electronic degrees of freedom, this type of coupling determines all first-order spectral changes of interest.

In particular, mode strengths and frequencies of all active normal modes can be calculated from the diagonalized quadratic part of the mode potential corresonding to a distorted phase. Using group theory the leading coupling term in the mode potential of the parent phase can be found which near a second-order transition determines the lowest power of η_s to which spectral changes are proportional. In general, this power depends on the symmetry of the parent phase as well as on the symmetry reduction due to an SPT. Nevertheless some generally valid conclusions can be drawn: The mean frequency shift defined as $(1/n) \sum_{i=1}^{n} [\omega_i(T < T_c) - \omega(T_c)]$ (n is the number of degenerate-mode components in the parent phase of frequency ω) of hard and soft modes is proportional to η_s^2 and η_s, respectively. Frequency splitting, if any, is proportional to η_s^s and η_s^{s-1} for hard and soft modes, respectively. The powers may be different for different types of SPTs, but for all investigated examples, s was found to be 1 or 2. The change of strength Δf of modes active already in the parent phase is proportional to η_s^2 unless *the splitting exponent $s = 1$* in which case $\Delta f \sim \eta_s$. The activation of a silent mode in the spectrum is caused by bilinear coupling of this mode to modes active already in the parent phase. This coupling occurring in the distorted phase originates from coupling terms in the parent phase which are specific for a particular SPT and therefore the power of η_s to which the mode strength is proportional is also not universal. In all investigated examples this power was equal to 2 or 4. The strength of the activated silent mode is taken from the strengths of active modes in the parent phase since the total sum of all mode strengths in a spectrum remains approximately constant throughout an SPT. This is a direct consequence of the sum rule (2.36) when the change of ionicity, i.e., of ion effective charges, is neglected.

The theory of Petzelt and Dvořák (1976a) was applied to 18 SPTs for which some experimental data were known until 1975 (Petzelt and Dvořák, 1976b). As far as the IR activation of hard modes was concerned the best agreement with the theory was found for quartz (Gervais and Piriou, 1975), the most striking disagreement for the E_u libration mode at 345 cm^{-1} in NH$_4$Br (Novák and Petzelt, 1976). In many cases mode overlapping and/or second-order effects prevent the theory to be quantitatively testified.

Damping $\Gamma(j,\omega_j)$ of IR-active modes (see Eq. (2.48)) is another important characteristic which exhibits temperature anomalies near an SPT and which can be studied by IR spectroscopy. Damping Γ of a mode in an ideal crystal is caused by the scattering of this mode by other thermally excited modes. If a mode is effectively scattered by modes from a soft branch the frequencies of which are strongly temperature-dependent, then temperature anomalies of Γ near T_c may be expected. There are several types of scattering processes. For example, damping due to three-phonon anharmonic interaction is given by (Maradudin and Fein, 1962)

$$\Gamma(j,\omega_j) = \frac{\pi\hbar}{16N\omega_j} \sum_{k_1,j_1,j_2} \left(\left| \phi_3 \begin{pmatrix} 0 & k_1 & -k_1 \\ j & j_1 & j_2 \end{pmatrix} \right|^2 \bigg/ \omega_1\omega_2 \right)$$
$$\times \{(n_1 + n_2 + 1)\delta(\omega_1 + \omega_2 - \omega_j) + 2(n_1 - n_2)\delta(\omega_1 - \omega_2 + \omega_j)\}, \qquad (2.64)$$

where ϕ_3 is the Fourier transform of the third-order anharmonic interaction constant, n_i is the population factor of the j_ith phonon with the frequency $\omega_{j_i}(k_{j_i})$ and N is the number of unit cells in the crystal. The first term in the braces describes the decay of the jth phonon into two other phonons and the second term describes a process in which the jth phonon together with another phonon are annihilated to create a single phonon. For derivation of the temperature dependence of Γ in an explicit form details of phonon dispersion curves are needed. Qualitatively, as it follows from Eq. (2.64), the temperature dependence of Γ comes from the temperature dependence of n_i and the two-phonon density of states via the temperature dependence of soft-mode frequencies. Indeed the temperature dependence of damping of hard modes in quartz has been qualitatively explained in this way (Gervais et *al.*, 1975). The type of the temperature dependence of Γ depends on the nature of scattering soft modes, i.e., whether they are in a particular temperature region of oscillator or relaxation character. Damping of a hard mode in an order–disorder system has been studied by Matsushita (1976). It turns out that damping, due to third-order scattering by pseudospins describing the hopping of atoms between potential minima, can be related to the pseudospin dynamical structure factor which near T_c exhibits temperature anomalies.

It should be pointed out that the origin of temperature-dependent damping of soft modes is better understood (Balagurov *et al.*, 1970). From Eq. (2.64) it is clear that the most effective processes are those in which lowest lying branches of the excitation spectrum, i.e., soft and acoustic branches, are taking part. The most important third-order processes are those in which two soft modes and one acoustic mode are involved and below T_c mainly interactions of three phonons from the soft branch. These processes give no anomaly in Γ as far as the soft branch retains its oscillator character (small damping). This is true for Brillouin-zone corner soft modes also (Pytte, 1970). In the most important fourth-order process, four modes from the soft branch take part. In this case the soft-mode damping behaves as $| T - T_c |^{-1/2}$ provided the mode-damping is small. Sufficiently near T_c the soft mode usually becomes overdamped. In such a case, as well as in order–disorder systems, soft-mode dynamics has a relaxation character with the relaxation time $\tau = \lambda^{-1}\chi_0$ (see Eq. (2.54)). Within the Landau theory (molecular field approximation) $\lambda^{-1} = \tau/\chi_0$ is temperature independent. The third- and fourth-order processes we have discussed give rise to anomalous corrections to λ^{-1} proportional to $| T - T_c |^{-1/2}$ and $| T - T_c |^{-1}$, respectively (Levanyuk and Schedrina, 1974).

III. EXPERIMENTAL TECHNIQUES

A. Powder Measurements

In the early days of IR spectroscopy the technique mostly used was transmission measurements on powder samples mixed with some transparent matrix and pressed into pellets. Until now this technique has been used for chemical analysis but in the physics of phase transitions it has little value. This is for two reasons. First, it averages all effects of crystal anisotropy which in the case of a lower crystal symmetry makes the assignment of vibrational modes difficult, especially in the low-frequency region of external lattice vibrations. Second, it is well known (see, e.g., Ruppin and Englman, 1970; Genzel, 1974) that the absorption peak corresponding to a single peak for an infinite crystal can reveal a complicated structure which in the limit of very small and dilute powder particles becomes a single, so-called Fröhlich mode (Fröhlich, 1949). Due to the depolarizing field of a particle, the Fröhlich mode frequency ω_F is shifted to higher frequencies with respect to the transverse mode frequency ω_T of an infinite crystal according to the formula

$$\frac{\omega_F^2}{\omega_T^2} = \frac{\epsilon_0 + \epsilon_M(\gamma^{-1} - 1)}{\epsilon_\infty + \epsilon_M(\gamma^{-1} - 1)}, \tag{2.65}$$

where γ is the depolarization factor [we suppose an ellipsoidal particle for which the depolarizing field is homogeneous (Landau and Lifshitz, 1960); e.g., for a sphere $\gamma = \frac{1}{3}$], ϵ_0 and ϵ_∞ are the static and optic permittivities, respectively (we assume only one optical mode), and ϵ_M is the permittivity of the medium in which the powder particles are embedded. It is supposed that ϵ_M is independent of ω. Therefore, especially for strong modes we observe a large Fröhlich shift from ω_T towards the corresponding ω_L ($\omega_L^2 = \omega_T^2 (\epsilon_0/\epsilon_\infty) > \omega_F^2$). For instance, in displacive proper ferroelectrics ω_F corresponding to the soft mode remains practically temperature-independent and high (Luxon et al., 1970). As the shape and size of powder particles varies in a real sample, the powder spectra can give only rough information about the lattice dynamics of phase transitions and are not at all suitable for revealing soft modes.

B. Bulk Reflectivity Measurements

Until now the most common technique used for the determination of the IR dielectric function is a normal bulk-reflectivity measurement. By this method we directly measure the power reflectivity R of a linearly polarized wave falling perpendicularly to a plane surface oriented in such a way that some principal axis of the crystal dielectric ellipsoid coincides with the polarization direction. The method can be used when the sample is sufficiently opaque so that we can neglect the multiple reflection, and the measured spectral range is sufficiently broad so that the Kramers–Kronig relations for calculating $\theta(\omega)$ can be used (see Eq. (2.22)). In the case of orthorhombic and higher symmetry the dielectric spectrum for the diagonal dielectric tensor component along the polarization direction can be obtained using Eqs. (2.20) and (2.23). Performing the measurements with the electric field E of the incident wave parallel to all nonequivalent principal axes of the dielectric ellipsoid we obtain the complete dielectric function of the crystal. In the case of monoclinic and triclinic crystal symmetry the situation is in general more complex. We need to analyze the polarization of all reflected waves and to perform a larger set of measurements and fit to more complicated formulae (Belousov and Pavinich, 1978; Pavinich and Belousov, 1978). Until now in most measurements on monoclinic or triclinic crystals these complications have been ignored.

Another method of evaluating the power reflectivity data is the oscillator dispersion analysis. It consists of a direct fit of $R(\omega)$ to various model formulae for $\epsilon(\omega)$, e.g., the sum of independent classical oscillators (Eq. (2.34)), or more generally, the product of generalized oscillators (Eq. (2.45)). In a special case of two oscillators we usually use formulae for coupled oscillators (Barker and Hopfield, 1964),

$$\epsilon(\omega) = \frac{f_1(\omega_2^2 - \omega^2 + i\omega\gamma_2) + f_2(\omega_1^2 - \omega^2 + i\omega\gamma_1) - 2\alpha\sqrt{f_1 f_2}}{(\omega_1^2 - \omega^2 + i\omega\gamma_1)(\omega_2^2 - \omega^2 + i\omega\gamma_2) - \alpha^2} + \epsilon_\infty, \tag{2.66}$$

$$\epsilon(\omega) = \frac{F_1(\Omega_2^2 - \omega^2 + i\omega\Gamma_2) + F_2(\Omega_1^2 - \omega^2 + i\omega\Gamma_1) - 2i\omega\Gamma\sqrt{F_1 F_2}}{(\Omega_1^2 - \omega^2 + i\omega\Gamma_1)(\Omega_2^2 - \omega^2 + i\omega\Gamma_2) + \omega^2\Gamma^2} + \epsilon_\infty. \tag{2.67}$$

The frequencies ω_i, damping constants γ_i, and strengths f_i in Eq. (2.66) refer to bare harmonic oscillators whereas Ω_i, Γ_i, and F_i in Eq. (2.67) refer to mixed normal modes arising from bilinear coupling between bare oscillators. The symbols α and Γ are coupling constants in the so-called real and imaginary representation of the mode coupling. Both these formulae are equivalent and it is the question of physical interpretation of individual parameters which coupling, i.e., real or imaginary, is preferably chosen for the fit. Without coupling both expressions (2.66) and (2.67) reduce to the formula for two classical oscillators (Eq. (2.34) with $n = 2$). Both Eqs. (2.66) and (2.67) are special cases of the more general Eq. (2.45) for $n = 2$.

The power reflectivity technique has a serious disadvantage in that the phase θ is not directly measured and therefore the accuracy of evaluating $\epsilon(\omega)$ is relatively low and dependent on the width of the spectral range measured. We overcome this deficiency by a novel technique called dispersive (or asymmetric) Fourier transform spectrometry (see, e.g., Birch and Parker, 1979). The technique is based on a two-beam interferometer with the specimen placed in one beam rather than in front of the detector as for conventional Fourier transform spectrometry. This enables us to determine both amplitude and phase of the reflected (or transmitted) wave while only the power reflectance (or transmittance) is measured in the conventional Fourier transform spectrometry. Unfortunately, presently no commercial devices for dispersive spectrometry have been produced, so that results concerning the spectroscopy of phase transitions using this technique are still scarce.

C. Transmission Measurements

When partially transparent single crystalline samples can be prepared, transmission measurements are more useful and accurate than bulk reflectivity measurements because they are much more sensitive to changes of the optical constants. This happens mostly in the very far or near IR, outside the region of strong first-order phonon absorption. The simplest method is to measure under conditions where the interference due to multiple passage of the beam through the sample is negligible. This can be achieved either by making the sample platelet slightly wedge-shaped (in the far IR) or merely by the noncoaxiality of the incident beam focused on the sample (in the near IR). In such cases the normal polarized transmittance, i.e., the ratio of transmitted to the incident radiation intensity (for $\kappa \ll n$) is

$$T(\omega) \sim \frac{(1 - R(\omega))^2}{e^{\alpha d} - R^2(\omega)e^{-\alpha d}}, \tag{2.68}$$

where α is the absorption coefficient and d the effective mean sample thickness. Knowing $T(\omega)$ and $R(\omega)$ or $n(\omega)$ (mostly constant over the spectral region investigated) from independent measurements, the absorption index $\kappa(\omega)$ or the dielectric losses $\epsilon''(\omega)$ can be calculated.

Transmission (or reflection) measurements on precisely plane parallel samples are more accurate and powerful. In this case the transmittance (or reflectance) spectrum alone, which has the form of channel spectra with interference due to multipass maxima and minima, is sufficient to determine the total $\epsilon(\omega)$ spectrum. The relevant formulae for the transmittance T and reflectance R (the ratio of the reflected and incident intensity) of radiation with wavenumber v which is incident normal to an absorbing layer of thickness d polarized along the principal axis of the dielectric tensor for orthorhombic and higher symmetry are (see Volkov *et al.,* 1979)

$$T(v) = \frac{(1 - R)^2 + 4R \sin^2\theta}{e^{\alpha d} + R^2 e^{-\alpha d} - 2R \cos 2 (\Phi + \theta)},$$

$$R(v) = \frac{1 + e^{-2\alpha d} - 2e^{-\alpha d} \cos 2\theta}{R^{-1} + Re^{-2\alpha d} - 2 e^{-\alpha d} \cos^2 2(\Phi + \varphi)}, \tag{2.69}$$

where $\alpha = 4\pi v\kappa$, $\Phi = 2\pi vnd$,

$$\varphi = \Phi - \arctan \frac{(n^2 + \kappa^2 - 1)\kappa}{(n^2 + \kappa^2)(n + 2) + n}$$

$$+ \arctan \frac{Re^{-\alpha d}\sin 2(\Phi + \theta)}{1 - Re^{-\alpha d}\cos 2(\Phi + \theta)}, \tag{2.70}$$

$$\theta = \arctan \frac{2\kappa}{n^2 + \kappa^2 - 1},$$

and R is given by Eq. (2.21). Analogous formulae for monoclinic samples were recently derived by Kroupa (1979). Let us assume that $n(v)$ and $\kappa(v)$ are weaker functions of v than $T(v)$ or $\mathcal{R}(v)$ (this can be achieved by employing a sufficient thickness of the platelet) and that n $\gg \kappa$. Then we can evaluate initially $n(v_m)$ at wavenumbers v_m, where $T(v)$ or $\mathcal{R}(v)$ reach their maxima or minima simply by measuring v_m and using the interference conditions for a transparent sample, and then using Eq. (2.67) for an iterative calculation of $\kappa(v_m)$. If these assumptions are not valid, additional independent measurements of $\varphi(v)$ are necessary using some interferometric method.

The method of transmission spectroscopy combined with phase measurements has been of late frequently used in the submillimeter monochromatic spectroscopic technique developed at the Moscow Physical Institute (Volkov et al., 1979, 1980c). The source of monochromatic radiation is provided by electron backward wave oscillators (BWOs). The main advantage of this new method consists in the possibility of continuous frequency tuning of BWOs by more than a factor of two on applying a bias electric field. About five such BWOs enable us to get a source of radiation in the $2-34$ cm^{-1} region with monochromaticity $v/\Delta v$ better than 10^4 and power of $10^{-3}-10^{-2}$ W. With such a spectrometer transmittance down to 10^{-5} and a phase shift with an accuracy of $1°$, are measurable.

Finally, let us mention that other experimental techniques have been developed in the middle and near IR, e.g., the attenuated total reflection method (see, e.g., Crawford et al., 1978), which are, however, until now of little use in the spectroscopy of SPTs in crystals. The same is true for tunable IR laser spectroscopy (see, e.g., McDowell, 1978) where, however, rapid and intensive development can be expected in the future.

IV. RESULTS ON PARTICULAR MATERIALS

A. Proper Ferroelectrics

Infrared and microwave spectroscopy played an important role in the history of proper ferroelectrics. It is the most useful technique for verification of the soft-mode idea in this class of SPTs, because the soft mode is active in both phases. In fact, soft modes were first found by far IR reflectivity in incipient ferroelectrics like SrTiO$_3$ (Barker and Tinkham, 1962) and KTaO$_3$ (Perry and McNelly, 1967), as well as in the ferroelectric perovskite BaTiO$_3$ (Ballantyne, 1964; Barker, 1966), and semiconductor SbSI (Petzelt, 1969), and by microwave waveguide technique in order–disorder ferroelectrics like TGS, DKDP (Hill and Ichiki, 1963), and NaNO$_2$ (Hatta, 1968).

During the last 15 years Raman scattering has been much more widely used for soft-mode spectroscopy of displacive SPTs because of its better accuracy and simpler evaluation of spectra than for IR reflection. However, in the last eight years the use of novel IR techniques (rapid scan Fourier transform, dispersive Fourier transform, BWO monochromatic spectroscopy) has revolutionized far IR soft-mode spectroscopy, with the results comparable to those obtained by Raman spectroscopy.

1. Incipient Ferroelectrics ($SrTiO_3$ and $KTaO_3$)

Although these materials are incipient ferroelectrics only and no ferroelectric transition occurs in the pure and unstressed $SrTiO_3$ and $KTaO_3$, $SrTiO_3$ was the first substance where the soft-mode idea was experimentally verified (by far IR reflection, Barker and Tinkham, 1962). On the other hand, $KTaO_3$ exhibits a very nice soft-mode behavior (Perry and McNelly, 1967), where the soft mode moves from 106 cm^{-1} at 463 K to 25 cm^{-1} at 12 K and accounts, as in $SrTiO_3$, for the whole ϵ_0.

Recently, the far IR response between 100 and 300 K was measured by dispersive Fourier transform spectroscopy in both substances (Pai et al., 1978a,b) and except for some fine structure between peaks the early results were confirmed. The most accurate data for $SrTiO_3$ in the 3–30 cm^{-1} region from 300 K down to 40 K were obtained using BWO spectroscopy by Irisova et al., (1974) and Bystrov et al., (1977). Even if the data are not in good quantitative agreement with the fit by Barker and Hopfield (1964), ϵ' (5.9 cm^{-1}) nicely fulfills the Curie–Weiss law above 50 K with $T_c = 36.5$ K and $C = 78,500$ which is in good agreement with static data. However, Servoin et al. (1980) measured the high-temperature reflectivity of $SrTiO_3$ from 300 to 1200 K and found that above 400 K the soft-mode frequency ω_s deviates from the classical Cochran law $\omega_s^2 \propto (T - T_c)$ (Cochran, 1960) and nearly saturates at ~ 160 cm^{-1}. This saturation cannot be explained only by a coupling between the soft mode and the TO mode at 180 cm^{-1}, which is very weak.

Very recently, Galzerani and Katiyar (1982) measured the low-temperature reflectivity of $SrTiO_3$ (300–15 K) with the emphasis on the antidistortive phase transition at 110 K. Below this transition the ferroelectric soft mode should split into A_{2u} and E_u components which were, however, not resolved in a polydomain sample. A new weak E_u mode, silent above 110 K, was observed at ~ 440 cm^{-1}, but its strength was temperature independent below ~ 100 K within the accuracy of experiment and fitting procedure, while the theory (Petzelt and Dvořák, 1976a) predicts proportionality to η_s^2.

2. Displacive Ferroelectrics

a. $BaTiO_3$ and $KNbO_3$

$BaTiO_3$ is a classical proper ferroelectric which undergoes the paraelectric–ferroelectric first-order transition at $T_{tr} = 395$ K (we shall reserve the symbols T_{tr} and T_c for first- and second-order transition temperatures, respectively). At lower temperatures $BaTiO_3$ undergoes two additional first-order transitions into orthorhombic and trigonal ferroelectric phases which were, however, not thoroughly investigated spectroscopically as no single-domain samples are available. The early far IR reflectivity measurements in the high temperature cubic phase performed by Ballantyne (1964) and better evaluated by Barker (1966) have shown that within the accuracy of the experiment, the Cochran law is fulfilled and, moreover, the soft-mode strength accounts for the total ϵ_0 (Curie–Weiss law). The new measurements performed in a much broader temperature region (300–1350 K) by rapid-scan Fourier spectroscopy (Luspin et $al.$, 1980) confirmed the Cochran law above ~ 500 K with an underdamped soft mode, but observed a stabilization of the (overdamped) soft-mode frequency at ~ 60 cm^{-1} in the 400–500 K region in contrast to Ballantyne's data.

In the tetragonal ferroelectric phase the F_{1u} soft mode splits into $A_1 + E$ components. The A_1 mode on single domain samples with properly etched surfaces was observed by Sanjurjo et $al.$ (1979 and 1980) at ~ 270 cm^{-1} with nearly no softening near T_{tr}. The E mode was most accurately evaluated from Raman scattering (Scalabrin et $al.$, 1977) and shows a further softening from 53 to 35 cm^{-1} on cooling from T_{tr} to 300 K. The far IR data does not account for the clamped static dielectric constant on single domain samples. The difference is especially pronounced for A_1 and F_{1u} spectra near T_{tr}. At room temperature a Debye type dispersion in the A_1 spectrum, which partially accounts for this difference, was observed at $3–4.10^9$ Hz (10^{-1} cm^{-1}) (Turik and Shevchenko, 1979), but comparison of the data at 1 cm^{-1} near T_{tr} (Benedict and Durand 1958) with the far IR reflectivity for $\omega \gtrsim 10$ cm^{-1} (Luspin et $al.$ 1980) leads to the conclusion that additional dispersion must occur in the $1–10$ cm^{-1} region revealing the characteristic features of a central peak. The existence of such a dispersion as well as the unusual character of the splitting of dielectric spectra in the tetragonal phase can be well explained by a partial order–disorder character of the transition as discussed in Section II.C.1 (Luspin et $al.$, 1981) which was also established in earlier structural studies.

Potassium niobate ($KNbO_3$) undergoes the same sequence of phase transitions as $BaTiO_3$ with a shift to higher temperatures. The reflectivity spectra in the high temperature cubic phase (700–1200 K) were performed by Quittet et $al.$ (1981) and Fontana et $al.$ (1981) and show a soft-mode behavior similar to $BaTiO_3$ with finite $\omega_s(T_{tr}) \simeq 90$ cm^{-1}. They also performed measurements in the orthorhombic phase (210–490 K), where further softening of the heavily damped B_2 soft-mode component was observed from ~70 to 50 cm^{-1} with decreasing temperature. For both $BaTiO_3$ and $KNbO_3$ it is supposed that the other two soft-mode components increase their frequencies in the orthorhombic phase, but no direct measurements are available. The discrepancy between ϵ_0 and $\epsilon(10$ cm$^{-1})$ determined from far IR measurements is large especially in the cubic phase so that, again, additional *central peak* dispersion is expected below 10 cm^{-1}.

b. LiTaO₃ and LiNbO₃

Lithium tantalate ($T_c = 890$ K) and lithium niobate ($T_c = 1480$ K) are isomorphous uniaxial ferroelectrics the properties of which have been intensively studied during the last two decades, both experimentally and theoretically (for a review see Lines and Glass, 1977). After a thorough theoretical analysis of many experimental data, Lines (1972) came to the conclusion that the phase transition (in $LiTaO_3$, at least) is intermediate between displacive and order–disorder. Spectroscopic data, among which the recent far IR reflectivity measurements (Servoin and Gervais, 1979, 1980) played the decisive role, have confirmed this conclusion. The spectra for the electric field parallel to the ferroelectric axis (for which the Curie–Weiss law is fulfilled by the free ϵ_0) which see the A_1 modes, evaluated by Kramers–Kronig analysis are shown in Figs. 2 and 3. Group theoretical analysis

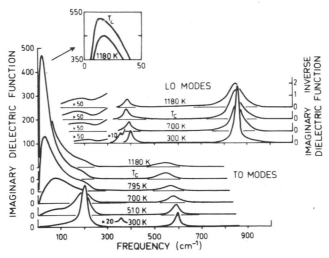

Fig. 2. Dielectric-loss spectra of $LiTaO_3$ for **E** ∥ **c** calculated from a Karmers–Kronig analysis of the reflectivity data (from Servoin and Gervais, 1979).

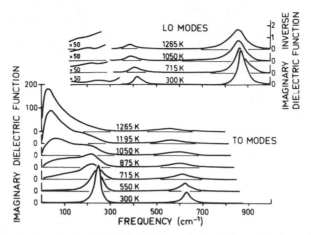

Fig. 3. Dielectric loss spectra of $LiNbO_3$ for $\mathbf{E} \parallel \mathbf{c}$ calculated from a Kramers–Kronig analysis of the reflectivity data (from Servoin and Gervais, 1979).

predicts $3A_{2u}$ and $4A_1$ modes for $\mathbf{E} \parallel \mathbf{c}$ in the paraelectric and ferroelectric phases, respectively. The fourth mode activated below T_c was observed only for $LiTaO_3$ (at ~ 360 cm^{-1}), whereas for $LiNbO_3$ it is known to be at 334 cm^{-1} from Raman measurements (Claus *et al.* 1972), but is too weak to be observed in IR reflectivity.

The most interesting is the region below 300 cm^{-1} consisting of two one-phonon absorption peaks which overlap at room temperature. Near T_c the spectrum is dominated by a strong overdamped low-frequency mode which nearly accounts for the whole static dielectric anomaly (except for about 100 K around T_c where additional microwave dispersion is therefore expected). This mode appears as a broad central peak in the Raman spectra and can be well fitted by the Debye relaxation (Penna *et al.,* 1976). However, it is not a central mode which occurs in addition to one-phonon spectral features. It is rather one of the $4A_1$ normal modes, which becomes nearly soft and heavily ovedamped near T_c. Therefore the displacive picture of the phase transitions seems to be more appropriate and only near T_c partial disorder (see Section II.C.1) is expected, in agreement with other experiments (see Lines and Glass, 1977). This disorder could be responsible for the additional dispersion which is expected below 10 cm^{-1}.

Whereas qualitatively the picture of the dielectric dispersion in $LiTaO_3$ and $LiNbO_3$ seems to be eventually clear, quantitatively there appeared serious problems with the fitting procedure of the reflectivity in several spectral regions, mainly below 300 cm^{-1} and around 450 cm^{-1} in both materials. Even the factorized 4-parameter oscillator model (Eq. (2.45)) was not sufficient to fit the dielectric spectra of the soft mode and the highest frequency mode. Servoin and Gervais (1979, 1976; Gervais and Servoin, 1977) succeeded in fitting the reflectivity spectra taking the phonon self-energy in the form

$$\Delta\omega(\omega) + i\Gamma(\omega) = \Delta\omega_0 + i\Gamma_0 + \frac{g^2}{\omega - \omega_{2ph} + (i/\tau)}, \qquad (2.71)$$

where ω_{2ph} is the frequency at which the two-phonon density of states is peaked (ω_{2ph} was set equal to zero for the fit of the soft-mode region) and τ is the mean lifetime of relevant phonons. This shows that anharmonicity plays a very important role in the lattice dynamics of these compounds. It remains to note that no such difficulties appear for the E spectra where the weak temperature dependence of the lowest frequency mode is also responsible for the slight increase of ϵ_0 near T_c, and no additional dispersion contribution is expected in the microwave region.

c. SbSI

Antimony sulfoiodide (SbSI) is a relatively simple semiconducting substance with a first-order proper ferroelectric transition at $T_{tr} \simeq 295$ K. It has a chain-like orthorhombic structure which is revealed by highly anisotropic optical and dielectric properties. The lattice dynamics of SbSI has been intensively studied since 1969. Like in ferroelectric pcrovskites and LiTaO$_3$, the soft mode is Raman inactive in the paraelectric phase (in ferroelectrics it can be Raman active only in noncentrosymmetric paraelectric phases) so that far IR spectroscopy is more suitable for studying the soft-mode dynamics. According to factor-group analysis, only two B_{1u} modes are active for polarization along the ferroelectric axis above T_{tr}, one of which should be soft if the transition were displacive. This theoretical expectation was confirmed first by Petzelt (1969). However, according to his results the soft mode does not soften sufficiently and in spite of the fact that it was found to be unusually strong (its contribution to ϵ_0 was $\Delta\epsilon_s \simeq 500$ at T_{tr}), it could not account for the total ϵ_0 which reaches the value of $\sim 3.10^4$ at T_{tr}. Several subsequent far IR measurements (Agrawal and Perry, 1971; Sugawara and Nakamura, 1972; Bartsokas and Siapkas, 1980; Massot et al., 1982) have questioned this result by finding a higher low-frequency reflectivity level $R(\omega) \simeq 0.90 - 0.95$ for $\omega < 80$ cm^{-1} at T_{tr}. This gives $\omega_s \simeq 5 - 10$ cm^{-1} and $\Delta\epsilon_s(T_{tr}) \simeq 2000$ to 5000 which is, however, still less than ϵ_0. Grigas and Beliackas (1978) measured the microwave response in the $0.1 - 2.6$ cm^{-1} region on several small needle-shaped crystals and found a *central mode*-like dispersion in the 0.7 cm^{-1} region. From T_{tr} to $T_{tr} + 10$ K the central mode is well described by an oscillator model (Eq. (2.34)) (surprisingly underdamped) with $f = 7.5 \times 10^3$, $\omega_0 = 0.18(T - T_0)^{1/2}$ cm^{-1}, $T_0 = T_{tr} - 8$ K, $\gamma \simeq 0.7$ cm^{-1}, and $\epsilon_\infty \simeq 1000 - 3000$. The last quantity is the far IR soft-mode contribution which is in this narrow temperature region only slightly T-dependent. This quantitative result was, however, questioned by the very recent BWO investigations of Volkov *et al.* (1984) who observed the microwave dispersion at higher frequency (5 cm^{-1}). The results are somehow sample-dependent, but qualitatively, similar microwave dispersion always occurs. It should be noted that a central peak of a comparable width was observed also in Raman scattering (Steigmeier *et al.*, 1975) where it was interpreted as due to phonon density fluctuations. As discussed in Section II.C.1, this explanation cannot be used for the microwave dielectric dispersion so that it seems that the interpretation analogous to the case of LiTaO$_3$ and BaTiO$_3$ is more appropriate and SbSI also belongs to displacive materials with some additional disorder near T_c.

The fitting procedure of the B_{1u} spectra in the 10–150 cm^{-1} region has shown the same difficulties as for LiTaO$_3$ and LiNbO$_3$. A good fit was achieved only by taking the self-energy of the soft mode in the form of Eq. (2.71), with $\omega_{2ph} \simeq 30$ cm^{-1} (Bartsokas and Siapkas, 1980; Massot *et al.*, 1982). The fitted eigenfrequencies are reproduced in Fig. 4. Note that for high temperatures the soft-mode frequency saturated below 20 cm^{-1} and does not fulfill the Cochran law. Knowing the B_{1u}-mode eigenfrequencies for SbSI and several isomorphs (SbSeI, BiSI, BiSeI, BiSBr, BiSeBr, SbSBr) we

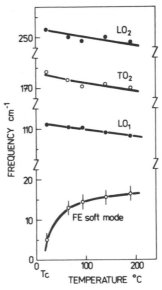

Fig. 4. Temperature dependence of the mode frequencies in the paraelectric phase of SbSI for **E ∥ c** (from Massot *et al.*, 1982).

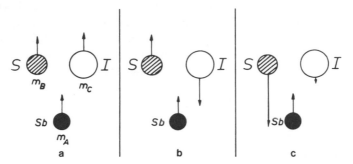

Fig. 5. Eigenvectors of the B_{1u} polar modes in SbSI from Fig. 4.   (a) Acoustic mode; (b) low-frequency mode; (c) high-frequency mode (from Riede and Sobotta, 1978).

can easily calculate analytically the B_{1u} eigenvectors (Riede and Sobotta, 1978).   The results for SbSI are shown in Fig. 5 and can be used for developing microscopic models of ferroelectricity in SbSI (Bilz *et al.*, 1980).

3. Hydrogen-Bonded Ferroelectrics

a. KH₂PO₄

Potassium dihydrogen phosphate (KDP) is certainly the most popular material among the ferroelectrics as far as the lattice dynamics is concerned. Enormous effort was exerted during the last fifteen years to understand especially the proton dynamics in this strongly hydrogen-bonded crystal.   In this effort the most important role was played by light scattering studies (see, e.g., Fleury and Lyons, 1981, for a brief recent review) because the soft mode is Raman active also in the (piezoelectric) paraelectric phase.   The soft mode manifests itself in the Brillouin spectra as well, because it interacts with the transverse acoustic wave governed by the elastic constant C_{66} and causes acoustic softening.   Dielectric spectroscopy in KDP gives, in principle, the same information as light-scattering studies (sometimes even more accurately), but was not yet reviewed thoroughly.   Here we shall briefly mention some recent aspects of the proton–deuteron dynamics in the KDP–DKDP system, review the most important IR investigations, and point out some open questions and possibilities for future IR studies.

KDP undergoes two phase transitions at 122 and ~450 K at normal pressure.   As the nature of the high-temperature reconstructive transition is not yet clear enough we shall discuss only the ferroelectric transition at 122 K.   Structural data (see Nelmes *et al.*, 1982, and references therein) show that the hydrogen atoms in the O—H $\cdots$ O hydrogen bonds move in a double minimum potential the accurate shape of which was not known until recently. In Figs. 6 and 7 we show the double-well potential for both KDP and DKDP together with energy levels according to the recent realistic model by Lawrence and Robertson (1981) (see also Robertson and Lawrence, 1981), which is consistent with almost all structural and spectroscopic data in the paraelectric phase including their temperature and pressure dependence.

This model is strongly based on the analysis of mid IR transmission data which reveal broad absorption maxima in the 4000–5500 (Viswanath and Miller, 1979) and 2000–3000 cm^{-1} (Hill and Ichiki, 1968) regions which are nearly temperature-independent and are evidently due to protonic absorption. The third region of protonic absorption, which is most important for the transition dynamics and which is strongly temperature-dependent, lies in the far IR region below 200 cm^{-1}. This is the region of proton tunneling modes through the potential barrier between both minima. The group-theoretical analysis shows that there are four tunneling mode branches because there are four H atoms in the primitive cell ($Z = 2$). In each of the far IR spectra with $\mathbf{E} \parallel \mathbf{c}$ and $\mathbf{E} \perp \mathbf{c}$ (KDP is tetragonal in the paraelectric phase) only one tunneling mode should be active. In the far IR region we can, in addition, expect $1B_2$ ($\mathbf{E} \parallel \mathbf{c}$) and $5E$ ($\mathbf{E} \perp \mathbf{c}$) external lattice modes to be active above T_c and a new librational mode is expected to appear for $\mathbf{E} \parallel \mathbf{c}$ below T_c. Moreover, all E modes have to split below T_c.

Of the many $\mathbf{E} \parallel \mathbf{c}$ far IR reflectivity measurements, in the paraelectric

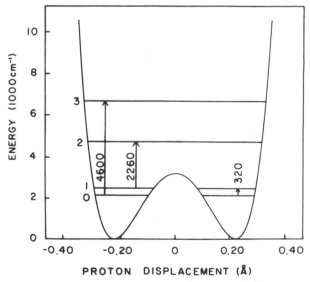

Fig. 6. Proton energy levels in KDP (from Lawrence and Robertson, 1981).

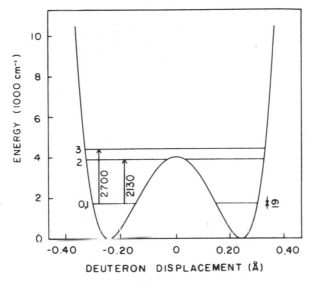

Fig. 7. Deuteron energy levels in DKDP (from Lawrence and Robertson, 1981).

phase the most accurate seem to be the data by Gauss *et al.* (1975) and Ledsham *et al.* (1977) obtained by dispersive spectroscopy in the 20–250 cm^{-1} region. The evaluated $\epsilon'(\omega)$ and $\epsilon''(\omega)$ spectra can be fitted well by two coupled oscillators. The lower frequency oscillator represents predominantly the H tunneling mode, the higher frequency mode is predominantly the $K^+ - (H_2PO_4)^-$ lattice vibration. Both modes are strongly coupled and the results are almost equivalent to earlier Raman data (see, e.g., Peercy, 1975) which were discussed using the microscopic model of Kobayashi (1968). This model explains the total dipole moment of the low frequency mode as due to the coupling of the H-tunneling mode with the high-frequency lattice mode. However, this is evidently not the case for the fit of Ledsham's data where both bare modes have comparable dipole moments (effective charges). Therefore it seems that the dipole moment of the soft mode arises mainly from the coupling between the H-tunneling mode and the high-frequency internal PO_4 vibrations, as recently suggested by Blinc and Žekš (1982).

The complicating feature is also that the tunneling mode is overdamped and near T_c the soft-mode dispersion falls below 20 cm^{-1}. The 5–20 cm^{-1} region was thoroughly investigated by Kozlov and coworkers (see Volkov *et al.*, 1980f and references therein) using BWO spectroscopy. They investigated the whole KDP–DKDP family for both **E** ∥ **c** and **E** ⊥ **c**. The dielectric spectra obtained with accuracy better than 5% could be fitted well to a simple Debye relaxation formula (Eq. (2.50)). The temperature dependence of the relaxation rate $1/(2\pi\tau)$ is shown in Fig. 8, where a nice example of critical slowing down can be seen. The inset shows the concentration dependence of the relaxation time ratio taken for a constant $(T - T_c)$ interval. The clear single-mode behavior of mixed crystals has important consequences for theoretical models of KDP–DKDP mixed crystals (Blinc *et al.* 1976b; Lage and Stinchcombe, 1976; Schreiber, 1977; Chaudhuri and Saha, 1978). The results are consistent with microwave investigations of KDP (Gauss *et al.*, 1975) and DKDP (Gauss and Happ, 1976) at 4.62 cm^{-1}. The fact that the low-frequency part of the B_2 spectra can be described by Debye relaxation is consistent also with Raman scattering results (Takagi and Shigenari, 1979) and does not contradict the coupled-mode approach, because the soft mode is heavily overdamped. For a higher frequency $\omega > 50$ cm^{-1} the Debye model, of course, fails (Takagi and Shigenari, 1979).

In the ferroelectric phase the **E** ∥ **c** reflectivity spectra drastically change (Sugawara and Nakamura, 1970a); Kawamura and Mitsuishi, 1973; Petzelt *et al.*, 1974), but no thorough analysis of the spectra seems to have been published. The corresponding low-frequency Raman spectra were thoroughly investigated (Peercy, 1975) and reveal two underdamped modes in the 150 and 210 cm^{-1} region. The low-frequency mode was assigned to the tunneling mode according to the theory of Blinc *et al.* (1973), because it weakens on deuteration and softens on applying hydrostatic pressure (Peercy, 1975, 1976). However, the corresponding far IR mode is very weak in KDP (it was seen only in the transmission experiment by Coignac and Poulet, 1971) but becomes very strong in mixed KDP–DKDP crystals (Petzelt *et al.*, 1974) and in DKDP (Kawamura *et al.*, 1974). It was, therefore

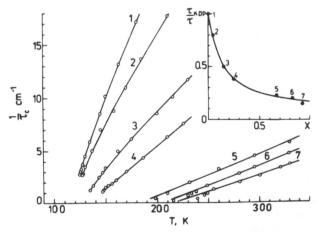

Fig. 8. Temperature dependence of the overdamped B_2 soft-mode frequencies in the $KH_{2(1-x)}D_{2x}PO_4$ system for **E** ∥ **c** (from Volkov *et al.*, 1980f). For curve 1, x = 0; 2, x = 0.05; 3, x = 0.15; 4, x = 0.23; 5, x = 0.67; 6, x = 0.84; 7, x = 0.93.

assigned to the missing A_1 libration mode activated below T_c rather than to the H-tunneling mode (see also Scott and Wilson, 1972).

Very recently, this point of view was strongly supported by Tominaga (1983) and Tokunaga and Tatsuzaki (1983) who on the basis of new Raman and structural data analysis (Nelmes et al., 1982) came to a rather surprising conclusion that the whole $H_2PO_4^-$ group is disordered in the paraelectric phase and its quantum tunneling is negligible. This point of view could explain several features of IR spectra which we have already discussed: the failure of Kobayashi's theory, pure relaxation character of the soft mode, large frequency shift of the high-frequency B_2 lattice mode from ~ 185 cm^{-1} above T_c to ~ 210 cm^{-1} below T_c, splitting of this mode above T_c (Petzelt et al., 1974) and the behavior of partially deuterated samples below T_c where no tunneling mode is expected.

The $E \perp c$ reflectivity spectra in the paraelectric phase also have been measured by several authors beginning with Barker and Tinkham (1963) and including measurements using the dispersive technique (Gauss et al., 1975; Ledsham et al., 1976). As expected from group theoretical analysis, the spectra below 300 cm^{-1} reveal five lattice modes and an overdamped H-tunneling mode in the 50 cm^{-1} region. The lattice mode parameters have been accurately evaluated only in the 300–400 K region (Brehat et al., 1981). The tunneling mode displays a slight softening near T_c in agreement with microwave and static dielectric data (Gauss et al., 1975) and theoretical calculations (Chaudhury et al., 1980). Its dependence on temperature and deuteration was investigated in the 5–20 cm^{-1} region by Volkov et al., (1980f) and the results were fitted to the Debye relaxation formula. The resulting relaxation rates are plotted in Fig. 9. However, in the case of pure KDP clear resonance features (maximum in the $\epsilon'(\omega)$ spectra) were observed, despite the relaxation fit in Fig. 10. The large effect of deuteration proves in the best way the tunneling nature of this mode. The sharp critical absorption observed near T_c in the microwave investigations of KDP and DKDP (Gauss et al., 1975; Gauss and Happ, 1976) proved to be an artifact connected with small temperature gradients in the sample (Volkov et al., 1980b).

Similar to $E \parallel c$ spectra, little data seem to exist on $E \perp c$ spectra below T_c. The reflectivity below 100 cm^{-1} shows a pronounced decrease (Petzelt et al., 1974) connected evidently with the disappearance of the tunneling mode. Single crystalline transmission measurements (Coignac and Poulet, 1971) show a splitting of some of the E modes at 90 K. The temperature dependence of this splitting was not investigated. In the mid IR region the reflectivity was measured for both polarizations by Kawamura and Mitsuishi (1973) and at room temperature by Onyango et al. (1975). No detailed discussion of the temperature changes was made.

In conclusion, we can state that despite the huge number of papers devoted

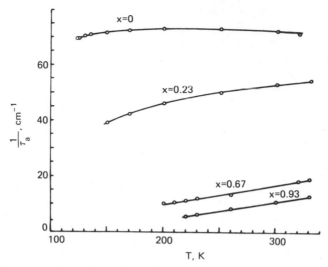

Fig. 9. Temperature dependence of the E proton tunneling mode in the $KH_{2(1-x)}D_{2x}PO_4$ system (from Volkov *et al.,* 1980f).

to the proton and lattice dynamics in the KDP–DKDP system, the field is still far from being completely understood and closed. Mainly, the far IR spectra below T_c are scarce, not properly evaluated and the differences between Raman and far IR spectra are not understood. Also the nature of the proton-lattice coupling is not quite clear so that the accurate eigenvector of the soft mode is still a matter of discussion.

b. PbHPO₄

Lead monohydrogen phosphate (LHP) is a new, simple hydrogen-bonded ferroelectric discovered in 1974 (Negran *et al.,* 1974). Despite its low symmetry (the structure is monoclinic in both phases, the space group changes from C_{2h}^4 to C_s^2 and $Z = 2$), the structure is simpler than that of other hydrogen-bonded ferroelectrics including KDP. The H bonds form linear zig zag chains and unlike in KDP the dipole moments of ordered protons seem to account directly for P_s. In the paraelectric phase the protons are believed to move in double-minimum potentials like in KDP. A serious shortcoming of these crystals, limiting the methods and accuracy of spectroscopic investigations, is their limited size due to difficulties with the sample growth (Březina and Havránková, 1980).

The initial IR and Raman spectroscopic investigations were performed on powders (Blinc *et al.,* 1976a). IR spectra above $1100\,cm^{-1}$ are very similar to KDP and are characteristic for medium strong O—H—O bonds with a double-minimum H potential. Subsequent single crystalline Raman mea-

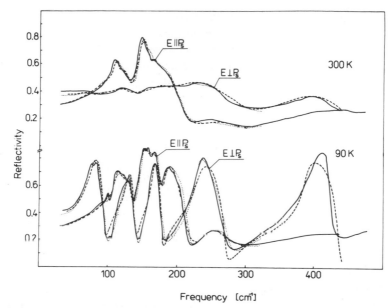

Fig. 10. Reflectivity of LHP for $\mathbf{E} \parallel \mathbf{P}_s$ and $\mathbf{E} \perp \mathbf{P}_s$. Experimental data (———); fit neglecting the monoclinic symmetry (– – –); fit using correct formulae ($\cdots$) (from Kroupa, 1982).

surements (Lavrenčič and Petzelt, 1977) enabled an assignment of most of the lattice modes and revealed a weak soft mode in the $60 - 100$ cm^{-1} region below $T_c = 310$ K (above T_c it should be only IR-active). However, the far IR reflectivity measurements (Kroupa *et al.*, 1978; Kock and Happ, 1980) have shown that this mode is too weak and its dipole moment is directed more or less perpendicular to P_s. The real soft mode was revealed by BWO transmission spectroscopy in the $6 - 20$ cm^{-1} region (Kroupa *et al.*, 1978). It has much lower frequency than in KDP and can be described well by a Debye relaxation, fulfilling the classical temperature behaviour $1/(2\pi\tau_P) = 1.0(T - T_c)$ cm^{-1} and $1/(2\pi\tau_f) = 4.0(T_c - T)$ cm^{-1} above and below T_c, respectively, accounting for the whole static ϵ_0. The microwave measurements at 8.2, 9.6, and 37 GHz by Kock and Happ (1980) show much smaller losses than required by the Debye model, but we believe this discrepancy to be caused by the monoclinic symmetry of LHP which apparently was not properly accounted for when evaluating the microwave measurements. The complicating feature of the monoclinic (and triclinic) symmetry is the fact that not all the principal axes of the ϵ'_{ij} and ϵ''_{ij} tensor ellipsoid coincide and their direction can be temperature- and frequency-dependent.

Recently, the problem associated with the monoclinic structure of LHP has been correctly treated by Kroupa (1982). In both $\mathbf{E} \parallel \mathbf{P}_s$ and $\mathbf{E} \perp \mathbf{P}_s$

spectra on (010) samples ($\mathbf{P}_s$ lies in the xz plane and otherwise is not fixed by symmetry) the same symmetry type of modes (B_u above T_c and A' below T_c) is active. Therefore the dipole moments of these modes are not fixed in the (010) plane and three dielectric-function components ϵ_{xx}, ϵ_{zz}, and ϵ_{xz} have to be evaluated from reflectivity or transmittance measurements of the (010) plates. The fit was performed to the correct formula for the normal reflectivity (Belousov and Pavinich, 1978) using the classical oscillator model for monoclinic symmetry (Claus, 1978),

$$
\begin{aligned}
\epsilon_{xx}(\omega) &= \sum_{i=1}^{6} \frac{f_i \cos^2\varphi_i}{\omega_i^2 - \omega^2 + i\omega\gamma_i} + \epsilon_\infty^{xx}, \\
\epsilon_{zz}(\omega) &= \sum_{i=1}^{6} \frac{f_i \sin^2\varphi_i}{\omega_i^2 - \omega^2 + i\omega\gamma_i} + \epsilon_\infty^{zz}, \qquad (2.72) \\
\epsilon_{xz}(\omega) &= \sum_{i=1}^{6} \frac{f_i \sin\varphi_i\cos\varphi_i}{\omega_i^2 - \omega^2 + i\omega\gamma_i} + \epsilon_\infty^{xz},
\end{aligned}
$$

where φ_i is the angle between the ith oscillator dipole moment and the x axis. The typical fitted spectra are shown in Fig. 10 together with the usual fit which neglects the monoclinic symmetry of the crystal. The resulting oscillator parameters for both fits are listed in Table I. Note that the proper *monoclinic* fit is better although it uses a smaller number of fitted parameters.

In the case of LHP it is even more important to take into account the monoclinic symmetry for evaluation of transmittance measurements. In Fig. 11 the temperature dependence of the extinction directions in a (010)-plane-oriented plate is shown for several frequencies between 4.8 and 30 cm^{-1}. Whereas the direction of maximum absorption (which practically coincides with the principal axis of the $\epsilon''(\omega)$ tensor) is temperature-independent, the extinction directions are strongly temperature-dependent. Therefore, the nondiagonal component ϵ_{xz} must be taken into account. By fitting the transmission data using the formulae derived by Kroupa (1979), Kroupa (1982) again succeeded with a Debye relaxation model and found $1/(2\pi\tau_p) = 0.7(T - T_c)$ cm^{-1} and $1/(2\pi\tau_f) = 2.8(T_c - T)$ cm^{-1} for the relaxation rate above and below T_c, respectively. The latter value is to be compared to the value $1/(2\pi\tau_f) \sim 0.6(T_c - T)$ cm^{-1} obtained from the fit of the temperature dependence of the elastic constant C_{22} from Brillouin measurements (Lavrenčič *et al.*, 1978). This difference which clearly lies outside the experimental error of the measurement, is not understood. Nor are the recent structural data of Nelmes *et al.* (1983) which show that the hydrogen bond direction below T_c differs from P_s by 40°. On the other hand, the ordering of protons closely follows the gradual $P_s(T)$ curve, which saturates about 100 K below T_c, whereas the displacements of the heavy atoms satu-

TABLE I

PARAMETERS OF THE REFLECTIVITY FIT IN LHP SHOWN IN FIG. 10

	90 K				300 K			
	ω_i (cm^{-1})	$\Delta\epsilon_i{}^a$	γ_i (cm^{-1})	$\varphi_i{}^a$ (°)	ω_i (cm^{-1})	$\Delta\epsilon_i{}^a$	γ_i (cm^{-1})	φ_i (°)
Fit neglecting the monoclinic symmetry								
$\mathbf{E} \parallel \mathbf{P}_s$	115	6.0	7.2		112	2.5	7	
	127	2.8	8.3		123	2.6	17	
	146	3.4	6.5		143	2.6	8	
	164	0.1	6.0		163	0.2	10	
	181	0.2	9.5		176	0.4	29	
	230	0.9	21		250	1.1	100	
$\mathbf{E} \perp \mathbf{P}_s$	76	9.8	6.5		75	1.8	15	
	91	0.4	9.0		—	—	—	
	127	2.5	11.1		129	0.8	18	
	163	1.8	5.4		171	0.5	22	
	224	2.4	13.7		221	7.3	98	
	378	1.3	14		379	2.0	102	
Fit accounting for the monoclinic symmetry								
	75.5	9.45	7.5	89	109.5	5.2	14.6	7.3
	111.6	6.17	13.7	62	123.5	3.1	16.4	42.5
	128.6	4.22	2.6	54	141.0	0.7	8.4	346
	143.8	1.02	5.0	351	168.1	0.6	26	57
	164.0	2.04	4.3	71	202.0	12.3	95	69
	224.5	2.24	5.2	73				

^{a} Angle between the ith mode dipole moment and $\mathbf{P}_s$, and $\Delta\epsilon_i = f_i/\omega_i^2$.

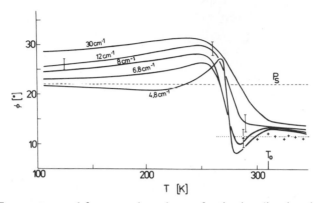

Fig. 11. Temperature and frequency dependence of extinction directions in LHP. The value $\varphi = 0$ corresponds to the crystallographic a axis. Crosses denote the direction of the light polarization where the absorption has a maximum (from Kroupa, 1982).

rate a few degrees below T_c. The former fact indicates a large proton-lattice coupling, whereas the latter contradicts it. Additional data, especially structural results concerning the proton distribution above T_c and soft-mode data on deuterated LHP are needed to clarify the phase-transition picture in LHP.

4. Order–Disorder Ferroelectrics

a. TGS

Triglycine sulfate [(NH$_2$CH$_2$COOH)$_3$H$_2$SO$_4$ (TGS))] with a classical second-order ferroelectric transition at 322 K is the most popular order–disorder ferroelectric despite its complex structure, mainly because large single crystals important for applications are easily available. The structure is monoclinic in both phases (the space group changes from $P2_1/m$ to $P2_1$) with P_s fixed by symmetry along the b axis. The paraelectric unit cell is schematically shown in Fig. 12. There are three glycinium ions GI, GII, and GIII in one formula unit; nearly planar GII and GIII are linked by a double-minimum hydrogen bond at the inversion center and the nonplanar GI are disordered above T_c. Below T_c the GI ions as well as protons in the double minimum bonds become ordered (see, e.g., Lines and Glass, 1977, and references therein). The GI ions consist of CH$_2$COOH skeletons and NH$_3^+$ ions which order with different temperature dependences (Stankowski, 1978): the temperature dependence of the skeleton saturates about 20 K below T_c whereas the NH$_3^+$ ion ordering saturates more than 100 K below T_c like P_s and probably accounts for the total P_s.

Despite this rather complex picture of the phase transition, the ferroelectric dispersion seemed, until recently, to be of a simple Debye type. Luther

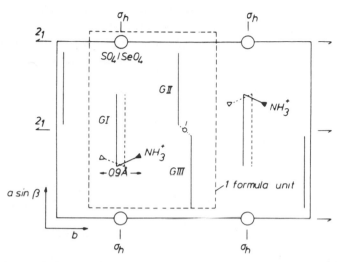

Fig. 12. Schematic [001] projection of the TGS(TGSe) unit cell (from Winterfeldt *et al.*, 1977).

(1973) performed microwave measurements in the $10^8 - 10^{10}$ Hz (0.003 – 0.3 cm^{-1}) region and found that ± 15 K around T_c the complex permittivity fulfills the simple Debye model

$$\epsilon(\omega) = \frac{\Delta\epsilon(T)}{1 + i\omega\tau(T)} + \epsilon_\infty \qquad (2.73)$$

with $\Delta c - 3190/(T - T_c)$ and $1/(2\pi\tau) = 0.027(T - T_c)$ cm^{-1} above T_c, $\Delta\epsilon = 670/(T_c - T)$ and $1/(2\pi\tau) = 0.13(T_c - T)$ cm^{-1} below T_c and $\epsilon_\infty = 9$. However, far IR transmission measurements by Hadni *et al.* (1970) are consistent rather with earlier microwave measurements by Hill and Ichiki (1963), who found a distribution of relaxation times. Recent precise BWO measurements by Kozlov *et al.* (1980) and Volkov *et al.* (1980d) in the 5 – 30 cm^{-1} region revealed an additional temperature-dependent dispersion. It can be described by another, much higher frequency Debye relaxation. Microwave data in a broader temperature region are needed, but it seems that the higher frequency relaxation causes a softening of the lower frequency relaxation and drives the phase transition. Such a picture is not surprising in light of the complex structural nature of the phase transition mentioned above. It is interesting to note that nearly the same dispersion has been observed in DTGS (Kozlov, 1982) so that no observed absorption is caused by proton tunneling. The situation in TGS resembles the microwave – far IR absorption in plastic crystals with polar molecules where an excess far IR absorption is always observed in addition to the microwave relaxation and is known to be caused by the librational motion of molecules, the so-called Poley absorption (see Section IV.H).

Let us now discuss the hard-mode behavior in TGS. The most complete reflectivity measurements and their temperature dependence as well as Raman measurements were performed by Winterfeldt *et al.* (1977). The most complete transmission measurements were performed by Hadni *et al.* (1969). Winterfeldt *et al.* found 4 types of temperature behavior of hard-mode frequencies around T_c, which are illustrated in Fig. 13. A-type behavior is not influenced by the phase transition. B-type behavior shows a

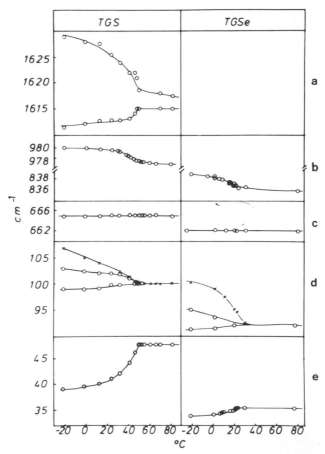

Fig. 13. Temperature dependence of frequencies of selected hard modes in TGS–TGSe. Infrared measurements (x); Raman data (O). (a) NH_3-deformation, type B + C; (b) v_1 (A_1) SO_4–SeO_4, type D; (c) COO′-bend, type A; (d) external lattice vibration, type B; (e) external lattice vibration GI, type C (from Winterfeldt *et al.*, 1977).

quasidegeneracy of some lines above T_c which is lifted below T_c. This is not expected from symmetry, but could be understood by the fact that considerable differences between the dimensions of glycinium ions appear only below T_c. C-type behavior shows changes $\Delta\omega \propto P_s^2$ as expected from the thermodynamic theory and symmetry considerations (Petzelt and Dvořák, 1976a,b). D-type behavior (Schaack and Winterfeldt, 1977) shows, moreover, some changes above T_c apparently caused by polarization fluctuations.

b. NaNO₂

Sodium nitrite has the simplest structure among order–disorder ferroelectrics and therefore its dynamic properties have been thoroughly investigated, mainly during the 1965–1975 decade. The unit cell contains only one formula unit. The phase transition takes place at $T_c \simeq 437$ K and consists of the ordering of the NO_2^- ions flipping between two positions. The complicating feature is the occurrence of a narrow incommensurate phase between T_c and $T_i \simeq 438.2$ K. As there are no spectroscopic data available for this narrow region, we shall neglect its existence in the further discussion. The dispersion in $\epsilon_b(\omega)$ along the ferroelectric axis is of a simple Debye type (Hatta, 1968) and the relaxation time satisfies the classical law $1/(2\pi\tau) = A(T - T_0)$ with $A = 1.6 \times 10^7$ Hz and $T_0 = 435$ K between T_i and ~ 455 K.

The list of normal modes and their symmetries and activities in both phases of NaNO₂ is given in Table II. The temperature dependence of IR

TABLE II

NORMAL MODES IN NaNO₂ AT ROOM TEMPERATURE[a]

Symmetry type C_{2v}^{20}	D_{2h}^{25}	Activity	External TO modes (cm⁻¹)	Internal TO modes (cm⁻¹)
A_1	A_g	$\alpha_{aa}, \alpha_{bb}, \alpha_{cc}$	—	1320 (ν_1)
	B_{2u}	e_b	186 (T_b)	825 (ν_2)
A_2	A_u	—	—	—
	B_{2g}	α_{ac}	120 (R_b)	—
B_1	B_{3g}	α_{bc}	154 (R_a)	—
	B_{1u}	e_c	187 (T_c)	1230 (ν_3)
B_2	B_{1g}	α_{ab}	220 (R_c)	—
	B_{3u}	e_a	144 (T_a)	—

[a] T_i and R_i ($i = a,b,c$) mean the translation along the i axis and libration about the i axis, respectively. Activity is shown for the paraelectric phase D_{2h}^{25}, for which nonzero components of the Raman tensor α_{ij} and effective-charge vector e_i are listed.

reflectivity was measured by Vogt and Happ (1966), Barnoski and Ballantyne (1968), Suzuki et al. (1969), and Brehat et al. (1982). The spectra are in good agreement with the group-theoretical predictions below T_c given in Table II. However, above T_c several modes (v_1, R_a, R_c) which have to disappear from the spectra survive more or less strongly until the highest temperatures measured (480 K). Moreover, all modes show a nonlinear increase of damping with increasing temperature. All these features are caused by the fact that the group theoretical analysis above T_c takes into account the long time-averaged symmetry whereas the activity of the modes is determined, in fact, by the immediate symmetry obtained by averaging over the time of the vibrational period only. The latter symmetry is substantially lower due to the lattice disorder and therefore the selection rules are relaxed.

No quantitative theory of these effects exists for $NaNO_2$. Attempts were made to explain the strong temperature dependence of the frequency and damping of the R_a libration mode via the temperature dependence of NO_2 flipping (Andrade et al., 1973, 1974). NO_2 groups lie in the (100) plane and their flipping was supposed to be realized mainly by a rotation about the a axis. This is structurally improbable. Moreover, the comparable temperature dependences of other external modes are not explained by their theory.

Much effort was exerted to investigate the second-order absorption spectra in $NaNO_2$ by transmission measurements. Of the most interesting features, Vogt and Happ (1968) have observed a rather underdamped mode at ~ 13 cm^{-1} for $\mathbf{E} \parallel \mathbf{b}$ whose presence is connected with the lattice disorder; it disappears far below T_c where the order parameter saturates. However, the recent BWO measurements by Kozlov (1982) have not confirmed this behavior. Whereas in the ordered phase their measurements agree with those of Vogt and Happ, in the paraelectric phase their absorption is much higher, with a broad minimum at ~ 15 cm^{-1}. The low-frequency (< 15 cm^{-1}) increase of absorption can be assigned to the high-frequency wing of the main ferroelectric dispersion. The high-frequency (> 15 cm^{-1}) increase is probably due to a disorder–induced absorption (proportional to the one-phonon density of states) which overlaps with the low-frequency wing of the basic one-phonon absorption.

In the mid IR region at ~ 1560 cm^{-1}, a mode was observed for $\mathbf{E} \parallel \mathbf{b}$ with a strange temperature dependence similar to that of the mode observed by Vogt and Happ (Holah, 1971). An explanation of this behavior offered by Holah is that the mode represents the v_1 mode having a shifted frequency in clusters where the neighboring NO_2 groups are in reversed positions.

The $\mathbf{E} \parallel \mathbf{a}$ and $\mathbf{E} \parallel \mathbf{c}$ spectra in the region of the v_2 mode appeared to be better understood. They show a *leakage* of the v_2 mode from the $\mathbf{E} \parallel \mathbf{b}$ polarization into both other polarizations, which are forbidden for an ordered crystal (Ivanova and Chisler, 1975; Suzuki and Takagi, 1976).   Again a large increase of the $E \parallel a$ and $E \parallel c$ mode strength is observed with increasing temperature in the region just below and above T_c.   This absorption is caused during the flipping of the NO_2 groups.   If the flipping involved a rotation about the a axis the ν_2 mode would absorb for $E \parallel c$, and if it were realized by a rotation about the c axis the ν_2 mode would absorb for $E \parallel a$.   From the temperature dependence of the $E \parallel a$ and $E \parallel c$ absorption the potential barriers for both of these flipping mechanisms were evaluated, with the conclusion that the rotation about the a axis is more probable.   However, the recent calculation based on the atomic sterical hindrance potential (Ehrhardt and Michel, 1981) has shown that the most probable is the rotation about the molecular c axis which occurs in such a way that during the N rotation, the $O-O$ axis tilts away from the c axis by as much as $40°$.   A reevaluation of the spectroscopic data is therefore needed.

An interesting application of IR spectroscopy in $NaNO_2$ was recently demonstrated by Suzuki et al. (1981).   It is well known that the ferroelectric domain walls in $NaNO_2$ are extremely thick (of the order of 1 μm) and can be made even more thick by applying an electric field during the polarization reversal process.   A question arises as to what the structure of the intermediate-state regions (domain walls) looks like.   The IR absorption topography in the ν_2 spectral region at room temperature revealed that the $E \parallel a$ absorption peak is strongly enhanced in the domain wall regions compared to the normal regions.   The domain walls were observed independently also by x-ray topography.   The $E \parallel c$ absorption peak is constant and weak over the whole sample.   A quantitative evaluation has shown that inside the domain walls the NO_2 groups are on the average rotated by $50°$ about the c axis from their regular orientation.   This shows that the polarization reversal as well as the dynamical flipping are realized by the rotation of the NO_2 groups about the c axis.

B. Displacive Improper Ferroelectrics

The improper (extrinsic) ferroelectric phase transitions are those where the symmetry of the order parameter differs from that of the polarization, nevertheless the spontaneous polarization occurs in the distorted phase as a result of higher order coupling terms in the thermodynamic potential of the schematic form $P\eta^n$ (n is a so-called faintness index of the polarization, see Aizu, 1974).   All known examples of improper ferroelectrics are zone boundary (nonequitranslational) transitions (this is not necessarily required by symmetry arguments, see Janovec et al., 1975).   The order parameter consists of at least two components (Levanyuk and Sannikov, 1974) so that the soft mode is at least doubly degenerate in the parent phase.   As discussed in Section I.C.2, it is IR-active only in the distorted phase where it splits into two or more components.

1. $Gd_2(MoO_4)_3$

Gadolinium molybdate [$Gd_2(MoO_4)_3$ (GMO)] is the best studied improper ferroelectric with $T_{tr} = 432$ K where the symmetry changes from the space group $P\overline{4}2_1m$ ($Z = 2$) into the ferroelectric one $Pba2$ ($Z = 4$). The transition is displacive which is proven by the existence of an underdamped soft mode (above 640 K) at the M-point ($\frac{1}{2}, \frac{1}{2}, 0$) of the Brillouin zone found in a thorough inelastic neutron scattering study of the isomorphous terbium molybdate (TMO) (Dorner *et al.*, 1972), which has nearly the same T_{tr} and is nearly indistinguishable from GMO concerning all the phase-transition phenomena. The soft mode fulfills the classical Cochran law $\omega_s^2 = 1.1(T - T_c)$ cm^{-1} K above T_{tr} with $T_c = 422$ K and damping $\gamma = 20 \pm 4$ cm^{-1} independent of T. The group-theoretical analysis (Petzelt and Dvořák, 1971) predicts that the soft mode is doubly degenerate above T_{tr}. Below T_{tr} the degeneracy is lifted and two totally symmetric A_1 soft modes are expected in both IR and Raman spectra. Their splitting is $\delta\omega(T) \propto \eta_s(T) \propto P_s^{1/2}(T)$ and their strengths $f(T)$ in both the IR and Raman spectra, is to a first approximation, proportional near T_{tr} to $\eta_s^2(T)$ (Petzelt and Dvořák, 1976a).

The experimental results of several Raman and far IR investigations are summarized in Fig. 14. We can see that Raman measurements have revealed two low-frequency doublets (in the 50 and 80 cm^{-1} region at low temperatures) which disappear above T_{tr}. Neither of them softens sufficiently, but their damping increases nonlinearly for $T \to T_{tr}$ (see Kim and

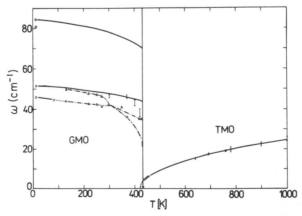

Fig. 14. Soft-mode frequencies in GMO-summary of spectroscopic data. Raman (O———O); IR ($\triangle-\cdot-\triangle$); neutron (l); theory ($\sim P_s^{1/2}$) (———·——).

Ullman, 1978, and references therein). In far IR transmission measurements (Petzelt, 1971 and Petzelt and Dvořák, 1971) the lower doublet was seen for the first time (the higher one is hidden by other stronger modes) and was assigned to the soft-mode doublet.

The soft-mode behavior in GMO has been reviewed several times (the most recent and thorough discussion is due to Fleury and Lyons, 1981), but has remained puzzling until recently. The insufficient softening and increase of damping calls for an additional central mode. However, acoustic investigations (see Yao et al., 1981, and references therein) revealed temperature anomalies but no dispersion in the 10^7–2×10^{10} Hz region. A larger softening of the classical soft mode is needed for the explanation of acoustic anomalies near T_{tr}.

Recently, thorough submillimeter and millimeter transmission measurements were performed in the 300–460 K region (Petzelt et al., 1984a). The resulting $\epsilon''(\omega)$ spectra are shown in Fig. 15. We can see that the peak in $\epsilon''(\omega)$ remains finite (greater than 30 cm^{-1}) for $T \to T_{tr}$, but an additional absorption arises in the low-frequency region near T_{tr}. This is obviously due to the occurrence of a central peak in the $S(\omega)$ spectrum, as shown in Fig. 16, where the $T\epsilon''(\omega)/\omega \propto S(\omega)$ spectrum is plotted. A simple fit to a phenomenological formula (see Eq. (2.55))

$$T\frac{\epsilon''(\omega)}{\omega} = Tf\left(\gamma + \frac{\tau\delta^2}{1 + \omega^2\tau^2}\right) \Bigg/$$

$$\left(\left(\omega_T^2 - \frac{\delta^2}{1 + \omega^2\tau^2} \quad \omega^2\right)^2 + \left(\gamma + \frac{\tau\delta^2}{1 + \omega^2\tau^2}\right)^2 \omega^2\right) + a \tag{2.74}$$

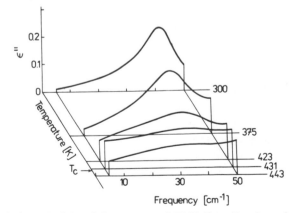

Fig. 15. Soft-mode dielectric loss spectra of GMO (from Petzelt et al., 1984).

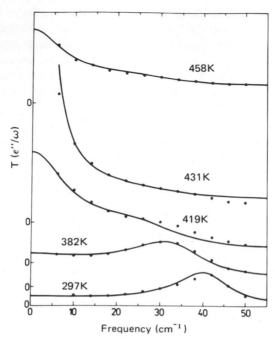

Fig. 16. The $\epsilon''(\omega)/\omega$ soft-mode spectra of GMO showing the central mode behavior. Experimental data (. . .); fit to Eq. (2.74) (————) (from Petzelt *et al.*, 1984).

is also shown in Fig. 16. Here it was assumed that $f(T) \propto P_s(T)$ as required by the thermodynamic theory and that τ is temperature-independent. The constant a accounts for a background absorption due to all higher frequency modes. The frequency ω_T represents the mean frequency of the bare soft-mode doublet and it was found to fulfill the classical law $\omega_T^2 \propto (T - T_0)$ with $T_0 \simeq 550$ K. As expected, the effective low-frequency limit of the soft-mode frequency $\tilde{\omega}_T^2 = \omega_T^2 - \delta^2$ tends to zero close above T_{tr}. The bare relaxation frequency $1/(2\pi\tau)$ was found to be $\simeq 20$ cm^{-1}. Until now, this is the highest frequency of a central mode ever found and therefore it is caused by a partial disorder rather than by defects or impurities as in most other cases. The most striking effect is the nonlinear increase of the coupling δ near T_{tr}. The presence of the central mode in the 20 cm^{-1} region is in perfect agreement with the weak anomaly observed in the clamped permittivity ϵ_c near T_c (about 2%) and with acoustic anomalies in longitudinal waves. It enabled also a good fit and better understanding of Raman data including the anomalous behavior of the higher frequency Raman doublet.

2. Benzil

Benzil [$(C_6H_5 - CO)_2$] is an organic molecular crystal which undergoes a first-order improper ferroelectric transition at $T_{tr} = 83.5$ K. Structural studies (Odou *et al.*, 1978) combined with a reinterpretation of their data by Tolédano (1979) have shown that the symmetry change is from $P3_121$ ($Z = 3$) to $C2$ ($Z = 12$) which would require an instability at the M point ($\frac{1}{2}$, 0, 0) of the hexagonal Brillouin zone. However, Raman (Sapriel *et al.*, 1979) and far IR transmission measurements (Wyncke *et al.*, 1980) have revealed a rather underdamped Γ-point E mode which partially softens from 15 cm^{-1} at 300 K to 8 cm^{-1} at T_{tr} and then splits into two ($A + B$) components which harden on further cooling to helium temperatures. In far IR transmission even more low-frequency modes have been observed below T_{tr}, but their detailed behavior is not clear.

To understand the E-mode softening, Tolédano (1979) worked out a thermodynamic theory which assumes that the primary instability takes place at the Γ point (with respect to the E mode) and the M-point instability is triggered as a secondary effect. The triggering is caused by a coupling term $\delta[\eta(2\xi_1^2 - \xi_2^2 - \xi_3^2) + \eta_y\sqrt{3}(\xi_2^2 - \xi_3^2)]$ (schematically $\eta\xi^2$) in the thermodynamic potential of the parent phase, where (η_x, η_y) is the two-dimensional primary order parameter and (ξ_1, ξ_2, ξ_3) the three-dimensional order parameter at the three M points. According to this theory no softening at the M point should take place in the parent phase which deserves experimental verification.

Finally, let us briefly discuss the static dielectric behavior. Sapriel *et al.* (1979) have observed a very small sharp peak ($\sim 0.5\%$) near T_{tr} and otherwise a temperature-independent value in the parent phase. Tolédano's theory explains this peak by a piezoelectric coupling between the soft E mode and acoustic modes driven by elastic constants ($c_{11} - c_{12}$) and c_{44}. Thus the clamped ϵ_0 should be practically temperature-independent. The very recent BWO submillimeter measurements (Petzelt *et al.*, 1984b) have confirmed this feature and have shown that the oscillator strength of the soft E mode is very small and roughly temperature-independent above T_{tr} ($f_s = 6 \pm 0.5$ cm^{-2}). The $\Delta\epsilon_s$ slightly grows with decreasing temperature to T_{tr}, although the $\omega_L - \omega_T$ splitting is only ~ 0.1 cm^{-1}, roughly independent of temperature and therefore ω_L softens like ω_T.

C. Incommensurate Ferroelectrics

1. Proper Ferroelectrics: Thiourea

Thiourea [$SC(NH_2)_2$] is a well-known proper incommensurate molecular ferroelectric with $T_i = 202$ K and $T_c = 169$ K. Using the crystallographic convention $c > b > a$ the incommensurate critical wavevector is $\mathbf{k}_i = \delta \mathbf{c}^*$, where δ varies from ~ 0.14 at T_i to a commensurate value $\frac{1}{6}$ near T_c and locks in $\mathbf{k}_c = 0$ at T_c (Moudden et al., 1979). Traditionally, the phases which were revealed by the static dielectric measurements by Goldsmith and White (1959) are denoted by I, II, III, IV, and V, respectively, with increasing temperature. I is the ferroelectric phase, II, III, and IV are incommensurate, and phase V is paraelectric.

It has been thought that phase III also possesses a very small spontaneous polarization. Recently, however, it has been shown that this spontaneous polarization is induced by an external electric field which, moreover, changes the incommensurate phase into the commensurate phase with $\delta = \frac{1}{8}$ (Gesi and Iizumi, 1982; Moudden et al., 1982). We shall not consider phase III further.

The structure consists of four chains of $SC(NH_2)_2$ molecules parallel to the c axis. The molecules are polar with the dipole moment in the (001) plane. In phase V the dipole moments of two pairs of adjacent chains cancel each other by symmetry. In the ferroelectric phase I the molecules tilt slightly and shift in the (001) plane giving rise to $\mathbf{P}_s \parallel \mathbf{b}$. In the incommensurate phase a purely transverse modulation of this distortion occurs in each chain. Projection onto the b axis of the dipole moments of adjacent chains are out of phase. As a result an incommensurate dipole moment wave $\mathbf{P}_i(\mathbf{k}_i)$ develops with wavelengths $(1/\delta)c$ and zero macroscopic P_s (Shiozaki, 1971).

The dynamic origin of the phase transition at T_i was believed to be of the order–disorder type in the earlier models (Calvo, 1960; Futama, 1962). However, using inelastic neutron scattering Moudden et al. (1978) succeeded in the observation of an underdamped soft mode at 300 and 263 K in the region of 10 cm^{-1} which becomes overdamped only closer to T_i. Moreover, far IR reflectivity, which sees the Γ-point mode of the soft branch, revealed an underdamped mode up to T_i accounting well for the static dielectric anomaly of the Curie–Weiss type (Brehat et al., 1976; Khelifa et al., 1977; Siapkas, 1978, 1980; Volkov et al., 1980a). A lattice dynamical calculation (Takahashi et al., 1967) has shown that the soft-mode eigenvector consists mainly of a polar molecular libration about the c axis combined with a nonpolar translation along the a axis (see also Wada et al., 1978). In contrast to the opinion of some authors (Winterfeldt and Schaack, 1980a,b), it can therefore be concluded that the phase transition is of the displacive type.

Let us now discuss in more detail the results of IR spectroscopy, especially below T_i. Concerning the low-frequency part, the most accurate are recent BWO measurements by Volkov et al. (1982). The resulting dielectric spectra are shown in Fig. 17. The spectrum in the paraelectric phase consists of two coupled modes. The higher frequency mode (at ~ 12 cm^{-1} for 280 K)

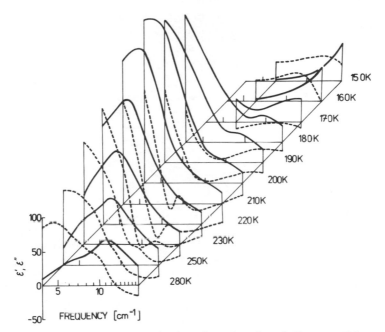

Fig. 17. Complex dielectric spectra in the soft-mode region of thiourea. ϵ'' (——); ϵ' (- - -) (from Volkov *et al.*, 1982).

softens and crosses the lower frequency mode (at ~ 7 cm^{-1} for 280 K) of much weaker strength. Due to the coupling, near T_i the strengths of both modes are exchanged. The stronger mode is clearly the Γ-point mode $P(0)$ from the soft branch. The origin of the extra hard mode at 7 cm^{-1} is not clear, but it cannot be any of the normal modes of the ideal lattice.

As was pointed out in Section II.C.4, in an incommensurate phase new modes which had nonzero wavevectors in the Brillouin zone of the parent phase, may become IR-active. To the first approximation such modes in thiourea are two $P(\pm 2\mathbf{k}_i)$ modes (see Fig. 18). This is because these modes are bilinearly coupled with the $P(0)$ mode. This coupling arises from the term $P_i^2 P(0)P^*(2\mathbf{k}_i) +$ c.c. in the thermodynamic potential of the parent phase, where P_i is the frozen-in incommensurate polarization wave. $P(2\mathbf{k}_i)$ and $P(-2\mathbf{k}_i)$ modes are split due to a term $P_i^4 P(-2\mathbf{k}_i)P^*(2\mathbf{k}_i) +$ c.c. and far away from T_i a strong coupling between $P(0)$ and $P(\pm 2\mathbf{k}_i)$ IR-active modes from the soft branch is expected. The lowest frequency mode of the coupled modes softens for $\delta \to 0$ and represents the phason sliding mode with wavevector equal to that of P_i. Its softening causes the large increase of $\epsilon_b(0)$ near T_c. The middle-frequency mode represents oscillations of discommensuration thickness and its IR strength is expected to decrease to zero for $\delta \to 0$.

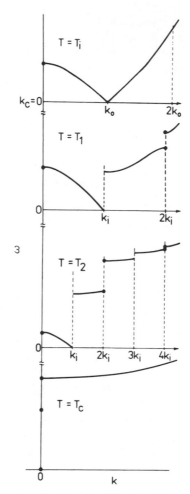

Fig. 18. Schematic soft-branch disperson and IR-active modes in incommensurate proper ferroelectrics. $T_i > T_1 > T_2 > T_c$, IR-active modes (●) (from Petzelt, 1981).

The highest frequency mode also remains active below T_c and represents the normal ferroelectric soft mode. Both lower frequency modes disappear from the IR spectrum of a single-domain sample below T_c.

The experimental results in Fig. 17 are in qualitative agreement with theoretical expectations. The two-coupled oscillator model (Volkov *et al.*, 1980a) does not fit the experimental spectra satisfactorily, especially in the low-frequency region near T_c. The fit was performed neglecting the micro-wave data of Toepfer and Helberg (1976) in the $0.3–2$ cm^{-1} region. Their spectra clearly show an additional strong mode which softens for $T \rightarrow T_c$

below 1 cm⁻¹. This mode represents the IR-active phason which contributes most strongly to the static dielectric anomaly.

The spectra below T_c were well fitted to a single oscillator model with the eigenfrequency nearly linearly increasing from 16 cm⁻¹ at T_c to 27 cm⁻¹ at 100 K. This mode is the ferroelectric soft mode whose frequency should be proportional to $\eta_s \propto P_s$ near the second-order transition temperature. The extrapolation of this relation below T_c in the case of thiourea is questionable

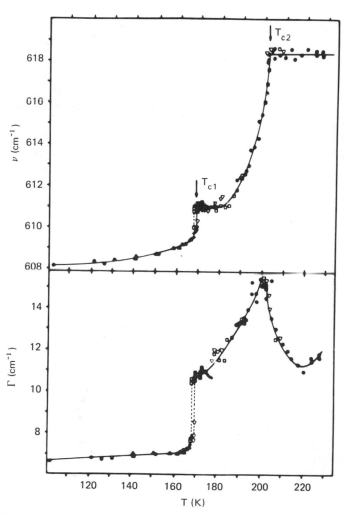

Fig. 19. Temperature dependence of the eigenfrequency and damping of the π(NCS) deformation vibration in thiourea. Sample A cooling (+), heating (●); sample B cooling (▲□), heating (▼■) (from Winterfeldt and Schaack, 1980b).

because the transition is strongly first order and P_s jumps at T_c to more than 70% of its saturated value (Goldsmith and White, 1959). In other words, T_c is far from the stability limit of the ferroelectric phase which approximately equals T_i. This does not mean, however, that T_c is also far from the stability limit of the incommensurate phase which is determined, e.g., by the divergence of $\epsilon_b(0)$. In principle, it can be arbitrarily close to T_c so that the incommensurate–commensurate transition can be nearly a continuous one. It is a specific feature of incommensurate–commensurate transitions that the order of the phase transition may depend on the direction of the temperature variation—it may be second order on cooling but it is always strongly first order on heating if the temperature region of the incommensurate phase is sufficiently broad (Hudák, 1983).

The hard-mode behavior in thiourea near T_i and T_c was most completely studied by Winterfeldt and Schaack (1980a,b) using IR reflectivity and Raman scattering measurements. A number of kinks at T_i and stepwise anomalies at T_c in mode frequencies and strengths have been observed in qualitative agreement with the general discussion in Section II.D. An illustrative example is shown in Fig. 19, where eigenfrequency and damping of the $\pi(NCS)$ deformation vibration of N—C—S atoms are plotted as a function of the temperature. The fit leads to $\delta v_\pi^2 \propto \eta_i^2 \propto (T - T_i)^{2\beta}$ with nonclassical $2\beta = 0.51 \pm 0.03$. Note that symmetry forbids the relation $\delta v^2 \propto \eta_i$ suggested by Winterfeldt and Schaack to save the classical dependence of $\eta_i(T)$. The explanation of the temperature dependence of $\eta_i(T)$ is not quite clear even after respecting other experimental data, e.g., the recent thorough ultrasonic investigations (Rehwald and Vonlanthen, 1982). Note also the pronounced maximum of the damping γ at T_i in Fig. 19 which might be expected according to the discussion in Section II.D.

2. Improper Ferroelectrics: K_2SeO_4

Potassium selenate (K_2SeO_4) is at present the best investigated substance exhibiting an incommensurate phase as far as lattice dynamics is concerned. Its room-temperature structure is isomorphous with the classical ferroelectric ammonium sulfate (space group D_{2h}^{16}, $Z = 4$). At $T_i = 129$ K it undergoes a second-order transition into the incommensurate phase with $\mathbf{k}_i = \frac{1}{3}(1 - \delta)\mathbf{a}^*$ with δ varying from 0.07 at T_i to ~ 0.02 near $T_c = 93$ K and locking slightly discontinuously in $\mathbf{k}_c = \mathbf{a}^*/3$ below T_c (Iizumi et al., 1977). The structure below T_c is an improper ferroelectric (C_{2v}^9, $Z = 12$) with small $P_s \propto \eta_s^3$ parallel to the c axis (Aiki et al., 1970). In the incommensurate phase the polarization wave $P_i(\mathbf{K})$ with $\mathbf{K} = \delta \mathbf{a}^*$ occurs as a third harmonic of η_i. Its wavelength increases from $\sim 14\mathbf{a}$ at T_i to more than $50\mathbf{a}$ near T_c.

The SPT at T_i is a purely displacive one—the soft mode in the parent phase was clearly observed in inelastic neutron scattering by Iizumi et al.,

(1977). Its frequency at $k_i = 0.31a^*$ fulfills the Cochran law $\omega_i \simeq 2.1(T - T_i)^{1/2}$ cm^{-1} and remains underdamped relatively close to T_i. Its eigenvector transforms according to the Σ_2 representation and consists of displacements of all atoms along the c axis and librations of the SeO$_4$ groups about the b axis. The lattice-dynamical calculation using the point-charge model and experimental Raman frequencies (Haque and Hardy, 1980) have shown that the instability at k_i is caused by a very delicate balance between the stabilizing Coulomb forces and destabilizing short-range forces between particular O and K atoms in the (001) plane.

To understand the IR and Raman soft-mode spectra below T_i, we first discuss qualitatively what is expected theroetically. The soft-mode branch and one polar ($\mathbf{P} \parallel \mathbf{c}$) hard-mode branch at four temperatures $T_i > T_1 > T_2 > T_c$ are schematically shown in Fig. 20. Note that gaps occur at the end of the new Brillouin zone, i.e., at $\mathbf{k} = \pm m\mathbf{k}_i$. Above T_i only the hard mode P_0 is active in the $\mathbf{E} \parallel \mathbf{c}$ spectrum. In the incommensurate phase $A(\pm \mathbf{K})$ and $\varphi(\pm \mathbf{K})$ modes are activated in the $\mathbf{E} \parallel \mathbf{c}$ IR spectrum due to the coupling with P_0 of the form $\eta_i^2 \eta^*(\mathbf{k}_i + \mathbf{K})P_0 +$ c.c. (Dvořák and Petzelt, 1978; Petzelt, 1981). Higher order coupling terms introduce gaps in both $A(\mathbf{q})$ and $\varphi(\mathbf{q})$ branches at $\mathbf{q} = \mathbf{K}$ so that two new doublets are expected in the low-frequency dielectric spectrum below T_i. Let us denote their eigenvectors by $A^+(\mathbf{K})$, $A^-(\mathbf{K})$, $\varphi^+(\mathbf{K})$, $\varphi^-(\mathbf{K})$ and the corresponding eigenfrequencies by $\omega_A^+ > \omega_A^- > \omega_\varphi^+ > \omega_\varphi^-$. Near T_c, $A^+(\mathbf{K})$ and $\varphi^+(\mathbf{K})$ represent the amplitudon and phason propagating in the commensurate regions between discommensurations. $A^-(\mathbf{K})$ represents the oscillations of the polarization domain-wall thickness whereas $\varphi^-(\mathbf{K})$ describes the anti-phase motion of domain walls. Passing through T_c, ω_A^+ has nearly no anomaly and remains IR-active and $A^-(\mathbf{K})$ disappears from the spectrum for a single domain sample. As $T \rightarrow T_c$, $\varphi^-(\mathbf{K}) \rightarrow \varphi(0)$ and therefore $\omega_\varphi^- \rightarrow 0$ which causes the divergence of $\epsilon_c(0)$. Modes $\varphi^+(\mathbf{K})$ and $\varphi^-(\mathbf{K})$ are both IR- and Raman active below T_i. However, close to T_c the IR strength of the $\varphi^+(\mathbf{K})$ mode and the Raman strength of the $\varphi^-(\mathbf{K})$ go to zero. The analytical formulae for the frequencies and strengths of both $\varphi^\pm(\mathbf{K})$ modes in both IR and Raman spectra near T_c were recently derived in the constant amplitude approximation (Dvořák and Hudák, 1982; Hudák, 1984). In the commensurate phase the $\varphi^+(\mathbf{K})$ remains Raman active and represents the locked-in phason, whereas the $\varphi^-(\mathbf{K})$ mode disappears from the single-domain sample.

Let us compare the theory with spectroscopic data. The observed frequencies are summarized in Fig. 21. All predicted selection rules are satisfied. The dielectric spectra in the $5 - 450$ cm^{-1} region were measured by Petzelt et al. (1979) and Volkov et al. (1980a). In the $5 - 31$ cm^{-1} region BWO spectroscopy was used, whereas in the higher frequency region the bulk reflectivity technique was used. The most interesting results relevant

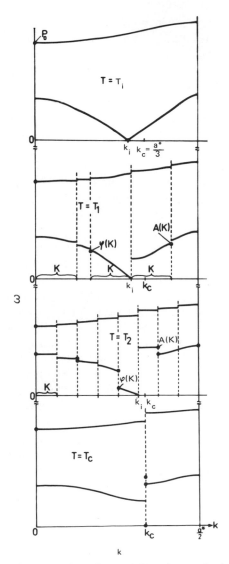

Fig. 20. Schematic soft-branch dispersion and IR-active modes in incommensurate improper ferroelectrics of the K_2SeO_4 symmetry ($K_c = \frac{1}{3}a^*$). For explanation see Fig. 18 (from Petzelt, 1981).

for our theoretical discussion have been obtained by the former method. In the $20-30$ cm^{-1} region the amplitudon $A(\mathbf{K})$ was observed below T_i with an abrupt increase in strength below T_c, in agreement with the theory (Dvořák and Petzelt, 1978). The frequency of $A(\mathbf{K})$ is in good agreement with the

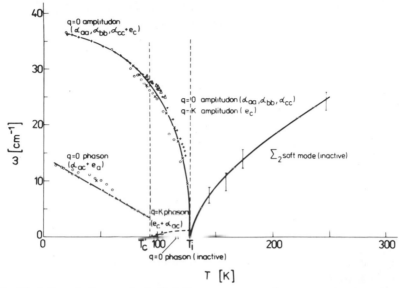

Fig. 21. Soft-mode frequencies in K_2SeO_4—a summary of spectroscopic data. Neutron scattering (I); far IR data ($\triangle$); Raman data (+, $\bigcirc$, $\times$) (from Petzelt, 1981).

$A(0)$ amplitudon from Raman data. The splitting of $A^+(\mathbf{K})$ and $A^-(\mathbf{K})$ modes near T_c was not observed due to its small value, high damping, and the low IR intensity of both modes.

The low-frequency spectra show an absorption increase specific for the incommensurate phase only (see Fig. 22). It is assigned to a high-frequency wing of the $\varphi^-(\mathbf{K})$ mode, which was found to be overdamped in agreement with theoretical expectation. The dielectric dispersion in the 5–900 MHz region close to T_c was measured by Horioka *et al.* (1980) and the ω_φ^- value at T_c was found to be 10^8 Hz. This value can be nonzero because of the slightly first-order nature of the incommensurate–commensurate transition or partially also because of the pinning of the polarization wave at defects. In fact, NMR experiments reviewed by Blinc (1981) bring some evidence of phason pinning of this order of magnitude. Despite this finite frequency, the $\varphi^-(\mathbf{K})$ softening is unusually large: from about 2 cm^{-1} near T_i till 3×10^{-3} cm^{-1} at T_c. This is in disagreement with the large finite value of $\mathbf{K}(T_c^+)$ from neutron scattering (Iizumi *et al.*, 1977). It seems likely that the accuracy of the neutron experiment is insufficient for a precise determination of $\mathbf{k}_i(T)$ close to T_c. Several other experiments show that the phase transition at T_c is nearly continuous on cooling and therefore no large discontinuous change of $\mathbf{k}_i(T)$ at T_c would be expected.

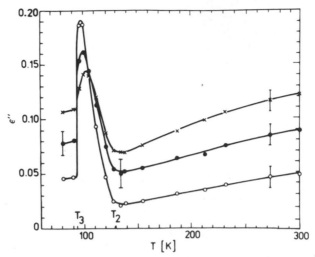

Fig. 22. Temperature dependence of millimeter dielectric losses in K_2SeO_4. Values of ϵ'' at $\omega = 11.7$ (x), 8.6 (●), and 5.7 (○) cm^{-1} (from Petzelt *et al.*, 1979).

D. Nonferroelectric Transitions in Dielectrics

1. Quartz

Quartz (SiO_2) is a classical material which is commonly used in IR, visible, and UV techniques as a filter or window. Therefore its IR properties have been intensively studied since the beginning of this century. The earlier bibliography can be found in the paper by Saksena (1940). Here we shall mention only more recent IR results connected with the $\alpha \rightarrow \beta$ phase transition at 846 K. The transition is displacive, slightly first order, nonferroelectric, and nonferroelastic with the order parameter at the Brillouin zone center. The list of all normal modes and their activities in both phases is given in Table III. The soft-mode behavior was studied by Raman and neutron spectroscopy and was reviewed by Scott (1974).

The temperature dependence of the IR reflectivity from 300–1300 cm^{-1} was most accurately measured and evaluated by Gervais and Piriou (1975). As expected from Table III, two of the four A_2 modes disappear above T_{tr}. In the E spectra two TO modes lie below 300 cm^{-1} so that only six modes are observed, three of which disappear above T_{tr}. The thermodynamic theory (Petzelt and Dvořák, 1976a,b) predicts the mode strength to be proportional to η_s^2 which is in approximate agreement with experimental data, taking into account that some ambiguity in the fitting procedure of η_s arises due to the first-order nature of the transition (Bachheimer and Dolino, 1975). The

TABLE III

NORMAL MODES IN SiO$_2$ AT ROOM TEMPERATURE[a]

Number of optic modes		Activity	TO frequencies (cm^{-1})				LO frequencies (cm^{-1})			
D_3^4	D_6^5									
$4A_1$	$1A_1$	$\alpha_{xx} + \alpha_{yy}, \alpha_{zz}$	464				equal to			
	$3B_1$	—	207	356	1085		TO frequencies			
$4A_2$	$2A_2$	e_z	495	1071			552	1229		
	$2B_2$	—	363	777			387	790		
$8E$	$4E_1$	$(e_x, e_y); (\alpha_{xz}, \alpha_{yz})$	263	450	797	1065	264	510	810	1226
	$4E_2$	$(\alpha_{xy}, \alpha_{xx} - \alpha_{yy})$	128	394	695	1158	128	402	698	1155

[a] The IR-active modes are taken from Gervais and Piriou (1975) and Loewenstein et al. (1973), the IR-active A_1 modes are from Fries and Claus (1971).

predicted temperature dependence is best fulfilled by the mode at 777 cm^{-1} which is well separated from other modes in the A_2 spectrum.

The frequency changes, which are very pronounced for most of the modes in quartz, satisfy the proportionality to η_s^2, as expected theoretically (see Fig. 23). Next, Fig. 24 illustrates the critical increase of damping of all IR modes near T_{tr}. Such an increase of the damping may be explained by three phonon scattering processes involving two phonons from the soft branch, as discussed in Section II.D. Gervais and coworkers (Gervais et al., 1975; Gervais, 1976; Billard et al., 1979) were able to fit this temperature dependence quantitatively (see Fig. 24 (———)) using a simplified model which neglects the phonon dispersion.

The temperature dependence of the weak IR modes at 128 and 263 cm^{-1} above room temperature (see Russell and Bell, 1967, for the most accurate room-temperature data) seems to have been uninvestigated until now. Especially, the temperature dependence of the strength of the isolated mode at 128 cm^{-1} which should disappear in the β phase is of interest. Below room temperature the mode strength surprisingly decreases (Loewenstein et al., 1973) although the thermodynamic theory requires proportionality to η_s^2 near T_{tr}.

2. NH$_4$Cl and NH$_4$Br

Ammonium halides exist in two different modifications: in the high-temperature disordered NaCl structure α (space group O_h^5, $Z = 1$) and the low

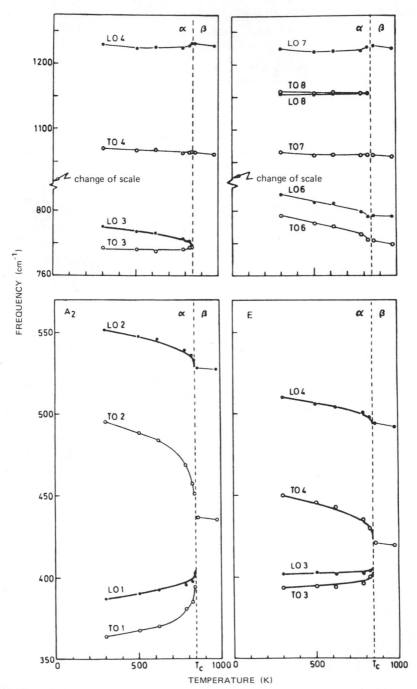

Fig. 23. Temperature dependence of polar hard-mode frequencies in quartz (from Gervais and Piriou, 1975).

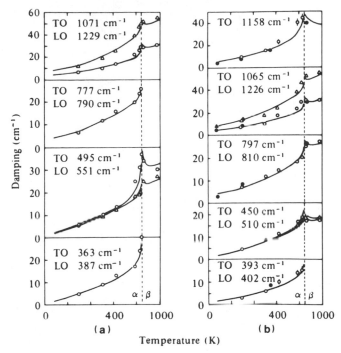

Fig. 24. Temperature dependence of hard-mode damping in quartz. (a) A_2-modes, (b) E-modes (from Billard *et al.*, 1979).

temperature CsCl structure. The reconstructive transition between these modifications (at 456 and 411 K for NH_4Cl and NH_4Br, respectively) was not thoroughly investigated spectroscopically. The CsCl structural modification is disordered at higher temperatures (phase β, space group O_h^1, $Z = 1$) and becomes ordered at lower temperatures (phase δ, space group T_d^1, $Z = 1$, or phase γ, space group D_{4h}^7, $Z = 2$). NH_4Cl undergoes this order–disorder transition at 243 K into phase δ, NH_4Br at 235 K into phase γ and at 78 K into phase γ. The disorder concerns the NH_4^+ tetrahedra which flip between two orientations mutually related by an inversion with the center at N atoms. In the case of the ferrodistortive (nonferroelectric and nonferroelastic) transition in NH_4Cl the order parameter (flipping of NH_4^+ ions) transforms according to the A_{2u} representation. The peculiarity of this SPT is that no external lattice vibration transforms according to this representation so that the SPT must be of the order–disorder type from symmetry arguments alone. In the case of antiferrodistortive (improper ferroelastic) transition in NH_4Br the order parameter is the same NH_4-flipping motion as in NH_4Cl, but with the wavevector $\mathbf{k} = \frac{1}{2}(\mathbf{a}_i^* + \mathbf{a}_j^*)$, $i \neq j$ (different combina-

TABLE IV

Mode Classification for NH_4Cl and NH_4Br and Observed Frequencies[a]

Mode	Disordered phase $\beta(0)_h^1$		Ordered phases					
	Symmetry type	Activity	$\delta(T_d^1)$ − NH_4Cl Symmetry type	Activity	Observed frequencies (cm⁻¹)	$\gamma(D_{4h}^7)$ − NH_4Br Symmetry type	Activity	Observed frequencies (cm⁻¹)
NH_4^+ internal								
ν_1	A_{1g}	$\alpha_{xx}+\alpha_{yy}+\alpha_{zz}$	A_1	$\alpha_{xx}+\alpha_{yy}+\alpha_{zz}$	3048	A_{1g}	$\alpha_{xx}+\alpha_{yy}+\alpha_{zz}$	3038
						B_{1u}	—	—
ν_2	E_g	$(2\alpha_{zz}-\alpha_{xx}-\alpha_{yy},$ $\alpha_{xx}-\alpha_{yy})$	E	$(2\alpha_{zz}-\alpha_{xx}-\alpha_{yy},$ $\alpha_{xx}-\alpha_{yy})$	1716	A_{1g}	$\alpha_{xx}+\alpha_{yy}+\alpha_{zz}$	1693 + 1697
						B_{1g}	$\alpha_{xx}-\alpha_{yy}$	—
						B_{1u}	—	—
						A_{1u}	—	—
ν_3	F_{1u}	(e_x,e_y,e_z)	F_2	(e_x,e_y,e_z) $\alpha_{xy},\alpha_{yz},\alpha_{zx}$	3126	B_{2g}	α_{xy}	3117 + 3126
						E_g	$(\alpha_{xz},\alpha_{yz})$	3124
						A_{2u}	e_z	—
						E_u	(e_x,e_y)	—
ν_4	F_{1u}	(e_x,e_y,e_z)	F_2	(e_x,e_y,e_z) $\alpha_{xy},\alpha_{yz},\alpha_{zx}$	1403	B_{2g}	α_{xy}	1400 + 1420
						E_g	$(\alpha_{xz},\alpha_{yz})$	1412 + 1435
						A_{2u}	e_z	—
						E_u	(e_x,e_y)	—
NH_4^+ libration	F_{1g}	—	F_1	—	—	A_{2g}	—	—
	$M_2^\dagger(A_{2g})$	—	$M_2(A_2)$	—	—	E_g	$(\alpha_{xz},\alpha_{yz})$	334
	$M_5^\dagger(E_g)$	—	$M_5(E)$	—	—	B_{2u}	—	—
						E_u	(e_x,e_y)	343
Translation	F_{1u}	(e_x,e_y,e_z)	F_2	(e_x,e_y,e_z) $\alpha_{xy},\alpha_{yz},\alpha_{zx}$	176	A_{2u}	e_z	152
	$M_2^\dagger(A_{2u})$	—	$M_4(B_2)$	—	—	E_u	(e_x,e_y)	134
	$M_5^\dagger(E_u)$	—	$M_5(E)$	—	—	B_{1g}	$\alpha_{xx}-\alpha_{yy}$	177
						E_g	$(\alpha_{xz},\alpha_{yz})$	—
M-point acoustic	$M_3^\dagger(B_{1u})$	—	$M_1(A_1)$	—	—	A_{1g}	$\alpha_{xx}+\alpha_{yy}+\alpha_{zz}$	66
	$M_5^\dagger(E_u)$	—	$M_5(E)$	—	—	E_g	$(\alpha_{xz},\alpha_{yz})$	80

[a] Mostly at ~180 K. The activity in the γ phase is related to the tetragonal coordinate system. The point-group representation in brackets are equivalent to small M-point representations. The unit-cell origin is chosen in N.

tions of i, j correspond to three types of ferroelastic domains) at the M-point of the Brillouin zone.   The results of the group analysis together with observed mode frequencies are summarized in Table IV.

Most spectroscopic work on NH_4Cl and NH_4Br was performed using Raman scattering.   As the selection rules for IR absorption are almost exclusive with those for Raman scattering, IR spectroscopy gives complementary spectroscopic information not available from Raman measurements.

The far IR region is dominated by the strong "reststrahlen" absorption due to the translational mode which was most thoroughly measured using bulk reflectivity and thin film transmission by Perry and Lowndes (1969). The classical oscillator fit to reflectivity spectra needs an additional weak oscillator on the high-frequency side for getting good agreement with experiment.   This is a sign of appreciable anharmonicity of these crystals even in the ordered phases.   The temperature dependence of the translational mode parameters through the SPTs was determined from thin-film transmittance, but comparison with the bulk Raman results in the δ phase of NH_4Cl has shown that the thin film data are not quantitatively reliable.

The E_u libration mode in the γ phase of NH_4Br was investigated by Novák and Petzelt (1976).   It consists of opposite rotations of adjacent NH_4^+ groups about an axis perpendicular to the tetragonal c axis which corresponds to the M-point of the Brillouin zone of the β phase.   The temperature dependence of the mode parameters evaluated from the transmittance of the 0.1-mm thick single crystalline platelet are shown in Fig. 25.   The most interesting temperature dependence is that of the strength which follows the propor-

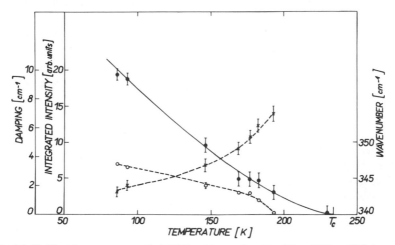

Fig. 25. E_u-libration parameters in NH_4Br.   Proportional to $(T_c - T)^{1.5} \propto \eta_s^6(T)$ (———), integrated intensity (. . .), damping (xxx), wavenumber (ooo) (from Novák and Petzelt, 1976).

tionality to $\eta_s^6(T) \propto (T_c - T)^{1.5}$. According to symmetry considerations, however, the strength should be proportional to $\eta_s^2(T)$ to the lowest order; only the next higher coupling leads to the observed dependence. We note, that in addition the Raman active E_g libration does not fulfill the thermodynamic theory by Petzelt and Dvořák (1976b) which predicts the strength $I_R \propto \eta_s^4$. Instead, unlike the E_u mode, a rapid increase of I_R close to but below T_c is observed (Wang and Wright, 1973). We conclude that the activation of both these modes is not yet understood.

The higher frequency region was thoroughly investigated by Garland and Schumaker (1967) and Schumaker and Garland (1970) by means of transmission spectroscopy of single crystals, sublimed films, and powders. The most interesting is the behavior near the strong v_4 vibration in the 1430–1450 cm^{-1} region where a sharp peak appears in the disordered phase. In the ordered δ phase of NH_4Cl its intensity decreases as $\eta_s^2(0) - \eta_s^2(T)$ (Garland and Schumaker, 1967). Like the 1560 cm^{-1} peak in $NaNO_2$ it represents a clear example of a disorder-induced mode. The appearance of this mode can be explained in the same way as for $NaNO_2$. The analogous peak in NH_4Br behaves in a more complex way (Schumaker and Garland, 1970). Its intensity remains finite in the γ phase and falls nearly to zero only in the δ phase for $T \rightarrow 0$. The situation is complicated also by the fact that the $\gamma \rightarrow \delta$ transition shows a large thermal hysteresis which depends on the thermal treatment of the sample.

The last feature which is worth noting is the appearance and behavior of librational overtones which are IR-active even in the disordered β phase up to 300 K. This is best seen for the binary overtones near 740 and 650 cm^{-1} in NH_4Cl and NH_4Br, respectively. Below the order–disorder transition temperature they become progressively sharper and stronger. Below the $\gamma \rightarrow \delta$ transition in NH_4Br a second component appears near 680 cm^{-1} whose intensity characterizes the quantitative occurrence of the δ phase which coexists with the γ phase. No theory which correlates the temperature dependence of these overtones with the order parameter seems to exist.

3. CsCuCl$_3$

Cesium trichlorocuprate (CsCuCl$_3$) is the only material known to the authors with an SPT into a helicoidally modulated structure. It occurs at 423 K, it is strongly first order and is connected with a tripling of the unit cell from the D_{6h}^4 or C_{6v}^4 ($Z = 2$) group into D_6^2 ($Z = 6$) group. The recent IR and Raman data (Akiyama et al., 1979; Petzelt et al., 1981) support rather the nonpolar D_{6h}^4 parent structure with a high degree of disorder in agreement with the Jahn–Teller origin of the transition (Hirotsu, 1977).

The observed TO frequencies and their assignment using the independent

TABLE V

NONSILENT TO MODES AT ROOM TEMPERATURE IN CsCuCl$_3$ AND THEIR ACTIVITY

D_6^2	D_{6h}^4	Activity	Observed TO frequencies (cm^{-1})
6A_1	1A_{1g}	$\alpha_{xx} + \alpha_{yy}, \alpha_{zz}$	288
	5Δ_5	—	27.5, 102.5, 178.5, 265
8A_2	1A_{2g}	—	95
	2A_{2u}	e_z	50, 142
	5Δ_5	—	17.4, 72, 90, 181, 260
14E_1	1E_{1g}	$(\alpha_{yz}, \alpha_{xz})$	189
	3E_{1u}	(e_x, e_y)	68, 158, 282
	10Δ	—	39, 54, 76, 94, 112, 172, 187, 258, 276, 292
15E_2	3E_{2g}	$(\alpha_{xx} - \alpha_{yy}, \alpha_{xy})$	43, 155, 194
	2F_{2u}	—	24, 53, 60, 66.5, 85, 132, 243
	10Δ_5	—	

data of Petzelt *et al.* and Akiyama *et al.* are listed in Table V. Most interesting temperature changes are observed in the low-frequency part of the **E** ∥ **c** (A_2) spectra where the mode at 50 cm^{-1}, which involves the Cs vibration along the *c* axis, becomes heavily damped for $T > T_{tr}$ probably in connection with an increase of the Cs ionic conductivity above T_{tr}. The low-frequency mode at 17 cm^{-1} was thoroughly investigated by Volkov *et al.* (1980e) using BWO spectroscopy and its parameters are shown in Fig. 26. The symmetry analysis shows that this mode is very probably connected with a phase shift of the modulation wave along the *c* axis. In other words, this mode corresponds to a phason of the commensurate modulation with a finite gap. The symmetry analysis (see Table V) predicts that another component which represents the amplitudon should appear in the A_1 spectrum. Fluctuations of the complementary enantiomorphic modulation should appear in the E_2 spectrum. Above T_{tr} all of these components are degenerate and transform according to the 4-dimensional Δ_5 representation like the order parameter. Table V shows that these modes were observed in Raman spectra at 27 and 24 cm^{-1}, respectively.

Because of the order–disorder character of the transition the soft mode is expected to be diffusive. Therefore the observed modes are not soft modes although they have geometrically identical eigenvectors. Even if the soft-mode eigenvector is not yet known in detail (the character of the structural disorder above T_{tr} was not investigated), it must represent the hopping of the soft-mode particles between several minima of an anharmonic potential well. On the other hand, the observed modes represent their underdamped

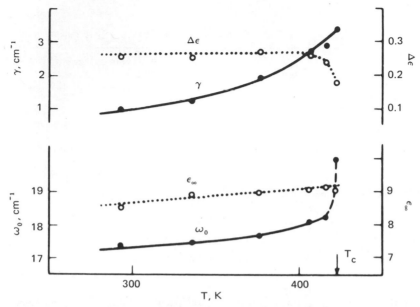

Fig. 26. Parameters of the A_2 hard phason in $CsCuCl_3$ (from Volkov *et al.*, 1980e).

vibrations in the central potential minimum. If this assignment is correct we should observe an additional microwave dispersion in the A_2 spectrum and central peaks in the A_1 and E_2 scattering spectra. No corresponding data are available.

Cesium trichlorocuprate represents the only case of a nonferroelectric nonpyroelectric phase transition known to the authors where some soft-mode component (in this case phason) becomes IR-active below T_{tr}.

E. Charge-density Wave Substances

Charge-density wave (CDW) substances have been most extensively studied in the last decade mainly because of the one- or two-dimensional character of their conductivity, which was theoretically promising from the viewpoint of high-temperature superconductivity. They exhibit a number of phase transitions, many of which are believed to be of electronic origin. If the Coulomb repulsion between electrons is negligible (free-electron gas) we can expect a Peierls phase transition with a critical wavevector $2\mathbf{k}_F$ ($\mathbf{k}_F$ is the Fermi wavevector). If the Coulomb repulsion between electrons is strong (localized electrons) a Peierls transition at $4\mathbf{k}_F$ or a spin-Peierls transition at $2\mathbf{k}_F$ can occur (see, e.g., Lépine *et al.*, 1978). In the latter case a spin-density wave (SDW) instead of CDW freezes-in below the transition temperature.

CDW and SDW can occur in various conductors and semiconductors with quasi-one-dimensional (see, e.g., André, *et al.*, 1976; Berlinsky, 1979), two-dimensional (Wilson *et al.*, 1975), or even three-dimensional (Overhauser, 1978) character. Their IR spectra are mostly dominated by a strong electronic absorption which makes difficult an accurate evaluation of vibrational-mode parameters. The exceptions are TCNQ salts the IR spectra of which have been intensively studied in recent years and will be briefly discussed here.

1. TCNQ Salts

Tetracyanoquinodimethane (TCNQ) $(C_{12}H_4N_4)$ is a planar molecule which often forms salts with segregated TCNQ stacks, having excess electronic charge (electronic acceptor), and with some other donor stacks. These compounds exhibit high electrical conductivity along the stacking axes. A vast number of such compounds is now known (see, e.g., André *et al.*, 1976) and many of them exhibit phase transitions which manifest themselves by pronounced anomalies in the electric conductivity. As a rule, the conductivity of the higher temperature phase is higher. Most of the investigated transitions could be understood considering just the electronic subsystem (Peierls and spin-Peierls transitions), but very often the structural ordering or displacive changes of the donor stacks play an important role as well.

The IR spectra of stacked TCNQ salts reveal several interesting pronounced features which are specific for this class of materials. The basic feature is the strongly IR-active electronic charge transfer mode polarized along the stacking axis. The band (or bands) due to this mode (or several modes) lies typically in the near or middle IR region, it is very strong and broad (highly damped) and causes in this way a very large anisotropy of absorption and reflection in the whole IR region. The linear coupling between this band and internal TCNQ molecular vibrations causes a strong enhancement of the vibrational mode strengths and their specific frequency shifts which enables us to calculate the electron–phonon coupling constants. This effect is the most pronounced and strongest for totally symmetric (IR-inactive) vibrations of isolated TCNQ molecules which become strongly IR-active due to this coupling.

Two qualitatively different IR spectra occur in two main classes of TCNQ salts, i.e., the conducting and semiconducting ones. In the case of semiconducting salts the excess (conducting) electrons are well localized on individual TCNQ molecules and the charge transfer mode has higher energy than vibrational modes. During the period of molecular vibration each TCNQ molecule keeps its charge so that the vibrational modes remain sharp (only slightly damped). The electron–phonon coupling shifts the vibrational frequencies downwards. On the other hand, in the case of conducting salts the conducting electrons are rather delocalized along the TCNQ stacks and the charge-transfer energy is comparable or smaller than that of TCNQ vibrations. In this case the TCNQ molecule changes its charge during the vibrational period causing in this way a large increase of vibrational mode damping. Nothing can be said generally about their frequency shifts.

It is clear that the classification mentioned above is rather crude. It loses its sense, e.g., when the TCNQ stack is strongly dimerized (trimerized, tetramerized) as usually happens in reality. In these cases we have to consider separately the intra- and inter-dimer (trimer, tetramer) charge transfer which can differ considerably. Whereas the electrical conductivity is determined by the inter-dimer transfer, the vibrational damping is determined by all charge-transfer excitations. Despite these complicating features the above qualitative considerations are very useful for understanding of the IR spectra of TCNQ salts. As will become clear from the following examples, the relation between the IR spectra and dc conductivity is valid also for two phases of a particular TCNQ salt exhibiting a phase transition.

Until now, phase transitions in three TCNQ salts have been investigated only by means of single crystal IR spectroscopy, namely in tetrathiafulvalene TCNQ (TTF-TCNQ), MEM(TCNQ)$_2$ (N-methyl-N-ethylmorpholinium-bis-TCNQ), and MTPP(TCNQ)$_2$ (methyltriphenylphosphonium-bis-TCNQ). We expect the number of investigated materials to increase considerably in the near future.

a. TTF-TCNQ

TTF-TCNQ is the most thoroughly studied TCNQ salt because of its highest known room-temperature conductivity ($\sim 10^3 \ \Omega^{-1}$cm^{-1}) which still increases on lowering the temperature to 54 K where a Peierls transition into an incommensurate structure with a frozen-in CDW occurs. The critical wavevector of this phase transition is $\mathbf{k}_i^I = \mathbf{a}^*/2 + 0.295\mathbf{b}^*$, where $0.295\mathbf{b} = 2\mathbf{k}_F$ ($\mathbf{b}$ is the stacking axis). The value of $\mathbf{k}_F$ is determined by the partial electronic charge transfer from the TTF to the TCNQ stack and is almost temperature-independent. Below 54 K two other phase transitions take place: at 49 K ($\mathbf{k}_i^{II} = (\frac{1}{2} - \delta)\mathbf{a}^* + 0.295\mathbf{b}^*$, $0 < \delta < \frac{1}{4}$) and at 38 K ($\mathbf{k}_i^{III} = \mathbf{a}^*/4 + 0.295\mathbf{b}$), (see the review by Comes and Shirane, 1979 and references therein). It is believed that at 54 K and 49 K the CDWs predominantly on the TCNQ and the TTF stacks, respectively, become long-range correlated. At 38 K a discontinuous transition into a structure with a different arrangement of adjacent CDWs occurs: in the a direction two adjacent CDWs are in-phase and the other two in antiphase. The high-temperature space group is $P2_1/c(C_{2h}^5)$ ($Z = 2$), below 38 K the point symmetry either remains $2/m$ or reduces to 2 (Bak and Janssen, 1978).

For such a complicated phase-transition sequence neither the group-theoretical analysis nor the detailed spectroscopic information on all vibrational
modes in all phases are available.   Recently rather detailed infrared powder
measurements as a function of temperature were performed (Etemad, 1981;
Bozio and Pecile, 1981) which have revealed several new modes in the
low-temperature phase.   Assignment of these new modes is still not unambiguous, as it follows from different interpretations suggested by Etemad and
Bozio and Pecile.   More physical information is contained in the single
crystalline far IR reflectivity recently measured in all phases by Tanner *et al.*
(1981).   The reflectivity (see Fig. 27) shows a pronounced temperature
dependence and gives evidence of several new modes activated below 54 K,
with the two strongest at ~ 40 and 290 cm^{-1}.   The latter was seen also in both
powder investigations, but at higher frequencies (at 317 and 350 cm^{-1}) due to
the Fröhlich shift discussed in Section III.A.   The former mode was assigned
to a pinned CDW phason (the so-called Fröhlich mode), but the absence of
its softening on approaching 54 K contradicts this suggestion.   More likely it

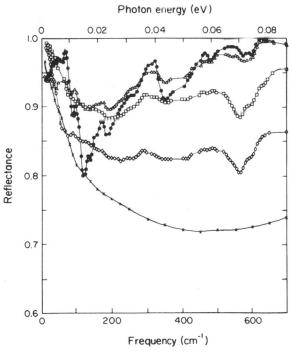

Fig. 27. Far IR reflectivity of TTF–TCNQ for **E ∥ b**.   25 K (●), 34 K (△), 60 K (□), 160 K
(◇), 300 K (x) (from Tanner *et al.,* 1981).

could be one of the many external vibrational hard modes activated below 54 K due to the Brillouin zone folding (see also the discussion in the review by Petzelt, 1981). It is an interesting feature of the reflectivity spectra that the results of the Kramers–Kronig analysis extrapolated below the measured region (7–700 cm^{-1}) are in good agreement with the direct measurements of ϵ' in the microwave region. This supports the view that no additional strong modes are pesent below ~ 10 cm^{-1} in contrast with previous suggestions (Jacobsen 1979; Eldridge and Bates, 1979).

b. MEM(TCNQ)$_2$

MEM(TCNQ)$_2$ belongs to the semiconducting class of TCNQ salts and undergoes two phase transitions: a second-order transition at 19 K and a first-order transition at 335 K. In the high-temperature (conducting) phase the TCNQ molecules are uniformly spaced in a stack, below 335 K a strong dimerization and below 19 K a tetramerization occurs in the TCNQ stack. If we suppose a full electronic charge transfer from the MEM to the TCNQ stacks, the transitions can be understood as Peierls ($k_c^I = 4k_F$) and spin-Peierls ($k_c^{II} = 2k_F$) transitions, respectively. However, the Peierls transitions is accompanied also by pronounced ordering of the MEM ions (Oostra *et al.*, 1981).

Infrared reflectivity of MEM(TCNQ)$_2$ was measured at room temperature (Rice *et al.*, 1980) and at 350 K (Yartsev and Jacobsen, 1981) and thoroughly interpreted theoretically. In the dimerized phase the electronic charge-transfer mode is modeled by a strong highly damped oscillator and the whole IR spectrum (in the 50–6000 cm^{-1} region) polarized along the TCNQ stacks is explained by a coupling between this oscillator and ten totally symmetric internal TCNQ vibrations (inactive unless this coupling is respected), analogous to other semiconducting TCNQ salts. In the conducting phase, on the other hand, the charge transfer oscillator was replaced by a function which describes the absorption of a one-dimensional free-electron gas due to its excitation across the Peierls gap at 0 K. The application of this model to high temperatures seems to be questionable. The vibrational spectrum is much broader than at 300 K and is again assigned to coupling with the electronic mode. The evaluated electron–molecular-vibrational coupling constants are approximately of the same magnitude in both phases. Quite recently, Sweitlik (1983) repeated the reflectivity measurements on MEM(TCNQ)$_2$ in the 200–4000 cm^{-1} region in detail as a function of temperature. Most of the reflectivity bands show abrupt decreases in intensity and smearing out at T_{tr}, but no other spectral changes inside each phase were observed. The value of T_{tr} shows a clear thermal hysteresis of about 3 K.   These facts confirm the purely first-order nature of the phase transition.

c. MTPP(TCNQ)₂

MTPP(TCNQ)$_2$ belongs also to the class of semiconducting TCNQ salts and undergoes a first-order phase transition at 316 K, connected with an abrupt increase of the electrical conductivity.   From the viewpoint of the electronic subsystem, the transition is not as simple as in previous cases because the TCNQ stacks remain tetramerized in both phases.   The phase transition is connected mainly with large rotations and partial disordering of phenyl groups in MTPP molecules (Konno and Saito, 1973).

The IR reflectivity (Graja *et al.*, 1982) at room temperature is similar to other semiconducting TCNQ salts with one important difference: many of the TCNQ vibrational modes consist of sharp narrow doublets which would be expected because there are two nonequivalent TCNQ molecules in the unit cell.   However, all these doublets transform abruptly into broader singlets above 316 K, as can be seen from Fig. 28.   This is strong evidence for the delocalization of electrons (at least inside the tetramers) in the high-temperature phase.

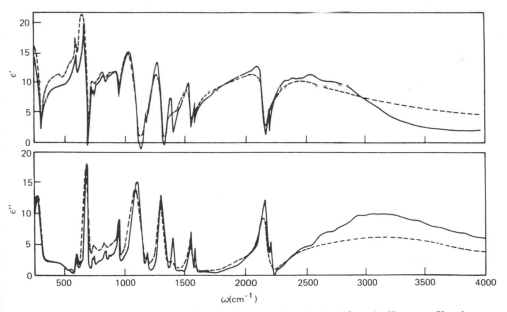

Fig. 28. Infrared dielectric spectra of MTPP(TCNQ)$_2$ calculated from the Kramers–Kronig analysis of the **E** ∥ **b** reflectivity: 292 K (———), 335 K (– – –) (from Graja *et al.*, 1982).

F. Metal – Nonmetal Transitions in Binary Compounds

A number of metal – nonmetal transitions are known in simple binary compounds like transition-metal oxides and chalcogenides or rare-earth chalcogenides (the so-called mixed valency compounds) (see, e.g., the monograph by Bugaev *et al.*, 1979). In most of these transitions electronic correlations are believed to play a decisive role but due to electron – phonon coupling it is not easy to decide whether in a particular transition the primary order parameter is predominantly of electronic or lattice origin. Infrared (together with visible) spectroscopy is a very important technique for solving such problems. The large increase of the static conductivity is expected to be accompanied by a drastic change of the IR spectra caused by the strong free carrier absorption. Nevertheless, very few accurate IR studies of metal – nonmetal transitions in these compounds currently exist, mainly due to the limited quantitative understanding of IR changes, necessity of investigations in a broad spectral region, and the lack of sufficiently large samples. Here we shall limit our discussion to two examples, VO_2 and NbO_2, for which the best IR data are available.

1. VO_2

Vanadium dioxide (VO_2) at $T_{tr} = 341$ K undergoes the most investigated metal – semiconductor transition. It seems to be strongly first order, because of a stepwise conductivity increase by a factor of 10^5 (see the review by Zylbersztejn and Mott, 1975) and stepwise anomalies in lattice parameters (Kucharczyk and Niklewski, 1979). The symmetry change D_{4h}^{14} ($Z = 2$) $\rightarrow C_{2h}^5$ ($Z = 4$) allows in principle a second-order transition which can be described by the Landau theory (Brews, 1970). In fact, dynamical properties indicate that critical changes occur in a rather broad region in both phases around T_{tr}, as we shall mention. From the structural point of view, the high-temperature hexagonal metallic rutile form of VO_2 is characterized by chains of short equidistant atoms along the rutile c_r axis whereas in the monoclinic form the atoms are dimerized forming a zigzag chain along the monoclinic a_m axis (c_r axis) (McWhan *et al.*, 1974).

The IR reflectivity was investigated by Barker *et al.* (1966). At room temperature the spectrum in the $100–800$ cm^{-1} region for both $\mathbf{E} \parallel \mathbf{a}_m$ and $\mathbf{E} \perp \mathbf{a}_m$ is dominated by 8 lattice modes which differ for both polarizations (group theory predicts 8 and 7 modes for $\mathbf{E} \parallel \mathbf{b}_m$ and $\mathbf{E} \perp \mathbf{b}_m$, respectively). Near T_{tr} a strong electronic absorption overlaps with the vibrational spectrum and 20 K above T_{tr} it dominates the spectrum so completely that no phonon structure is seen at all (1 and 3 modes should be active above T_{tr} for $\mathbf{E} \parallel \mathbf{c}_r$ and $\mathbf{E} \perp \mathbf{c}_r$, respectively). No fit of the intermediate region was attempted. The electronic absorption was more thoroughly investigated by

Verleur *et al.* (1968) in the $(2-40) \times 10^3$ cm^{-1} region.   A band gap energy $E_g = 0.6$ eV at 300 K was found, but its temperature dependence near T_{tr} (above which $E_g = 0$) was not determined.

Recently Bianconi *et al.* (1981) determined the temperature dependence of the plasmon frequency ω_p above T_{tr} from thermoreflectance measurements and found a pronounced softening of ω_p as shown in Fig. 29.   The softening may be caused by a decrease in the number of conduction electrons or an increase in their effective mass near T_{tr}.   In terms of existing electronic band-structure calculations (Gupta *et al.*, 1977) it is caused by a critical increase of the interelectron correlation.   The softening of ω_p strongly supports the Mott–Hubbard mechanism in which the interelectron correlation is considered as the driving force of the phase transition.

This picture was further developed in the thermodynamic study of Paquet and Leroux–Hugon (1980) who introduced two order parameters, the lattice η and the averaged amplitude of the local magnetic moment μ These authors came to the conclusion that the electronic parameter μ triggers the

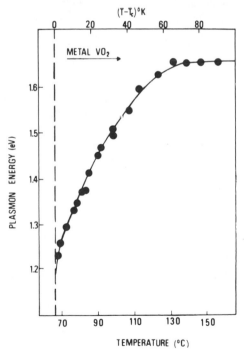

Fig. 29. Temperature dependence of the plasmon frequency in VO$_2$ determined from thermoreflectance measurements (from Bianconi *et al.*, 1981).

phase transition in η. The usefulness of their treatment consists of calculating the explicit temperature dependence of several measurable parameters, like the gap energy E_g and the lattice distortion, in a broad temperature range. However, their E_g value at 300 K is only about one half of the experimental value. Moreover, the theory predicts no large lattice softening at the R point of the rutile Brillouin zone [$\mathbf{k} = (1, 0, 1)$] to which the lattice order parameter belongs.

On the other hand, there are strong indications that the transition is induced by a lattice instability due to electron–phonon interaction. Gupta *et al.* (1977) performed an electron-band calculation and found that electron nesting occurs which leads to a maximum in the static electronic susceptibility at the R point. This results in a Kohn anomaly and subsequent Peierls instability as in CDW substances (see, also, Kopaev and Mokerov, 1982). No inelastic neutron scattering data, however, exist (due to the large incoherent-scattering cross section of vanadium) which could directly confirm this picture. However, clear indirect evidence of lattice softening is obtained from Raman scattering (Srivastava and Chase, 1971; Aronov *et al.*, 1977), which revealed a critical broadening of some lines near T_{tr}. Similarly, ultrasonic anomalies near T_{tr} were observed (Prieur *et al.*, 1977) and x-ray diffuse scattering studies (Terauchi and Cohen, 1978) revealed a critical intensity increase at the R point with an extrapolated stability limit at ~ 330 K.

2. NbO$_2$

The metal–nonmetal transition in niobium dioxide occurring at T_{tr} $\simeq 1080$ K seems to be of second order. At T_{tr} the conductivity increases by a factor of 10 only. The high-temperature phase is isomorphous with VO$_2$ and the structural change below T_{tr} is similar to VO$_2$ (involving dimerization of Nb atoms, although the space group and unit-cell parameters, C_{4h}^6, $Z = 16$, are different). The order parameter lies on the P line of the Brillouin zone ($\mathbf{k} = (\frac{1}{4}, \frac{1}{4}, \frac{1}{2})$). The soft mode is overdamped with a frequency of about 3 cm^{-1} observed in neutron scattering (Pynn *et al.*, 1978) which suggests that the transition is of an order–disorder nature as far as lattice dynamics is concerned.

The IR reflectivity was measured at room temperature by Gervais and Baumard (1979) and at elevated temperatures by Gervais (1981). The spectra below T_{tr} were fitted to the formula

$$\epsilon(\omega) = \epsilon_\infty \prod_j \frac{\omega_{Lj}^2 - \omega^2 + i\omega\gamma_{Lj}}{\omega_{Tj}^2 - \omega^2 + i\omega\gamma_{Tj}} \frac{\omega_P^2 - \omega^2 + i\omega\gamma_P}{-\omega^2 + i\omega\gamma_0} \qquad (2.75)$$

which represents the genralization of Eq. (2.45) with a generalized Drude

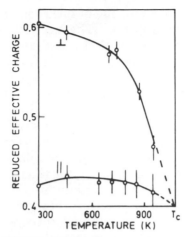

Fig. 30. Temperature dependence of effective charges in NbO_2 measured parallel (‖) and perpendicular (⊥) to the c axis (from Gervais, 1981).

term describing the free-carrier absorption. The term ω_p is the plasmon frequency, γ_p the plasmon damping, and γ_0 the damping in the $\omega \rightarrow 0$ limit. The plasmon is overdamped at all temperatures and the electronic absorption near T_{tr} increases appreciably. On the other hand, the strength of all phonon modes decreases with increasing temperature. In binary compounds the dynamic effective ionic charge can be evaluated from the IR spectra according to the formula

$$\sum_j (\omega_{Lj}^2 - \omega_{Tj}^2)_\alpha = \frac{1}{\epsilon_v V} \sum_k \frac{(Ze)_{k\alpha}}{m_k}, \tag{2.76}$$

where V is the volume occupied by the formula unit, ϵ_v is the permittivity of vacuum, m_k is the mass of the kth atom, and e the electronic charge. The temperature dependence of the reduced effective charge Z/Z_0 (the nominal charge $Z_0 = 4$) is plotted in Fig. 30. The decrease of Z, which is more pronounced for the $E \perp c$ spectra, is balanced by the increase of delocalized electron absorption to satisfy the sum rule (2.15). The interesting feature is that in the high-temperature rutile phase, Z tends to be isotropic, in agreement with other crystals of the rutile structure such as TiO_2, SnO_2, GeO_2, and TeO_2.

G. Superionic Conductors

Superionic conductors (solid electrolytes) represent a very important class of materials where the high ionic conductivity (of the order of 1 Ω^{-1} cm^{-1}) is caused by the melting or disordering of one sublattice, whereas the other sublatttices form the solid skeleton. The mechanical properties resemble those of the normal solids, but the electrical conductivity is comparable to molten salts. With increasing temperature sublattice melting occurs either continuously without any other structural changes or continuously with additional structural changes or discontinuously. The latter two cases are accompanied by second- and first-order phase transitions, respectively. Because of numerous practical applications and interesting physical phenomena superionic conductors have been intensively studied in the last decade. However, the complex structures and the large diversity of these materials and their behavior have prevented a good and unique understanding of the dynamical processes in the substances. There is not the space here to discuss fully all the dynamical properties of superionic conductors which manifest themselves in the frequency-dependent conductivity $\sigma(\omega)$ (as a rule in the $10^{10} - 10^{13}$ Hz region). This subject was reviewed or investigated, e.g., by Hayes (1978), Delaney and Ushioda (1979), Funke (1980, 1981), and more theoretically by Lam and Bunde (1978), Beyeler et al. (1979), Geisel (1979), Boyce and Huberman (1979), Dietrich et al. (1980), and Dietrich (1982). Instead, we shall briefly mention some recent work where the temperature dependence of the far IR dynamical conductivity was experimentally investigated through the phase transitions. Very few accurate investigations of this type have been performed until now. Most of them concern the reconstructive $\alpha \rightarrow \beta$ transition in AgI; some recent studies are devoted also to Ag_3SI and CuTeBr.

The most investigated superionic conductor, AgI, undergoes a dicontinuous transition from the normal β phase with the wurtzite structure (space group C_{6v}^4, $Z = 2$) to the superionic α phase with the body-centered cubic phase (O_h^9, $Z = 2$) at 420 K. Although the symmetries of both phases are not group–subgroup related, the local iodine tetrahedral coordination around the Ag ions is the same in both phases. The main structural change consists of a strong disordering of the Ag ions which is connected with a stepwise increase of conductivity from $\sim 10^{-4}$ Ω^{-1} cm^{-1} to ~ 1 Ω^{-1}cm^{-1}.

Until now the most accurate far IR data are the reflectivity and transmission data of Brüesch et al. (1980). The reflectivity data are shown in Fig. 31. The main absorption peak at 110 cm^{-1} which survives through the phase transition (with an increase of damping) corresponds to the stretching vibration of Ag against the I ions. The weaker peaks near 80 and 30 cm^{-1} in the β phase are probably of two-phonon origin. The evaluation of the low-frequency conductivity in the α phase depends strongly on the extrapolation into the microwave region. Earlier microwave data (for a review, see Funke, 1980) revealed a complicated structure in the $10^{10} - 10^{11}$ Hz region which was, however, not confirmed in a recent more accurate measurement by Luther and Roemer (1981) (see also Roemer and Luther, 1981). The latter authors found the microwave conductivity in the 18–26.5 GHz region to be frequency independent and equal to the dc conductivity throughout the whole α phase. This result can influence also the evaluated conductivity in the 3–10 cm^{-1} region and make questionable the existence of the conductivity minimum in the 1–3 cm^{-1} region obtained from the Kramers–Kronig analysis by Brüesch et al. (1980). It seems more likely that in the 1–20 cm^{-1} region the conductivity increases monotonically above its dc value. In this case the simple single particle Ag hopping mechanism for the conductivity in the α − AgI phase would be more appropriate than other complex models which account for the correlation effects (Funke, 1980).

Ag$_3$SI undergoes two phase transitions, a first-order transition from the high temperature α phase, $O_h^9 (Z = 1)$, into the β phase, $O_h^1 (Z = 1)$, at 519 K, and then a nearly second-order transition into a pyroelectric $C_3^4 (Z = 1)$ phase γ at 157 K (Hoshino et al., 1981). In all three phases the Ag ions are distributed near the face centers of iodine cubes with S atoms inside, in the γ phase the I and S atoms are, moreover, statistically distributed between S and I positions. In this phase the Ag ions can move diffusively between different

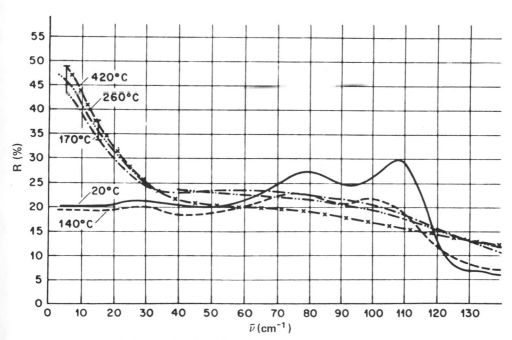

Fig. 31. Far IR reflectivity of AgI (from Brüesch et al., 1980).

faces causing a conductivity of $\sim 1 \ \Omega^{-1}cm^{-1}$. In the β phase the anions become ordered, but the Ag ions can still hop between neighboring faces over a potential barrier of about 0.17 eV, estimated from the conductivity of 0.02 $\Omega^{-1}cm^{-1}$ at 300 K. Moreover, Ag ions can jump between four equivalent sites near the face center over a much smaller barrier of ~ 0.014 eV estimated on the basis of x-ray data (Perenthaler et al., 1981). In the γ phase the four sites for the Ag ions become inequivalent and the Ag ions order in one of them causing in this way the lowering of symmetry to the polar rhombohedral one.

The far IR reflectivity at room temperature was measured by Gras and Funke (1981) and through the $\beta - \gamma$ transition by Brüesch et al. (1982). The room-temperature conductivity spectrum is dominated by two strong peaks at about 60 and 250 cm^{-1}. The frequency of the former increases below the $\beta - \gamma$ transition to 82 cm^{-1} and a complicated fine structure due to new modes and/or splitting of degenerate modes is seen. The mode at 60 cm^{-1} was assigned to *attempt* vibrations of Ag ions in a single potential minimum. At the low-frequency end below 30 cm^{-1} the reflectivity remains constant in the γ phase, but increases appreciably in the β phase. This increase can be assigned to the hopping process of Ag ions among the four potential minima. A fit to a simple Debye formula gives $1/(2\pi\tau) = 7.3$ cm^{-1} at 300 K. The more complicated microscopic models (Gras and Funke, 1981) give no better agreement with experiment and do not elucidate the detailed picture of the Ag hopping process.

Our last example, CuTeBr, has not been studied as intensively as the Ag-ionic conductors. At 343 K it undergoes a first-order displacive transition from the Ag-ionic conductors. At 343 K it undergoes a first-order displacive transition from the $D_{4h}^{19}(Z = 16)$ high-temperature form (Carkner and Haendler, 1976) into the D_{2h}^{24} ($Z = 32$) low temperature phase. The phase transition was studied using BWO spectrometry in the 1.3–3 cm^{-1} region (Chandrasekhar and Genzel, 1978). An increase of conductivity with increasing frequency and temperature was observed in both phases similar to other superionic conductors without phase transitions, like β-alumina (Barker et al., 1976). At the phase transition a simple stepwise increase of microwave conductivity by about 10% was observed.

H. Plastic Crystals

Many molecular crystals consisting of globular molecules display a plastic crystalline phase near their melting temperature. In this phase which is translationally ordered but rotationally disordered, the molecules exhibit large, somewhat chaotic rotational motions as in a liquid, or at least large reorientations between several fixed orientations. Except for rare exceptions, (e.g., solid hydrogen), the rotational motion is always hindered, i.e., the molecule has to overcome some potential barrier during its reorientation. If dynamical disorder occurs this potential barrier should not be higher than kT in order of magnitude. At sufficiently low temperatures, a phase transition to an orientationally ordered phase occurs, as a rule, where the molecules can librate only with small angular amplitudes about their equilibrium positions. Therefore such a phase is sometimes called librator phase whereas the plastic phase is called a rotator phase.[†]

There is a large number of simple plastic crystals which were thoroughly investigated by IR as well as Raman spectroscopy; see, e.g., the review by Bailey (1979). Most of them appear in a gaseous (e.g., H_2, HCl, CO, N_2, H_2S, PH_3, CH_4, SiH_4, GeH_4) or liquid (e.g., CCl_4, CBr_4) phase at room temperature. The spectroscopic investigation of such crystals has been initiated by molecular spectroscopists who look rather at the differences in the vibrational spectra between gaseous, liquid, and solid phases than at the nature of rotator–librator phase transitions. We shall not dwell on the discussion of these investigations which certainly have a rich and interesting history and refer the interested reader to the review by Bailey (1979). Here we shall only briefly discuss the dielectric spectra due to the rotational and librational motion of polar molecules in plastic crystals. The best investigated family of this kind is derivatives of methane of the general formula CX_4, where X can be CH_3, Cl, Br, NO_2, CN, or various combinations of these groups, especially $(CH_3)_3CX$, $X = $ Cl, Br, NO_2, or CN. We shall illustrate the behavior in tertiary nitrobutane $(CH_3)_3CNO_2$(TBN), where the most complete spectral data became recently available.

TBN — as with all other members of the $(CH_3)_3CX$ family — undergoes two first-order phase transitions below the melting point 299 K: at $T_1 = 260$ K and $T_2 = 215$ K (Urban et al., 1975). The phase I (299–260 K) is orthorhombic ($Z = 2$), slightly distorted cubic ($Z = 1$). In this phase the whole molecule performs liquid-like reorientational motions which due to the dipole moment of $(CH_3)_3C^+(NO_2)^-$ essentially contribute to the static permittivity of ϵ_0(I) $\simeq 25$. This represents the mean value over all crystal orientations and it roughly equals ϵ_0 in the liquid phase. In phase II (260–215 K) which is triclinic ($Z = 2$) the rotational motion reduces to uniaxial reorientation about the polar C—N axis consisting of jumps of CH_3 groups by an angle of 120° (Mayer et al., 1977). In an undeformed molecule such a motion is nonpolar and does not contribute to ϵ_0. In fact the mean ϵ_0 value

---

† It should be noted that mechanical plasticity is a rather general phenomenon which occurs at temperatures close to the melting point and is not a specific feature of an orientationally disordered phase. Therefore the term *rotator phase* seems to be more appropriate than the historical term *plastic phase*.

in this phase drops to ~3–4. In phase III (librator phase) (below 214 K) which is also triclinic, all rotational degrees of freedom are frozen-in and ϵ_0 further reduces to ~2.3.

Haffmans and Larkin (1972) performed far IR transmission measurements of TBN and several related substances in the 20–110 cm^{-1} region and evaluated the absorption coefficients for all phases (probably neglecting the reflection losses between the sample and the polypropylene cell). They found a broad absorption band in this region which in phase III consists of several peaks (at 42, 68, 82, and 92 cm^{-1} at 133 K). Their total contribution to ϵ_0 amounts to ~0.6. In phase II the absorption is of a single-peak form at ~65 cm^{-1} and width ~75 cm^{-1} independent of temperature approximately with the same contribution to ϵ_0. In phase I this peak suddenly shifts to ~30 cm^{-1} and remains more or less temperature-independent even through melting.

Recently Freundlich and Sobczyk (1981) performed high-frequency dielectric measurements on TBN at 5.10^5, 2.10^9, and 3.8×10^{10} Hz for all phases. Using the far IR data and Kramers–Kronig relation, Eq. (2.8), they were able to calculate the whole dielectric spectrum up to 100 cm^{-1} which fits all measured data. A monotonic decrease of $\epsilon'(\omega)$ in the 1.3–20 cm^{-1} region where measurements are missing was assumed. The resulting spectra for phases I and II are shown in Fig. 32. Note that the $\epsilon''(\omega)$ spectra in phase II have a different scale so that they fall below the spectra of phase I for all ω. Furthermore, let us note the interesting fact that in phase I the peak of $\epsilon''(\omega)$ in the ~0.3 cm^{-1} region shifts due to its large width in the absorption spectrum $\alpha(\omega) = 2\pi\omega\epsilon''/n$ up to ~30 cm^{-1} (for small damping both peaks appear at the same frequency). Finally, let us mention that the spectra in phase III (not shown in Fig. 32) show negligible microwave losses so that the small increase of ϵ_0 in phase II with respect to phase III is clearly connected to the weak microwave absorption tail in phase II. Its orgin is most probably in the deformation of the TBN molecules permitted by symmetry which presumably causes a slight dielectric activity of their rotation about the C—N axis.

Let us say a few words about the interpretation of the spectra obtained in phase I. Whereas in phases II and III the main contribution to $\epsilon''(\omega)$ is due to a librational motion of TBN molelcules in the 10–100 cm$^-$ region, the dominant contribution to $\epsilon''(\omega)$ in phase I is due to reorientation jumps of the TBN molecules in the 0.1–1 cm^{-1} region. In the low-frequency spectral range (up to 10^9 Hz) such a spectrum could be fitted to the Debye relaxation formula, Eq. (2.50) (Clemett and Davies, 1962). For the high-frequency tail $\omega \gg 1/2\pi\tau$ this description clearly fails because it neglects the excess absorption due to the librational motion in the far IR (the so-called Poley absorption) and the return to transparency at still higher ω due to molecular

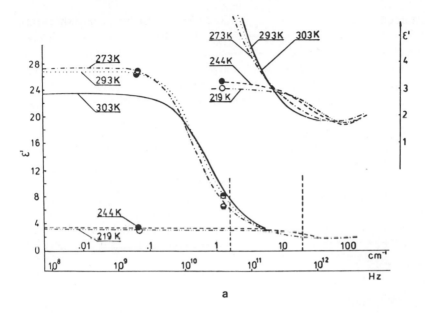

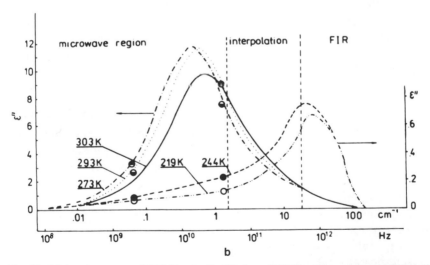

Fig. 32. Dielectric spectra of TBN in the liquid phase (303 K), rotatory phase I (293 and 273 K) and rotatory phase II (244 and 219 K): (a) $\epsilon'(\omega)$, (b) $\epsilon''(\omega)$ (from Freundlich and Sobczyk, 1981).

inertial effects. There are several models which improve the shortcomings of the Debye model (see, e.g., Bailey, 1979). They are based mainly on the description of rotational diffusion or on the description of stochastic jumps between fixed orientations combined with librations. Even if the spectral differences between particular models are small, conceptually the former models are better suited for liquids whereas the latter ones are more applicable to solids. Two semiempirical models of the latter type, worked out by Larkin (1973), were successfully used to fit the TBN far IR absorption spectra in phase I (Haffmans and Larkin, 1972). Assuming a sinusoidal orientational potential with a periodicity of 70° as it follows from structural data, the barrier height ~ 7 kJ/mol ($kT \simeq 2.5$ kJ/mol for $T = 300$ K) and Debye relaxation rate $1/(2\pi\tau) \simeq 0.6$ cm^{-1} were obtained in reasonable agreement with the low-frequency ($2-9 \times 10^8$ Hz) data of Clemett and Davies. Larkin's dispersion formulae are rather complicated and will not be dicussed here, but they can be brought to a form of two generalized oscillators (cf. Eq. (2.45)).

I. Liquid Crystals

Liquid crystalline phases represent another type of so-called mesophases between the crystalline and liquid state. Liquid crystals consist of elongated rod- or lath-like molecules having a tendency to align parallel to each other. According to the type of this alignment we distinguish nematic, cholesteric, and smectic liquid crystals (see, e.g., de Vries, 1979). Usually several phase transitions (first or second order) occur in these mesogenic materials between the crystalline and the isotropic liquid phase so that they provide rich material for phase-transition studies.

The vibrational spectroscopic work done until 1979 was thoroughly reviewed by Bulkin (1981) (see, also, his earlier review in 1979) so that we shall confine ourselves to brief comments on the most important applications of IR spectroscopy in investigations of phase transitions in liquid crystals.

Until now, the greatest attention was paid to nematic phases, particularly to crystal–nematic and nematic–isotropic liquid phase transitions. The former phase transition manifests itself mostly in the low-frequency external mode region. As we would expect, some of the translational external modes are seen only in the crystal phase and become overdamped in the liquid crystalline phase. For instance, Afanas'eva *et al.* (1976) observed a mode at 24 cm^{-1} in the transmission spectra of butoxybenzilidene amino benzonitrile BBAB1

$$(C_4H_9-O-\text{\textcircled{}}-CH = N-\text{\textcircled{}}-C \equiv N)$$

which gradually disappears (within ~ 3 K) at the crystal–nematic phase transition at 336 K. These authors have assumed the proportionality between the integral absorption due to this mode and η_s^2 and close to T_c they have determined the order-parameter critical index $\beta = 0.4 \pm 0.1$. The narrowness of the temperature interval where the pronounced spectral changes occur (~ 1 K) and the first-order nature of the transition make this interpretation questionable. The gradual decrease of the integral absorption could well be caused by a coexistence of both phases.

The determination of the temperature dependence of the order parameter for the isotropic liquid–nematic phase transition is more reliable. Neff (1974) derived formulae which enable the determination of the order parameter from dichroism studies of aligned samples if we know the dipole-moment direction of the measured mode. In some cases [see, e.g., Kirov et al. (1980a,b)]this represents the first or (until now) the only method of quantitative determination of η_s. (The alignment of nematics can be done by mechanical rubbing or by applying an electric or magnetic field.)

Interesting but not yet fully understood phenomena are the pronounced spectral changes induced by an external electric field which aligns the liquid crystals. Depending on the sign of the dielectric anisotropy of the molecules, the damping of many internal vibrational modes decreases (positive dielectric anisotropy) or increases (negative dielectric anisotropy) with increasing applied field (even with an ac field). In the former case the field aligns the sample homogeneously (molecules are parallel to the sample cell surfaces) and the decrease of damping is interpreted as the freezing-in of the reorientational motion about the short molecular axes in the aligned sample. In any case, this motion is too slow to account for the observed large changes of damping (by $\sim 10\%$). Presumably, the mode broadening in unaligned samples is due to sample inhomogeneity which then decreases with the applied field. Striking (but not understood) effects have been observed also in the far IR region where the broad absorption of an unaligned nematic, 4-cyano-4'-heptylbiphenyl (HCB), changed under an applied field into a series of rather sharp peaks (Evans and Evans, 1978a,b).

Much effort has also been exerted in studying the molecular dynamics of liquid crystals. The situation is more complicated than in plastic crystals and polar liquids due to the large molecular anisotropy in liquid crystals. We can expect several microwave relaxation-type dispersions due to reorientations about different axes and a composite Poley absorption in the far IR due to librations about different axes. Let us illustrate the situation in 4-nitrophenyl-4-n-octyloxybenzoate (NPOB) which was recently thoroughly investigated by Janik (1980) and his collaborators. This substance has both smectic A and nematic phases. The dielectric dispersion in the isotropic liquid phase consists of two Debye relaxations with $\tau_1 = 1.2 \times 10^{-8}$ s and $\tau_2 = 4.3 \times 10^{-10}$ s. As in many other liquid crystals, the former relaxation is believed to be caused by molecular reorientations about the short axes and the latter by molecular reorientations about the long axes. In both liquid crystalline phases an additional relaxation with $\tau_3 \simeq 5 - 10 \times 10^{-9}$ s exists which can be caused by small fluctuations of the direction of the long molecular axis about the director, i.e., about the mean direction of this axis.

In cholesteric phases the medium becomes optically active due to its chirality. Many new effects like circular dichroism or R and A Cotton effects can be expected and observed if the radiation wavelength is comparable to the modulation periodicity (pitch). In normal cholesterics this appears in the visible region but in chiral smectics or in various cholesteric solutions the magnitude of the pitch corresponds typically to the mid IR or even far IR region. We refer readers interested in these problems to the recent review by Korte and Schrader (1981).

Infrared spectroscopy has been shown to be useful also in investigations of new types of mesophases like discotic phases; they consist of disc-like molecules in a columnar arrangement with irregular spacing. For instance, in benzene-hexa-n-hexanoate $C_6(OCOC_5H_{14})_6$ five phases were found between 383 and 100 K accompanied by pronounced changes in the IR region between 30 and 1500 cm^{-1} (Sorai et al., 1980).

Finally, we mention lyotropic liquid crystals in which phase transitions into liquid crystalline phases are realized in a solution by changing the solvent (mostly water) concentration. Biological membranes, for example, belong to these systems; they undergo a gel – liquid crystal phase transition at about the human-body temperature. The far IR and microwave spectroscopy is of special interest for studying such systems since it has been suggested that a system of biological cells in the living state emit coherent far IR or microwave radiation (Fröhlich, 1980 and Chapter 4).

V. CONCLUSIONS

Because of the development of new IR techniques the IR spectroscopy of SPTs has undergone a revolution during the last eight years and has given results of comparable or even better accuracy than Raman spectroscopy. Still the number of quantitatively reliable IR data is much smaller than the number of good Raman results. This is because in the case of IR spectroscopy quantitative measurements of intensity are required which are rather elaborate especially in the far IR and microwave regions. Only relative spectral intensity measurements are sufficient for Raman spectroscopy. On the other hand, dielectric spectroscopy is in principle more informative and efficient since it makes possible the direct determination of both the $\epsilon'(\omega)$

and $\epsilon''(\omega)$ spectra. The disadvantage of IR spectroscopy is in the selection rules which are in general slightly more restrictive than those for light scattering.

As far as dielectric soft-mode spectroscopy is concerned, the most important result which has been achieved in recent years is probably the discovery of microwave dispersion in addition to the Cochran-type soft mode in most of displacive SPTs, at least near T_c. This is analogous to the central-mode phenomenon in light scattering and indicates the existence of clusters with their own nonlinear (soliton-like) dynamics near T_c. These effects are still understood only qualitatively and very likely the cluster dynamics near T_c is appreciably influenced by defects. Much more thorough investigations are needed, especially in the hardly accessible $0.3 - 3$ cm^{-1} range.

Concerning hard-mode spectroscopy, the anomalies around T_c deserve more quantitative studies which in some cases could be used for the evaluation of critical indices. Order–disorder SPTs display some specific features in IR spectra. Disorder introduces a specific relaxation of selection rules. This leads in some cases to the occurrence of sharp IR peaks which disappear in the ordered phase (e.g., in $NaNO_2$ and NH_4Cl). The origin of these peaks is not yet fully understood. In the far IR region we can sometimes observe a disorder-induced continuous absorption proportional to the one-phonon density of states [e.g., for $(NH_4)_2BeF_4$; see Petzelt et al. (1980)].

Dielectric spectroscopy has been shown to be especially useful for the investigation of incommensurate ferroelectrics. The phason absorption in K_2SeO_4 was the first spectroscopic observation of a phason mode. Many other subtle effects as, e.g., mode splitting and activation of new mode series could be expected in incommensurate phases, particularly at low temperatures.

The dielectric spectroscopy of various metal–nonmetal transitions is another very interesting field, where until now only scarce quantitative data are available. It makes possible the determination of the mechanism of conductivity which is operative in these transitions. In the case of electronic conductivity dielectric spectroscopy moreover provides a deeper insight into low-lying electronic excitations and can be used for the determination of various electron–phonon coupling strengths.

Infrared and microwave spectroscopy is also useful in the investigation of various mesophases between the crystalline and isotropic liquid phases, especially in systems with polar molecules. More quantitative data, which are still lacking, could bring important information about the molecular dynamics and the degree and range of molecular order.

Finally, far IR and microwave radiation is supposed to play an important role in biological systems with cell membranes. Here the theoretical speculations still await basic experimental data.

REFERENCES

Afanas'eva, N. I., Burlakov, V. M., and Zhizhin, G. N. (1976). *Pis'ma Zh. Eksp. Teor. Fiz.* **23**, 506–508.
Agrawal, D. K., and Perry, C. H. (1971). *Phys Rev. B* **4**, 1893–1902.
Aiki, K., Hukuda, K., Koga, H., and Kobayashi, T. (1970). *J. Phys. Soc. Jpn.* **28**, 389–394.
Aizu, K. (1972). *J. Phys. Soc. Jpn.* **33**, 629–634.
Aizu, K. (1974). *J. Phys. Soc. Jpn.* **37**, 885–896.
Akiyama, K., Morioka, Y., and Nakagawa, I. (1979). *Bull. Chem. Soc. Jpn.* **52**, 1015–1018.
Andrade, P. daR., Prasad Rao, A. D., Katiyar, R. S., and Porto, S. P. S. (1973). *Solid State Commun.* **12**, 847–851.
Andrade, P. daR., and Porto, S. P. S. (1979). *Ann. Rev. Mat. Sci.* **4**, 287–310.
André, J. J., Bieber, A., and Gautier, F. (1976). *Ann. Phys. (Paris)* **1**, 145–256.
Aronov, A. G., Mirlin, D. N., Reshina, I. I., and Chudnovski, F. A. (1977). *Fiz. Tverd. Tela* **19**, 193–200.
Bachheimer, J. P., and Dolino, G. (1975). *Phys. Rev. B* **11**, 3195–3205.
Bailey, R. T. (1979). *In* "The Plastically Crystalline State" (J. N. Sherwood, ed.), pp. 233–284. Wiley, New York.
Bak, P., and Janssen, T. (1978). *Phys. Rev. B.* **17**, 436–439.
Balagurov, B. Ya., Vaks, V. G., and Shklovskii, B. I. (1970). *Fiz. Tverd. Tela* **12**, 89–99.
Ballantyne, J. M. (1964). *Phys. Rev.* **136A**, 429–436.
Barker, Jr., A. S., (1966). *Phys. Rev.* **145**, 391–399.
Barker, Jr., A. S., and Hopfield, S. S. (1964). *Phys. Rev.* **135A**, 1732–1737.
Barker, Jr., A. S., and Tinkham, M. (1962). *Phys. Rev.* **125**, 1527–1530.
Barker, Jr., A. S., and Tinkham, M. (1963). *J. Chem. Phys.* **38**, 2257–2264.
Barker, Jr., A. S., Verleur, H. W., and Guggenheim, H. J. (1966). *Phys. Rev. Lett.* **17**, 1286–1289.
Barker, Jr., A. S., Ditzenberger, J. A., and Remeika, J. P. (1976). *Phys. Rev. B* **14**, 4254–4265.
Barnoski, M. K., and Ballantyne, J. M. (1968). *Phys. Rev.* **174**, 946–952.
Bartsokas, A., and Siapkas, D. (1980). *Ferroelectrics* **25**, 561–563.
Baumard, J. F., and Gervais, F. (1977). *Phys. Rev. B* **15**, 2316–2323.
Belousov, M. V., and Pavinich, V. F. (1978). *Opt. Spektrosk.* **45**, 920–926.
Benedict, T. S., and Durand, J. L. (1958). *Phys. Rev.* **109**, 1091–1093.
Berlinsky, A. J. (1979). *In* "Physics of Solids and Liquids: Highly Conducting One-Dimensional Solids" (J. T. Devreese, R. P. Evrard, and V. E. van Doren, eds.), pp. 1–16. Plenum, New York.
Berreman, D. W., and Unterwald, F. C. (1968). *Phys. Rev.* **174**, 791–799.
Beyeler, H. U., *et al.* (1979. *In* "Topics in Current Physics: Physics of Superionic Conductors" (M. B. Salamon, ed.), pp. 77–110. Springer-Verlag, Berlin, Heidelberg, New York.
Bianconi, A., Stizza, S., and Bernardini, R. (1981). *Phys. Rev. B* **24**, 4406–4411.
Billard, D., Servoin, J. L., Gervais, F., and Piriou, B. (1979). *High Temp.—High Pressures* **11**, 415–422.
Bilz, H., Bussmann, A., and Benedek, G. (1980). *Ferroelectrics* **25**, 339–342.
Birch, J. R., and Parker, T. J. (1979). *In* "Infrared and Millimeter Waves" (K. J. Button ed.) Vol. 2, pp. 137–271. Academic Press, New York.
Birman, J. L. (1974). "Theory of Crystal Space Groups and Infra-Red and Raman Lattice Processes of Insulating Crystals." Handbuch der Physik/Encyclopedia of Physics, Vol. XXV/2b. Springer-Verlag, Berlin and New York.
Blinc, R. (1981). *Phys. Rep.* **79**, 332–398.
Blinc, R., and Žekš, B. (1982). *J. Phys. C* **15**, 4661–4670.

Blinc, R., Lavrenčič, B., Levstek, I. Smolej, V., and Žekš, B. (1973). *Phys. Status Solidi B,* **60,** 255–259.

Blinc, R., Arend, H., and Kanduŝer, A. (1976a). *Phys. Status Solidi B* **74,** 425–435.

Blinc, R., Pirc, R., and Žekš, B. (1976b). *Phys. Rev. B* **13,** 2943–2949.

Born, M., and Huang, K. (1954). "Dynamical Theory of Crystal Lattices." Oxford Univ. Press, London and New York.

Born, M., and Wolf, E. (1964). "Principles of Optics." Pergamon, Oxford.

Boyce, J. B., and Huberman, B. A. (1979). *Phys Rep.* **51,** 190–265.

Bozio, R., and Pecile, C. (1981). *Solid State Commun.* **37,** 193–197.

Brehat, F., Claudel, J., Strimer, P., and Hadni, A. (1976). *J. Phys. Lett.* **37,** L229–231.

Brehat, F., Wyncke, B., and Hadni, A. (1981). *Phys. Status Solidi B* **107,** 723–727.

Brehat, F., Wyncke, B., and El Sherif, M. (1982). *Phys. Status Solidi B* **110,** 449–506.

Brews, J. R. (1970). *Phys Rev. B* **1,** 2557–2568.

Březina, B., and Havránková, M. (1980). *Krist. Tech.* **15,** 1447–1456.

Bruce, A. D. (1982). *In* "Nonlinear Phenomena at Phase Transitions and Instabilities" (T. Riste, ed.), pp. 35–68. Plenum, New York.

Bruce, A. D., and Cowley, R. A. (1980). *Adv. Phys.* **29,** 219–321.

Brüesch, P., Bührer, W., and Smeets, H. J. M. (1980). *Phys. Rev. B* **22,** 970–981.

Brüesch, P., Beyeler, H. U., and Strässler, S. (1982). *Phys. Rev. B* **25,** 541–547.

Bugaev, A. A., Zakharchenya, B. L., and Chudnovskii, F. A. (1979). "Fazovyi Perekhod Metall-Poluprovodnik i ego Primenenie." Nauka, Leningrad 1979.

Bulkin, B. J. (1979). *In* "Liquid Crystals — The Fourth State of Matter" (F. D. Saeva, ed.), pp. 365–410. New York.

Bulkin, B. J. (1981). *In* "Advances in Infrared and Raman Spectroscopy." (R. J. H. Clark and R. E. Hester, eds.), Vol. 8, pp. 151–225. Heyden, London.

Bystrov, V. P. *et al.* (1977). *Izv. Akad. Nauk SSSR, Ser. Fiz.* **41,** 485–492.

Calvo, C. (1960). *J. Chem. Phys.* **33,** 1721–1731.

Carkner, P. M., and Haendler, H. M. (1976). *J. Solid State Chem.* **18,** 183–189.

Chandrasekhar, H. R., and Genzel, L. (1978). *Solid State Commun.* **25,** 73–75.

Chaudhuri, B. K., and Saha, M. (1978). *Ferroelectrics* **18,** 213–218.

Chaudhury, B. K., Ganguli, S., and Nath, D. (1980). *Solid State Commun.* **33,** 775–779.

Claus, R. (1978). *Phys. Status Solidi B* **88,** 683–688.

Claus, R., Borstel, G., Wiesendanger, E., and Steffan, L. (1972). *Phys. Rev. B* **6,** 4878–4879.

Clemett, C., and Davies, M. (1962). *Trans. Faraday Soc.* **58,** 1705–1728.

Cochran, W. (1960). *Philos. Mag. Suppl.* **9,** 387–423.

Cochran, W. (1971). *In* "Structural Phase Transitions and Soft Modes" (E. J. Samuelsen, E. Andersen and J. Feder, eds.), pp. 1–13. Universitetsforlaget, Oslo.

Coignac, J. P., and Poulet, H. (1971). *J. Phys. Colloq, (Orsay, Fr.)* **32,** 679–684.

Comès, R., and Shirane, G. (1979). *In* "Physics of Solids and Liquids: Highly Conducting One-Dimensional Solids" (J. T. Devreese, R. P. Evrard, and V. E. van Doren, eds.), pp. 17–67. Plenum, New York.

Cowley, R. A. (1963). *Adv. Phys.* **12,** 421–480.

Crawford, B. Jr., Goplen, T. G., and Swanson, D. (1978). *In* "Advances in Infrared and Raman Spectroscopy." (R. J. H. Clark and R. E. Hester, eds.), Vol. 4, pp. 47–83. Heyden, London.

Delaney, M. J., and Ushioda, S. (1979). *In* "Topics in Current Physics: Physics of Superionic Conductors" (M. B. Salamon, ed.), pp. 111–139. Springer-Verlag, Berlin and New York.

de Vries, A. (1979). *In* "Liquid Crystals — The Fourth State of Matter" (F. B. Saeva, ed.), pp. 1–72. Dekker, New York.

Dietrich, W. (1982). *In* "Trends in Physics 1981" (I. A. Dorobantu, ed.), pp. 698–705, Central Institute of Physics, Bucharest.

Dietrich, W., Fulde, P., and Peschel, I. (1980). *Adv. Phys.* **29,** 527–605.
Dorner, B., Axe, J. D, and Shirane, G. (1972). *Phys. Rev. B* **6,** 1950–1963.
Dvořák, V. (1973). *Phys. Status Solidi B* **55,** K59–62.
Dvořák, V. (1974). *Ferroelectrics* **7,** 1–9.
Dvořák, V. (1980). *In* "Modern Trends in the Theory of Condensed Matter" (A. Pekalski and J. Przystawa, eds.), Lecture Notes in Physics, Vol. 115, pp. 447–477. Springer-Verlag, Berlin and New York.
Dvořák, V. (1984). *In* "Structural Phase Transitions II" (K. A. Müller and H. Thomas, eds.), Topics in Current Physics, Vol. 23, Springer-Verlag, Berlin, Heidelberg, New York, in press.
Dvořák. V., and Hudák, O. (1982). *Ferroelectrics* **46,** 19–24.
Dvořák, V., and Petzelt, J. (1978). *J. Phys. C* **11,** 4827–4835.
Ehrhardt, K. D., and Michel, K. H. (1981). *Phys. Rev. Lett.* **46,** 291–294.
Ehrhardt, K. D., and Michel, K. H. (1981). *Z. Phys B* **41,** 329–339.
Eldridge, J. E., and Bates, F. E. (1979). *Solid State Commun.* **30,** 195–200.
Etemad, S. (1981). *Phys. Rev. B* **24,** 4959–4971.
Evans, G. J., and Evans, M. W. (1978a). *Infrared Physics* **18,** 863–866.
Evans, G. J., and Evans, M. W. (1978b). *J. Chem. Soc. Chem. Commun.,* 267–268.
Feder, J. (1976). *In* "Local Properties at Phase Transitions" (K. A. Müller and A. Rigamonti, eds.), pp. 312–332. North-Holland, Amsterdam.
Fleury, P. A., and Lyons, K. (1981). *In* "Structural Phase Transitions I" (K. A. Müller and H. Thomas, eds.), Topics in Current Physics, Vol. 23, pp. 9–92. Springer-Verlag, Berlin and New York.
Fontana, M. D., Metrat, G., Servoin, J. L., and Gervais, F. (1981). *Ferroelectrics* **38,** 797–800.
Freundlich, P., and Sobczyk, L. (1981). *Mol. Cryst. Liq. Cryst.* **65,** 197–214.
Fries, J., and Claus, R. (1973). *J. Raman Spectrosc.* **1,** 71–81.
Fröhlich, H. (1949). "Theory of Dielectrics," Oxford Univ. Press, Clarendon, London and New York.
Fröhlich, H. (1980). *In* "Advances in Electronics and Electron Physics" (L. Marton and C. Marton, eds.), Vol. 53, pp. 85–152. Academic Press, New York.
Funke, K. (1980). *Adv. Solid State Phys.* **20,** 1–18.
Funke, K. (1981) *Solid State Ionics* **3–4,** 45–52.
Futama, H. (1962). *J. Phys. Soc. Jpn.* **17,** 434–441.
Galzerani, J. C., and Katiyar, R. S. (1982). *Solid State Commun.* **41,** 515–519.
Garland, C. W., and Schumaker, N. E. (1967). *J. Phys. Chem. Sol.* **28,** 799–803.
Gauss, K. E., and Happ, H. (1976). *Phys. Status Solidi B* **78,** 133–138.
Gauss, K. E., and Happ, H., and Rother, G. (1975). *Phys. Status Solidi B* **72,** 623–630.
Geisel, T. (1979). *In* "Topics in Current Physics: Physics of Superionic Conductors" (M. B. Salamon, ed.), pp. 201–246. Springer-Verlag, Berlin and New York.
Genzel, L. (1974). *In* "Festkörperprobleme XIV, Advances in Solid State Physics" (O. Madelung and H. J. Queisser, eds.), pp. 183–203, Pergamon, Vieweg, Stuttgart.
Gervais, F. (1976). *Ferroelectrics* **13,** 555–557.
Gervais, F. (1981). *Phys. Rev. B* **23,** 6580–6584.
Gervais, F., and Baumard, J. F. (1979). *J. Phys. C* **12,** 1977–1983.
Gervais, F., and Piriou, B. (1974). *J. Phys. C* **7,** 2374–2386.
Gervais, F., and Piriou, B. (1975). *Phys. Rev. B* **11,** 3944–3950.
Gervais, F., and Servoin, J. L. (1977). *Phys. Rev. B* **15,** 4532–4536.
Gervais, F., Piriou, B., and Billard, D. (1975). *Solid State Commun.* **17,** 861–865.
Gesi, K. and Iizumi, M. (1982). *J. Phys. Soc. Jpn.* **51,** 1047–1048.
Goldsmith, G. J., and White, J. G. (1959). *J. Chem. Phys.* **31,** 1175–1187.

Golovko, V. A., and Levanyuk, A. P. (1979). *Zh. Eksp. Teor. Fiz.* **77**, 1556–1573.
Golovko, V. A., and Levanyuk, A. P. (1981). *Zh. Eksp. Teor. Fiz.* **80**, 2296–2313.
Graja, A., Swietlik, R., Petzelt, J. and Dobiášová, L. (1982). *Phys. Status Solidi A* **69**, K205–208.
Gras, B., and Funke, K. (1981). *Solid State Ionics* **2**, 341–346.
Grigas, J., and Beliackas, R. (1978). *Ferroelectrics* **19**, 113–118.
Gupta, M., Freeman, A. J., and Ellis, D. E. (1977). *Phys. Rev. B* **16**, 3338–3351.
Hadni, A. *et al.* (1969). *J. Phys. Colloq.* (*Orsay, Fr.*) **30**, 377–388.
Hadni, A., Grandjean, D., Claudel, J., and Gebraux, X. (1970). *J. Phys. Colloq.* (*Orsay, Fr.*) **31**, 899–902.
Haffmans, R., and Larkin, I. W. (1972). *J. Chem. Soc. Faraday Trans.* 2 **68**, 1729–1741.
Happ, H., and Rother, G. (1977). *Phys. Status Solidi B* **79**, 473–477.
Haque, M. S., and Hardy, J. R. (1980). *Phys. Rev. B* **21**, 245–259.
Hatta, I. (1968). *J. Phys. Soc. Jpn.* **24**, 1043–1053.
Hayes, W. (1978). *Contemp. Phys.* **19**, 469–486.
Hill, R. M., and Ichiki, S. K. (1963). *Phys Rev.* **132**, 1603–1608.
Hill, R. M., and Ichiki, S. K. (1968). *J. Chem. Phys.* **48**, 838–842.
Hirotsu, S. (1977). *J. Phys. C* **10**, 967–985.
Holah, G. D. (1971). *J. Phys. C.* **4**, 2191–2201.
Horioka, M., Sawada, A., and Abe, R. (1980). *Jpn. J. Appl. Phys.* **19**, L145–147.
Hoshino, S., Fujishita, H., Takashige, M., and Sakuma, T. (1981). *Solid State Ionics* **3–4**, 35–39.
Hudák, O. (1984). *J. Phys. C,* in press.
Iizumi, M., Axe, J. D., Shirane, G., and Shimaoka, K. (1977). *Phys. Rev. B* **15**, 4392–4411.
Irisova, N. A., Kozlov, G. V., Narytnik, T. N., Smirny, V. V. and Chernyshev, I. M. (1974). *Kristallografiya* **19**, 403–404.
Ivanova, Y. A., and Chisler, E. V. (1975). *Fiz. Tverd. Tela* **17**, 2873–2882.
Jacobsen, C. S. (1979). *In* "Lecture Notes in Physics," *Quasi One-Dimens. Conduct. Proc. Int. Conf. Pt. 1–2,* 1978 (S. Barišić, A. Bjeliš, J. R. Cooper, and B. Leontič, eds.), Vol. I, pp. 223–229.
Janik, J. A. (1980). *In* "Advances in Liquid Crystal Research and Applications" (L. Bata, ed.) Vol. 1, pp. 371–382. Pergamon, Akadémiai Kiadó, Budapest.
Janovec, V., Dvořák, V., and Petzelt, J. (1975). *Czech. J. Phys. Sect. B* **25**, 1362–1396.
Kawamura, T., and Mitsuishi, A. (1973). *Technol. Rep. Osaka Univ.* **23**, 365–384.
Kawamura, T., Mitsuishi, A., Furuya, N. and Shimomura, O. (1974). *Technol. Rep. Osaka Univ.* **24**, 429–441.
Khelifa, B., Delahaigue, A., and Jouve, P. (1977). *Phys. Status Solidi B* **83**, 139–145.
Kim, Q., and Ullman, F. G. (1978). *Phys Rev. B* **18**, 3579–3584.
Kirov, N., Simova, P., and Ratajczak, H. (1980a). *Mol. Cryst. Liq. Cryst.* **58**, 285–298.
Kirov, N., Simova, P., and Ratajczak, H. (1980b). *Mol. Cryst. Liq. Cryst.* **58**, 299–309.
Kobayashi, K. K. (1968). *J. Phys. Soc. Jpn.* **24**, 497–508.
Kock, E. J., and Happ, H. (1980). *Phys. Status Solidi B* **97**, 239–246.
Konno, M., and Saito, Y. (1973). *Acta Crystallogr. Sect. B* **29**, 2815–2824.
Kopaev, Y. V., and Mokerov, V. G. (1982). *Dokl. Akad. Nauk SSSR* **264**, 1370–1374.
Korte, E. H., and Schrader, B. (1981). *In* "Advances in Infrared and Raman Spectroscopy." (R. J. H. Clark and R. E. Hester, eds.), Vol. 8, pp. 226–281. Heyden, London.
Kozlov, G. V. (1982). Dissertation, unpublished.
Kozlov, G. V., Lebedev, S. P. Prokhorov, A. M., and Volkov, A. A. (1980). *J. Phys. Soc. Jpn.* **49** Suppl. B, 188–190.
Kroupa, J. (1979). *Opt. Commun.* **30**, 282–285.

Kroupa, J., Petzelt, J., Kozlov, G. V., and Volkov, A. A. (1978). *Ferroelectrics* 21, 387–389.
Kroupa, J. (1982). Dissertation unpublished.
Kubo, R. (1957). *J. Phys. Soc. Jpn.* 12, 570–586.
Kucharczyk, D., and Niklewski, T. (1979). *J. Appl. Crystallogr.* 12, 370–373.
Kurosawa, T. (1961). *J. Phys. Soc. Jpn.* 16, 1298–1308.
Lage, E. J. S., and Stinchcombe R. B. (1976). *J. Phys. C* 9, 3681–3689.
Lam, L., and Bunde, A. (1978). *Z. Phys. B* 30, 65–78.
Landau, L. D., and Khalatnikov, I. M. (1965). *In* "Collcted Papers of L. D. Landau" (D. ter Haar, ed.), pp. 626–629. Pergamon, London.
Landau, L. D., and Lifshitz, E. M. (1960). "Electrodynamics of Continuous Media." Pergamon, Oxford.
Larkin, I. W. (1973). J. Chem. Soc. Faraday Trans. 2 69, 1278–1290.
Lavrenčič, B. B., and Petzelt, J. (1977). *J. Chem. Phys.* 67, 3890–3896.
Lavrenčič, B. B., Čopič, M., Zgonik, M., and Petzelt, J. (1978). *Ferroelectrics* 21, 325–327.
Lawrence, M. C., and Robertson, G. N. (1981). *Ferroelectrics* 34, 179–186.
Ledsham, D. A., Chambers, W. G., and Parker, T. J. (1976). *Infrared Phys.* 16, 515–522.
Ledsham, D. A., Chambers, W. G., and Parker, T. J. (1977). *Infrared Phys.* 17, 165–172.
Lépine, Y., Caillé, A., and Larochelle, V. (1978). *Phys. Rev. B* 18, 3585–5592.
Levanyuk, A. P., and Sannikov, D. G. (1974). *Usp. Fiz. Nauk* 112, 561–589.
Levanyuk, A. P., and Schedrina, N. V. (1974). *Fiz. Tverd, Tela* 16, 1439–1443; *Sov. Phys. Solid State Eng. Transl.* 16, 923–928.
Lines, M. E. (1972). *Solid State Commun.* 10, 793–796.
Lines, M. E., and Glass, A. M. (1977). "Principles and Applications of Ferroelectrics and Related Materials." Oxford Univ. Press (Clarendon).
Loewenstein, E. V., Smith, D. R., and Morgan, R. L. (1973). *Appl. Opt.* 12, 398–406.
Lowndes, R. P. (1970). *Phys. Rev. B* 1, 2754–2763.
Luspin, Y., Servoin, J. L., and Gervais, F. (1980). *J. Phys. C.* 13, 3761–3773.
Luspin, Y., Servoin, J. L., Gervais, F., and Quittet, A. M. (1981). *In* "Symmetries and Broken Symmetries in Condensed Matter Physics" (N. Boccara, ed.), pp. 277–284. Idset, Paris.
Luther, G. (1973). *Phys. Status, Solidi A* 20, 227–236.
Luther, G., and Roemer, H. (1981). *Phys. Status Solidi B* 106, 511–517.
Luxon, J. T., Montgomery, D. J., and Summit, R. (1970). *J. Appl. Phys.* 41, 2303–2307.
Maradudin, A. A., and Fein, A. E. (1962). *Phys Rev.* 128, 2589–2608.
McWhan, D. B., Marezio, M., Remeika, J. P., and Dernier, P. D. (1974). *Phys. Rev. B* 10, 490–495.
Massot, M., Teng, M. K., Vittori, J. F., and Balkanski, M. (1982). *Ferroelectrics* 45, 237–242.
Matsushita, M. (1976). *J. Chem. Phys.* 65, 23–28.
Mayer, J., Natkanies, I., and Ściesiński, J. (1977). *Acta Phys. Pol. A* 52, 665–677.
McDowell, R. S. (1978). *In* "Advances in Infrared and Raman Spectroscopy" (R. J. H. Clark and R. E. Hester, eds.), Vol. 5, pp. 1–66. Heyden, London.
Mori, H. (1965). *Prog. Theor. Phys.* 33, 423–455.
Moudden, A. H., Denoyer, F., Benoit, J. P., and Fitsgerald, W. (1978). *Solid State Commun.* 28, 575–580.
Moudden, A. H., Denoyer, F., Lambert, M., and Fitzgerald, W. (1979). *Solid State Commun.* 32, 933–936.
Moudden, A. H., Svensson, E. C., and Shirane, G. (1982). *Phys. Rev. Lett.* 49, 557–560.
Nattermann, T. (1982). *Sol. State Commun.* 49, 869–871.
Neff, V. D. (1974). *In* "Liquid Crystals and Plastic Crystals" (G. W. Gray and P. A. Winsor, eds.), Vol. 2, pp. 231–253.

Negran, T. J. et al. (1974). Ferroelectrics 6, 179–182.
Nelmes, R. J., Meyer, G. M., and Tibballs, J. E. (1982). J. Phys. C 15, 59–75.
Nelmes, R. J., Choudhary, R. N. P., and Březina, B. (1984). To be published.
Ngai, K. L. (1979). Comments Solid State Phys. 9, 127–140.
Novák, L., and Petzelt, J. (1976). Solid State Commun. 19, 947–949.
Odou, G., More, M., and Warin, V. (1978). Acta Crystallogr. A 34, 459–462.
Onyango, F., Smith, W., and Angress, J. F. (1975). J. Phys. Chem. Sol. 36, 309–313.
Oostra, S. et al. (1981). Phys. Rev. B 24, 5004–5013.
Overhauser, A. W. (1978). Adv. Phys. 27, 343–363.
Pai, K. F., Parker, T. J., and Lowndes, R. P. (1978a). J. Opt. Soc. Am. 68, 1322–1325.
Pai, I. F., Parker, T. J., Tornberg, N. E., and Lowndes, R. P. (1978b). Infrared Phys. 18, 327–336.
Paquet, D., and Leroux–Hugon, P. (1980). Phys. Rev. B 22, 5284–5301.
Pavinich, V. F., and Belousov, M. V. (1978). Opt. Spektrosk. 45, 1114–1118.
Peercy, P. S. (1975). Phys Rev. B 12, 2725–2740.
Peercy, P. S. (1976). Phys. Rev. B 13, 3945–3947.
Penna, A. F., Chaves, A. and Porto, S. P. S. (1976). Solid State Commun. 19, 491–494.
Percnthaler, E., Schulz, H., and Beyeler, H. U. (1981). Solid State Ionics, 5, 493–496.
Perry, C. H., and Lowndes, R. P. (1969). J. Chem. Phys. 51, 3648–3660.
Perry, C. H., and McNelly,T. F. (1967). Phys. Rev. 154, 456–458.
Petzelt, J. (1969). Phys. Status Solidi 36, 321–333.
Petzelt, J. (1971). Solid State Commun. 9, 1485–1488.
Petzelt, J. (1974). Phys. Lett. 48A, 341–342.
Petzelt, J. (1981). Phase Transitions, 2, 155–230.
Petzelt, J., and Dvořák, V. (1971). Phys. Status Solidi B 46, 413–423.
Petzelt, J., and Dvořák, V. (1976a). J. Phys. C 9, 1571–1586.
Petzelt, J., and Dvořák, V. (1976b). J. Phys. C 9. 1587–1601,
Petzelt, J., Horák, V., Mayerová, I., and Březina, B. (1974). Czech. J. Phys. Sect. B 24, 121–124.
Petzelt, J., Kozlov, G. V., Volkov, A. A., and Ishibasi, Y. (1979). Z. Phys. B 33, 369–379.
Petzelt, J., Volkov, A. A., and Kozlov, G. V. (1980) Phys. Status Solidi B 99, 189–194.
Petzelt, J. et al. (1981). J. Raman Spectrosc. 10, 187–193.
Petzelt, J. et al. (1984a). Phys. Rev. B, in press.
Petzelt, J. et al. (1984b). Czech. J. Phys. Sect. B, in press.
Prieur, J. Y., Seznec, P., and Ziolkiewicz, S. (1977). J. Phys. Lett. 38, L25–28.
Pynn, R., Axe, J. D., and Raccah, P. M. (1978). Phys. Rev. B 17, 2196–2205.
Pytte, E. (1970). Phys. Rev. B 1, 924–930.
Quittet, A. M., Servoin, J. L., and Gervais, F. (1981). J. Phys. 42, 493–498.
Rehwald, W., and Vonlanthen, A. (1982). J. Phys. C 15, 5361–5370.
Rice, M. J., Yartsev, V. M., and Jacobsen, C. S. (1980). Phys. Rev. B 21, 3437–3446.
Riede, V., and Sobotta, H. (1978). Czech. J. Phys. Sect. B 28, 886–893.
Robertson, G. N., and Lawrence, M. C. (1981). J. Phys. C 14, 4559–4574.
Roemer, H., and Luther, G. (1981). Ferroelectrics 38, 919–921.
Roos, J., Kind, R., and Petzelt, J. (1976). Z. Phys. B 24, 99–112.
Ruppin, R., and Englman, R. (1970). Rep. Prog. Phys. 33, 149–196.
Russell, E. E., and Bell, E. E. (1967). J. Opt. Soc. Am. 57, 341–348.
Saksena, B. D. (1940). Proc. Indian Acad. Sci. 12A, 93–139.
Sanjurjo, J. A., Porto, S. P. S., and Silberman, E. (1979). Solid State Commun. 30, 55–57.
Sanjurjo, J. A., Katiyar, R. S., and Porto, S. P. S. (1980). Phys. Rev. B 22, 2396–2403.

Sapriel, J., Boudou, A., and Perigaud, A. (1979). *Phys Rev. B* **19**, 1484–1491.
Scalabrin, A., Chaves, A. S., Shim, D. S., and Porto, S. P. S. (1977). *Phys. Status Solidi B* **79**, 731–742.
Schaack, G., and Winterfeldt, V. (1977). *Ferroelectrics* **15**, 35–41.
Schneider, T., Srinivasan, G., and Enz, C. P. (1972). *Phys. Rev. A.* **5**, 1528–1536.
Schreiber, J. (1977). *Phys. Status Solidi B* **81**, 371–378.
Schumaker, N. E., and Garland, C. W. (1970). *J. Chem. Phys.* **53**, 392–407.
Scott, J. F. (1974). *Rev. Mod. Phys.* **46**, 83–128.
Scott, J. F., and Wilson, C. M. (1972). *Solid State Commun.* **10**, 597–600.
Servoin, J. L., and Gervais, F. (1976). *High Temp.—High Pressures* **8**, 557–563.
Servoin, J. L., and Gervais, F. (1979). *Solid State Commun.* **31**, 387–391.
Servoin, J. L., and Gervais, F. (1980). *Ferroelectrics* **25**, 609–612.
Servoin, J. L., Luspin, Y., and Gervais, F. (1980). *Phys. Rev. B* **22**, 5501–5506.
Shiozaki, Y. (1971). *Ferroelectrics* **2**, 245–260.
Siapkas, D. I. (1978). *In* "Lattice Dynamics" (M. Balkanski, ed.), pp. 692–694. Flammarion, Paris.
Siapkas, D. I. (1980). *Ferroelectrics* **29**, 29–32.
Sorai, M., Tsuji, K., Suga, H., and Seki, S. (1980). *In* "Advances in Electronics and Electron Physics" (L. Marton and C. Marton, eds.), Vol. 53, pp. 85–152. Academic Press, New York.
Srivastava, R., and Chase, L. L. (1971). Phys. Rev. Lett. **27**, 727–730.
Stankowski, J. (1978). *Ferroelectrics* **29**, 109–120.
Steigmeier, E. F., Auderset, H., and Harbeke, G. (1975). *Phys. Status Solidi B* **70**, 705–716.
Stern, F. (1963). *In* "Solid State Physics" (F. Seitz and D. Turnbull, eds.), Vol. 15, pp. 299–408. Academic Press, New York.
Sugawara, F., and Nakamura, T. (1970a). *J. Phys. Soc. Jpn.* **28**, 158–160.
Sugawara, F., and Nakamura, T. (1970b). *J. Phys. Soc. Jpn., Suppl.* **28**, 221–222.
Sugawara, F., and Nakamura, T. (1972). *J. Phys. Chem. Solids* **33**, 1665–1668.
Suzuki, K., Sugawara, F., Sawada, S., and Nakamura, T. (1969). *J. Phys. Soc. Jpn.* **26**, 1199–1203.
Suzuki, S., and Takagi, M. (1976). *Phys. Status Solidi A* **33**, 789–792.
Suzuki, S., Murakami, H., and Takagi, M. (1981). *J. Phys. Soc. Jpn.* **50**, 555–562.
Swietlik, R. (1983). *Solid State Commun.* **45**, 27–29.
Takagi, Y., and Shigenari, T. (1979). *J. Phys. Soc. Jpn.* **47**, 576–584.
Takhashi, H., Schrader, B., Meier, W., and Gottlieb, K. (1967). *J. Chem. Phys.* **47**, 3842–3850.
Tanner, D B., Cummins, K. D., and Jacobsen, C. S. (1981). *Phys. Rev. Lett.* **47**, 597–600.
Terauchi, H., and Cohen, J. B. (1978). *Phys. Rev. B* **17**, 2494–2496.
Toepfer, K. D., and Helberg, H. W. (1976). *Phys. Status Solidi A* **35**, 131–136.
Tokunaga, M., and Tatsuzaki, I. (1983). *Ferroelectrics* **52**, 81–90.
Tolédano, J. C. (1979). *Phys. Rev. B* **20**, 1147–1156.
Tominaga, Y. (1983). *Ferroelectrics* **52**, 91–100.
Turik, A. V., and Shevchenko, N. B. (1979). *Phys. Status Solidi B* **95**, 585–592.
Urban, S., Tomkowicz, Z., Mayer, J., and Waluga, T. (1975). *Acta Phys. Pol. A* **48**, 61–67.
Verleur, H. W., Barker, A. S., Jr., and Berglund, C. N. (1968). *Phys Rev.* **172**, 788–798.
Viswanath, R. S., and Miller, P. J. (1979). *Solid State Commun.* **29**, 163–166.
Vogt, H., and Happ, H. (1966). *Phys. Status Solidi* **16**, 711–719.
Vogt, H., and Happ, H. (1968). *Phys. Status Solidi* **30**, 67–72.
Volkov, A. A., Kozlov, G. V., and Lebedev, S. P. (1979). *Radiotekh. Elektron.* **6**, 1405–1412.

Volkov, A. A. *et al.* (1980a). *J. Phys. Soc. Jpn. Suppl. B* **49**, 78–80.
Volkov, A. A., Kozlov, G. V., and Lebedev, S. P. (1980b). *Fiz. Tverd. Tela* **22**, 2851–2854.
Volkov, A. A., Kozlov, G. V., and Lebedev. S. P. (1980c). *Zh. Exp. Teor. Fiz.* **79**, 1430–1437.
Volkov, A. A., Kozlov, G. V., Lebedev, S. P., and Chernyshev, I. M., (1980d). *Kratk. Soobshch. Fiz. 5,* 39–45.
Volkov, A. A., Kozlov, G. V., Lebedev, S. P., Petzelt., J., and Březina, B. (1980e). *Pis´ma Zh. Eksp. Teor. Fiz.* **31**, 107–109.
Volkov, A. A. Kozlov, G. V., Lebedev, S. P., and Prokhorov, A. M. (1980f). *Ferroelectrics* **25**, 531–534.
Volkov, A. A., Kozlov, G. V., Lebedev, S. P., Petzelt, J., and Ishibashi, Y. (1982). *Ferroelectrics* **45**, 157–162.
Volkov, A. A. *et al.* (1984). To be published.
Wada, M., Sawada, A., Ishibashi, Y., and Takagi, Y. (1978). *J. Phys. Soc. Jpn.* **45**, 1905–1910.
Waluga, T. (1975). *Acta Phys. Pol. A* **48**, 61–67.
Wang, C. H., and Wright, R. B. (1973). *J. Chem. Phys.* **58**, 2934–2939.
Wilson, J. A., DiSalvo, F. J., and Mahajan, S. (1975). *Adv. Phys.* **24**, 117–201.
Winterfeldt, V., and Schaack, G. (1980a). *Z. Phys. B* **36**, 303–310.
Winterfeldt, V., and Schaack, G. (1980b). *Z. Phys. B* **36**, 311–317.
Winterfeldt, V., Schaack, G., and Klöpperpieper, A. (1977). *Ferroelectrics* **15**, 21–34.
Wyncke, B., Brehat, F., and Hadni, A. (1980). *Ferroelectric* **25**, 617–620.
Yao, W., Cummins, H. Z., and Bruce, R. H. (1981). *Phys. Rev. B* **24**, 424–444.
Yartsev, V. M., and Jacobsen, C. S. (1981). *Phys. Rev. B* **24**, 6167–6169.
Zylbersztejn, A., and Mott, N. F. (1975). *Phys. Rev. B* **11**, 4383–4395.

3

Raman and Brillouin Scattering Spectroscopy of Phase Transitions in Solids

C. H. WANG

Department of Chemistry
University of Utah,
Salt Lake City, Utah

I. INTRODUCTION

Light is scattered by fluctuations in the dielectric tensor in a material. Fluctuations of certain physical quantities are coupled to the fluctuations in the dielectric tensor. Near phase transitions, the fluctuations of some of these quantities are enhanced. This makes light scattering an important tool for the study of the phenomena of phase transitions. In this review, we will discuss the application of Raman and Brillouin light scattering spectroscopic techniques to the study of phase transitions in ionic and molecular solids. Despite their great technical importance, metallic and polymeric solids are not included in this review. Special emphasis will be placed on the discussion of the spectral density of the scattered light, despite the fact that the measurement of the integrated scattered intensity also provides very useful information about the total fluctuation of the appropriate physical quantity involved in the phase transition. Measurements of the peak frequency and the linewidth of the spectral power density yield information about the structure and dynamics of the solid undergoing the phase transition.

Raman and Brillouin scattering techniques have proved to be very useful for the study of the effects on the normal modes of vibrations in crystals which undergo phase transitions. There have been many experimental investigations (as reviewed, e.g., by Scott, 1974) of the temperature dependence of the spectra as the phase transition is approached from above or below. Many of these experimental results for structural phase transitions have been interpreted in terms of the dynamic behavior of the quasi-harmonic soft modes which display critical behavior in the vicinity of the phase transition temperature. Although the effects of phase transitions on other lattice and internal vibration modes are considered, the present review is devoted mostly to a discussion of phase transitions in terms of the dynamics of soft modes using the experimental data which have been published since 1977.

II. THEORETICAL BACKGROUND

We are interested in the scattering of light from solids in the vicinity of phase transitions. Consider that the scattered light, polarized in the direction $\hat{e}_s$ at frequency ω_s and at wavevector $\mathbf{K}_s$ propagating in the medium, is induced by the incident light polarized in the direction $\hat{e}_i$ at frequency ω_i and at wavevector $\mathbf{K}_i$. The scattered light with $\omega_s \neq \omega_i$ and $\mathbf{K}_s \neq \mathbf{K}_i$ is induced because of the temporal and spatial fluctuations of the dielectric tensor of the medium. It is convenient to write the spatial and temporal dependence of the dielectric constant tensor $\epsilon_{ij}(\mathbf{r},t)$ as

$$\epsilon_{ij}(\mathbf{r},t) \equiv \hat{e}_i \cdot \boldsymbol{\epsilon}(\mathbf{r},t) \cdot \hat{e}_j = \epsilon_{ij}^0 + \delta\epsilon_{ij}(\mathbf{r},t), \tag{3.1}$$

where ϵ_{ij}^0 is the homogeneous part and is time- and space-independent. $\delta\epsilon_{ij}(\mathbf{r},t)$ is the inhomogeneous part, responsible for light scattering. In the vicinity of the phase transition, it is assumed that the fluctuations of some physical quantity known as the order parameter make the dominant contribution to the light scattering intensity.

It is useful to decompose $\delta\epsilon_{ij}(\mathbf{r},t)$ in terms of Fourier components in frequency Ω and in wavevector $\mathbf{q}$ according to

$$\delta\epsilon_{ij}(\mathbf{q},\Omega) = \frac{1}{2\pi V} \int_{\infty}^{\infty} \int \delta\epsilon_{ij}(\mathbf{r},t) \exp(+i\mathbf{q}\cdot\mathbf{r} - i\Omega t) \, d^3r \, dt \qquad (3.2)$$

$$= \frac{1}{2\pi} \int_{-\infty}^{\infty} \delta\epsilon_{ij}(\mathbf{q},t) \, e^{-i\Omega t} \, dt,$$

where V is the scattering volume which is microscopically large (compared to the range of the spatial fluctuation).

The conservation of energy and momentum in the scattering process require that

$$\Omega = \omega_i - \omega_s \qquad (3.3)$$

and

$$\mathbf{q} = \mathbf{K}_i - \mathbf{K}_s. \qquad (3.4)$$

For scattering with a small change of frequency such that $|\Omega| \equiv |\omega_i - \omega_s| \ll \omega_i \approx \omega_s$, it follows from Eq. (3.4) that the wavelength (Λ) of the fluctuation in the medium as selected by the scattering process is given by

$$\Lambda = \frac{2\pi}{|\mathbf{q}|} = \lambda_0(n_i^2 + n_s^2 - 2n_i \, n_s \cos \theta)^{-1/2}, \qquad (3.5)$$

where n_i and n_s are the refractive indices associated with the incident and the scattered light, respectively, of the medium, θ is the scattering angle, and λ_0 is the wavelength of the incident light in vacuum.

The spectral power density of the scattered light is obtained from Eq. (3.2) by

$$I_{ij}(\mathbf{q},\Omega) \propto |\delta\epsilon_{ij}(\mathbf{q},\Omega)|^2$$

$$\propto \frac{1}{2\pi} \int_{-\infty}^{\infty} dt \, e^{-i\Omega t} \langle \delta\epsilon_{ij}(\mathbf{q},t) \, \delta\epsilon_{ij}(\mathbf{q},0) \rangle \qquad (3.6)$$

$$\propto [n(\Omega) + 1] \, \text{Im} \, \chi_{ij}^{(\epsilon)}(\mathbf{q},\Omega),$$

where the second identity is the result of the Wiener–Khinchine theorem and the angle brackets represent the ensemble average. The third identity is the fluctuation–dissipation theorem, $\chi_{ij}^{(\epsilon)}$ is the generalized susceptibility, $n(\Omega)$ is the Bose–Einstein occupation number at Ω and is given by $[\exp(\hbar\Omega/kT) - 1]^{-1}$. Equation (3.6) shows that the spectral power density of the scattered light is proportional to the Fourier transform of the time correlation function of the fluctuation of the dielectric tensor $\delta\epsilon_{ij}(\mathbf{q},t)$. Thus, the mechanism underlying the phase transition in solids is contained in the time correlation function $\langle \delta\epsilon_{ij}(\mathbf{q},t)\delta\epsilon_{ij}^*(\mathbf{q}) \rangle$. If the time correlation function at the phase transition is dominated by a physical quality η, known as the order parameter, then we can approximately characterize the order parameter by two quantities — the coherence length ξ_c and the correlation time τ_c. The spectral line which follows the dynamic behavior of the order parameter is known as the soft mode. As mentioned above, the reason that the light scattering spectral density is affected by the phase transition is due to the fact that near the phase transition, $\delta\epsilon_{ij}$ is dominated by the static and dynamic behavior of the soft mode. There may be several soft modes for the phase transition, and in this case the order parameter becomes multidimensional. However, for simplicity, we here assume that η is one dimensional.

An approximate equation of motion of the order parameter η is given by

$$m\ddot{\eta} + \gamma\dot{\eta} + \frac{\partial\phi}{\partial\eta} = f(t), \tag{3.7}$$

where m is the effective mass of the soft mode and γ is the damping constant. Both m and γ are assumed to be insensitive to the temperature. The function $f(t)$ is the sum of the random force and the external force conjugate to η and ϕ is the thermodynamic potential which may be expanded in a power series of η and of the gradient of η according to Landau's theory (Landau and Liftshitz, 1970). For small η, it can be shown that $\partial\phi/\partial\eta = (\partial^2\phi/\partial\eta^2)_0\eta = A\eta$, where the coefficient A is proportional to $|T - T_c|$ according to the Landau mean field theory (Landau and Liftshitz, 1970).

Solving Eq. (3.7) yields the susceptibility $\chi^{(\eta)}$ at frequency Ω as

$$\chi^{(\eta)} = \frac{f(\Omega)}{\eta(\Omega)} = (\Omega_0^2 - i\Omega\Gamma)^{-1}, \tag{3.8}$$

where $\Omega_0^2 = A/m$, $\Gamma = \gamma/m$, and $f(\Omega)$ and $\eta(\Omega)$ are, respectively, the Fourier components of $f(t)$ and $\eta(t)$ at frequency Ω.

Since $\delta\epsilon_{ij} = (\delta\epsilon_{ij}/\partial\eta)_0 \eta \equiv e_{ij}\eta$, it follows that $\chi_{ij}^{(\epsilon)} = |\epsilon_{ij}|^2\chi^{(\eta)}$. Substituting Eq. (3.8) into Eq. (3.6), we obtain an expression for the spectral power density of the scattered light as

$$I_{ij}(\mathbf{q},\Omega) \propto [n(\Omega) + 1]|e_{ij}\eta|^2 \, \text{Im}(\Omega_0^2 - \Omega^2 - i\Omega\Gamma)^{-1}$$

$$\propto [n(\Omega) + 1] \, P^2 \frac{\Omega\Gamma}{(\Omega_0^2 - \Omega^2)^2 + \Omega^2\Gamma^2}, \tag{3.9}$$

where $P = e_{ij}\eta$. If the soft mode is not Raman active in the high temperature phase, simple one-phonon theory predicts that $P^2 = b^2(T_c - T)$, where b is a constant.

Equation (3.9) shows that the spectrum of the scattered light displays two maxima at the frequencies $\Omega = \pm(\Omega_0^2 - \Gamma^2/2)^{1/2}$ and a minimum at $\Omega = 0$.

Since $\Omega_0{}^2 = A/m = a|T - T_c|$, on approaching the phase transition, the peaks draw nearer to each other as $|T - T_c|^{1/2}$ at the temperature range of $\Omega_0 > \Gamma$. When $\Omega_0^2 < \Gamma^2/2$, the two side peaks merge into a single peak centered at $\Omega = 0$. The spectra predicted by Eq. (3.9) are plotted in Fig. 1 for several values of the parameter $y_0 = \Omega_0/\Gamma$.

When the effective mass $m = 0$, which is appropriate for the order–disorder phase transition, Eq. (3.7) reduces to a Langevin equation. Solving the Langevin equation and substituting the result into Eq. (3.6) gives

$$I_{ij}(\mathbf{q},\Omega) \propto P^2 \frac{\tau}{1 + (\Omega\tau)^2}, \tag{3.10}$$

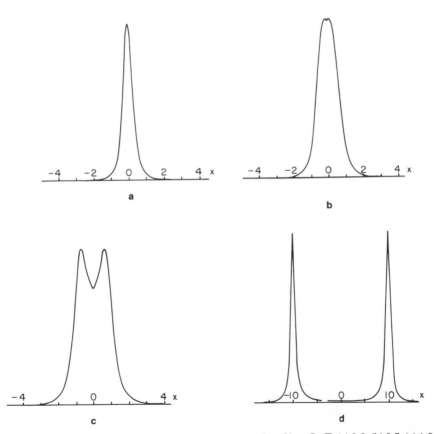

Fig. 1. Spectra calculated from Eq. (3.9) for several values $Y_0 = \Omega_0/\Gamma$: (a) 0.5, (b) 0.7, (c) 1.0, and (d) 10; $\Gamma = 0.5 \text{ cm}^{-1}$. The horizontal axis x is scaled in terms of Γ ($x = \Omega/\Gamma$). Temperature is equal to 500 Γ/k, k being the Boltzmann constant. Variation of temperature only affects the height but not the shape of the spectrum.

where $\tau = \gamma/A = \gamma/a|T - T_c|$ is the relaxation time which diverges as the phase transition point is approached. This phenomenon is known as critical slowing down.

To obtain Eq. (3.10), it is assumed that the random force $f(t)$ does not correlate with the order parameter and the correlation time of the random force is very short. Equation (3.10) predicts that the soft mode for transitions of the order–disorder type is of a purely relaxation character. On approaching the phase transition point, the linewidth increasingly narrows. Because of the contribution from the elastic peak originating from defects which is difficult to remove, Eq. (3.10) has not been used as extensively in interpreting the experimental results.

For the underdamped soft mode, the expression given in Eq. (3.9) is frequently used to fit the experimental spectra. The fit gives the values of the parameters P, Ω_0, and Γ at each temperature.

There have been several attempts to provide quantitative tests of the soft mode theory given in Eq. (3.9). One of the best candidates for testing the theory is lead germanate, $Pb_5Ge_3O_{11}$ ($T_c = 450$ K). The Raman spectrum of this compound is not contaminated by Rayleigh scattering or a central peak. Careful Raman measurements have recently been carried out by Hosea et al. (1979). Yacoby (1976) has tried to fit the experimental spectrum of this compound to the single soft-mode theory. He shows that Ω_0^2 indeed decreases to zero according to $\Omega_0^2 = a(T_c - T)$, and the linewidth is temperature-independent, according to the prediction of the mean field theory. However, a detailed comparison of the measured spectral shape with the theory does not yield a quantitative agreement; it provides only a qualitative agreement with the experiment.

Although the single-mode theory is unsatisfactory in detail, in several cases it is also found that:

(1)   the frequency of the soft mode Ω_0 does not decrease as $|T - T_c|^{1/2}$, predicted by the theory;

(2)   the damping constant Γ increases rapidly as $T \rightarrow T_c$ and possibly even diverges as $T \rightarrow T_c$;

(3)   the experimental lineshape is not accurately described by Eq. (3.9) (Yacoby, 1976; Burns and Scott, 1970; Lockwood and Torrie, 1974).

Explanations for the descrepancy between theory and experiment are provided (Yacoby et al., 1978). For molecular solids the interactions of the soft mode with other modes of motion, such as the molecular reorientational motion or other phonons of the same branch, are responsible for the discrepancy. For lead germanate the discrepancy is due to the failure of considering the two-phonon and one- and two-phonon interference terms in the scattering expression (Satija and Cowley, 1982). However, for a large number of systems, as long as T is not too close to T_c, the experimental results are in reasonable agreement with the simple soft mode theory. In this review, this simple theory will thus be used as a guideline to describe the connection between the vibrational spectra and the phase transition in solids. In the remaining sections of this review, experimental techniques and recent results obtained for several specific substances representing different transition types (cf. Chapter 1) will be described. These will show the importance of the light scattering technique and the important role played by the soft mode as well its interactions with other modes in affecting phase transitions in solids.

III. EXPERIMENTAL BACKGROUND AND BASIC CONCEPTS

Laser Raman scattering techniques remain the same as those used prior to 1977. Emphasis on Raman scattering of solids is directed at the low frequency region, and the iodine cell absorption filter is often used to remove elastically scattered light. Computers are widely used to control the spectrometer and to effect analysis of the spectral profile.

Raman scattering is usually carried out using a double grating monochromator, which is often optically interfaced in tandem to a triple monochromator to enhance contrast so that Raman lines near the laser excitation frequency can be observed.

In Brillouin scattering, multipass Fabry–Perot interferometers which yield a contrast greater than 10^{17} are used (Sandercock, 1971). Another advantage of these instruments is that they can be feedback-stabilized so that very weak Brillouin peaks can be detected by accumulation of many scans.

Scattered light corresponding to Rayleigh, Brillouin, and Raman scattering can be observed during irradiation of molecular or condensed systems with monochromatic light at a frequency ν_0. Rayleigh scattering corresponds to the elastic component at ν_0 and Stokes and anti-Stokes Raman scattering to the inelastic components $\nu_0 - \Omega$ and $\nu_0 + \Omega$, respectively. The spatial line shift Ω can be related to rotational, vibrational (long wavelength, $\mathbf{K} \sim 0$, phonons in solids), and electronic transition frequencies.

Brillouin scattering is the scattering of light from thermally induced acoustic phonons in a given medium. The acoustic phonon interacts and shifts the frequency of the incident light in the scattering event. The velocity of the acoustic phonon measured from the Brillouin scattering technique is obtained from Eq. (3.5) as

$$V_s = f_B \Lambda = f_B \lambda_0 (n_i^2 + n_s^2 - 2n_i n_s \cos \theta)^{-1/2}, \qquad (3.11)$$

where f_B, known as the Brillouin shift, is the frequency of the acoustic wave (in Hz) and is directly measureable with the Brillouin scattering apparatus.

Since in Brillouin scattering the fluctuation in the dielectric constant tensor is due to acoustic phonons, in a simple case, we may relate $\delta\epsilon_{ij}$ to the strain tensor S_{kl} according to Pockel's law by (Born and Huang, 1962),

$$\delta\epsilon_{ij} = -n_i^2 n_j^2 \sum_{k,l} p_{ijkl} S_{kl}, \tag{3.12}$$

where p_{ijkl} are Pockel's photoelastic constants and S_{kl} are the strain tensors. Both $\delta\epsilon_{ij}$ and S_{kl} are functions of time and space.

Calculation of the time correlation function of the dielectric tensor given in Eq. (3.6) can then be carried out by using the elastic theory of the solid which relates the sound velocity to the elastic constants and associated damping constants in accordance to the standard techniques (cf. Vacher and Boyer, 1972).

IV. RESULTS FOR SPECIFIC TRANSITION TYPES AND SUBSTANCES

A. Transitions in the Order–Disorder Limit

1. KCN and NaCN

One class of materials which has received attention is the alkali metal cyanides. Potassium cyanide and sodium cyanide crystals are of NaCl-type structure (O_h^5) at room temperature, with the orientation of the CN^- ions randomly distributed among the various (111) directions. The disordered KCN and NaCN crystals undergo first order–disorder phase transitions at 168 and 288 K, respectively. Below these transition temperatures (T_c) the CN^- ions assume a preferential orientation along the (110) direction, with little change in the unit cell dimensions at the phase transitions. KCN and NaCN undergo another phase transition at 83 and 172 K, respectively. Except for the usual contraction of the crystal, there is again no significant change in the unit cell dimensions at these transitions; however, not much is known about the lower transitions and we shall only discuss the data obtained for the order–disorder transitions.

While this transition has been studied extensively using several techniques, including thermodynamics (Matsuo et al., 1968), NMR (Coogan and Gutowsky; 1964, O'Reilly et al., 1973), neutron scattering (Price et al., 1972; Rowe et al., 1973, 1975) and Raman scattering (Daubert et al., 1976; Dultz, 1974, 1976), a clear understanding of the phase transition in KCN (and NaCN) was not obtained before the ultrasonic measurements of Haussuhl (1973). Haussuhl has shown that in KCN a dramatic decrease of the elastic constant C_{44} occurs as the phase transition temperature T_c is approached from above. This result has been confirmed using Brillouin scattering (Krasser *et al.*, 1976; Satija and Wang, 1977; Wang and Satiya, 1977). Brillouin scattering of NaCN has also been carried out (Wang and Satiya, 1977; Boissier *et al.*, 1978). The result demonstrates a clear softening of the long wavelength transverse acoustic phonon propagating along (110) and polarized along (001) (Fig. 2) as the temperature of the crystal is decreased toward T_c. A plot of ω_T^2 versus $(T - T_c)$ displays the expected mean-field linear dependence; however, it displays a finite intercept (Fig. 3) which disagrees with the soft-mode theory.

The thermoelastic anomalies (softening of elastic constants) and the reason for the disagreement with the simple soft-mode theory displayed in KCN and NaCN have also been considered theoretically by Michel and Naudts (1977a,b). These authors have developed a microscopic theory by considering the static coupling between translation (strain) and reorientation of the molecules (the order parameter) in solids. They show that the rotational–translational coupling leads to an effective orientational interaction among the CN⁻ ions, and the change of the effective orientational interaction is

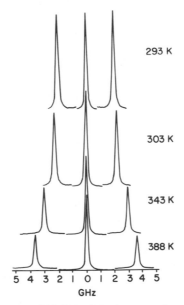

293 K

303 K

343 K

388 K

5 4 3 2 1 0 1 2 3 4 5
GHz

Fig. 2. The Brillouin spectra of NaCN of the long wavelength transverse (ω_T) acoustic phonon propagation along (110) and polarized along (001). (From Satija and Wang, 1977. Used with the permission of the American Institute of Physics.)

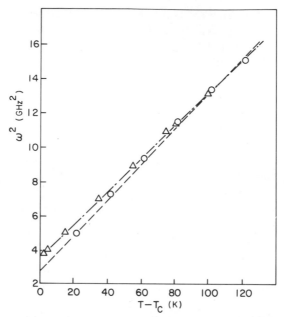

Fig. 3. The squares of the TA phonon frequencies [$\omega_T(110)$] of KCN (O) and NaCN (Δ) (GHz²) plotted as a function of $T - T_c$. T is equal to 168 K for KCN and equal to 288 K for NaCN. (From Satija and Wang, 1977. Used with permission of the American Institute of Physics.)

responsible for the anomalous behavior of the elastic constants and of the transverse – acoustic phonons. It appears that the theory qualitatively explains the temperature behavior of C_{44} and C_{11} in KCN above the 168 K phase transition (Fig. 4).

To further substantiate the theoretical model, Brillouin scattering experiments have been carried out in $(KCN)_x X_{1-x}$ mixed crystals, with $0 < x < 1$ and $X =$ Br and Cl. On replacing CN⁻ with bromide ions, the effective orientational interaction among the CN⁻ ions is reduced. This leads to a decrease of the critical temperature T_c with increasing concentration of x. The lowering of T_c with increasing x is obtained experimentally (Satija and Wang, 1978). However, experimentally it is found that below a critical concentration x_c, no obvious structural phase transitions for KCN_xBr_{1-x} or KCN_xCl_{1-x} are observed (Durand and Luty, 1977). For $x < x_c$, the elastic constant C_{44} (or $\omega_{TA}(110)$) decreases to a minimum when the temperature of the crystal is lowered to some value below which C_{44} increases with decreasing the temperature (Fig. 5). The position of the minimum (T_i) is found to linearly decrease with decreasing x. The value of x_c is 0.58 for KCN_xBr_{1-x} and is about equal to 0.79 for KCN_xCl_{1-x} (Durand and Luty, 1977; Wang *et*

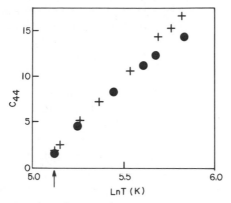

Fig. 4. Increase of C_{44} in KCN, with T (logarithmic scale); experiment (+), theory (●). Units are 10^9 dyn cm^{-2}. C_{44} is related to $\omega_{TA}(110)$. (From Michel and Naudts, 1977. Used with the permission of the American Institute of Physics.)

al., 1982). The result has recently been interpreted in terms of the formation of an orientationally disordered *electric dipole glass*, resembling the spin-glass phase in magnetic systems in which the spins have random orientations without long-range order (Michel and Rowe, 1980). However, recent Brillouin scattering results on the $KCN_x X_{1-x}$ mixed crystals do not yield consistent parameters to support the spin-glass picture (Wang *et al.*, 1982). Obviously, a great deal of work requiring measurements performed using

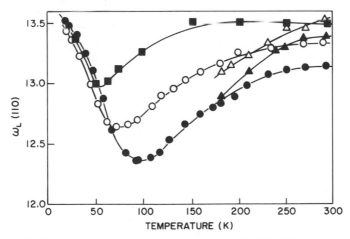

Fig. 5. Longitudinal acoustic phonon frequency $\omega_{LA}(110)$ for $KCN_x Br_{1-x}$ for several values of x [1.00 (△), 0.75 (▲), 0.56 (●), 0.34 (○), and 0.19 (■)] plotted as a function of temperature. The $\omega_{LA}(110)$ values are obtained using the 90° scattering geometry. (From Satija and Wang, 1978. Used with the permission of Pergamon Press Ltd.)

different techniques on the same sample needs to be done before an unambiguous answer can be obtained for the KCN_xX_{1-x} mixed crystal system.

2. Squaric Acid

The variation of the order parameter with temperature may manifest itself also in the intensity of the Raman lines. To illustrate this, we consider the phase transition of squaric acid ($H_2C_4O_4$). In the solid state, the C_4O_4 groups link together by hydrogen bonds in a planar configuration (Semmingsen 1973, 1975). The structural phase transition of squaric acid occurs at $100°C$. The transition temperature is strongly isotope-dependent. The transition temperature increases to $250°C$ for the deuterated squaric acid, indicating that hydrogen bonding plays a key role in the phase transition. The low temperature structure is $P2_1/m$ and the high temperature structure is tetragonal $I/4m$ (Hollander et al., 1977), indicating a doubling of the unit cell volume in the low temperature phase. Neutron scattering studies indicate that the transition is essentially two-dimensional, with an order parameter critical exponent of $\beta = 0.137 \pm 0.01$ (Nakashina and Balkanski, 1976; Samuelsen and Semmingsen, 1977). Raman scattering studies have revealed no evidence of an underdamped soft mode. However, low frequency Raman lines at 83 and 157 cm^{-1} existing in the low temperature phase disappear above T_c. The combination of neutron and Raman scattering data shows that the 83 and 157 cm^{-1} bands are the zone boundary $(0,1,0)$ transverse and longitudinal acoustic phonons, respectively (Samuelsen et al., 1979). Although the 157 cm^{-1} line is close to a zone center band at 150 cm^{-1} and is not studied in detail, careful studies of the 83 cm^{-1} line indicate that its integrated intensity varies very strongly with temperature just below T_c, and it can be represented as (Samuelsen et al., 1979)

$$I \propto \epsilon^{2\beta}, \tag{3.13}$$

where $\epsilon = (T_c - T)/T_c$, with $\beta = 0.137$. Above T_c, the 83 cm^{-1} line remains as a weak diffusive structure, indicating the presence of short range order above T_c. The presence of the 83 cm^{-1} band (and also the 157 cm^{-1} band) above T_c is considered to be due to the bilinear coupling of the in-plane transverse translational motion of the rigid squaric acid molecules with the molecular rotation. Following the formalism developed by Geisel and Keller (1975) for the order-disorder phase transition in NH_4Br, Fjaer et al. (1980) calculated the profile of the 83 cm^{-1} line as a function of temperature with the help of the one-dimensional density of state in the $(0,\zeta,0)$ direction (Fig. 6). The calculation includes only the nearest neighbor coupling and assumes that the correlation between layers decreases according to some power of the order parameter η, which represents the orientational behavior of the squaric acid molecules.

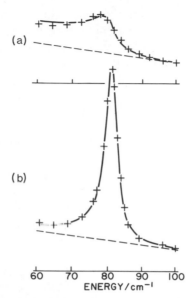

Fig. 6. Observed intensity profile (+) of the 83 cm⁻¹ line, compared to calculated profile
(———) for two different temperatures in squaric acid; fitted background (---). (a) $\eta = 0$,
105°C, (b) $\eta = 0.82$, 80°C. (From Fjaer *et al.*, 1980. Used with the permission of Gordon &
Breach, Science Publications, Inc.)

Preliminary Brillouin scattering data of the squaric acid crystal at the
temperature between 80 and 130°C have been published (Kruger *et al.*,
1980). The result reveals an elastic anomaly of C_{11} and C_{66} in the vicinity of
T_c. However, the dynamics of the molecular motion associated with the
observed elastic anomaly in the vicinity of the phase transition remains
unclear. A further study of the temperature dependence of the elastic constants of the squaric acid crystal will be helpful.

3. Inorganic Nitrates

Raman scattering studies of the phase transition in ammonium nitrate
(NH$_4$NO$_3$) single crystals have been carried out by Akiyama *et al.*
(1981a,b). At room temperature, the observed Raman spectra in the low-
frequency lattice vibration region as well as in the internal vibration region
are well interpreted based upon a D_{2h}^{13} structure (orthorhombic with $Z = 2$,
phase IV). The splitting of the A_g and B_{1g} components of ν_3 (the asymmetric
stretching mode of the NO$_3^-$ ion) in phase IV is found to be quite large
(≈ 35 cm⁻¹). This is believed to be due to the strong ionic interaction between NH$_4^+$ and NO$_3^-$ ions (Tang and Torrie, 1978), and is not associated
with the transverse and longitudinal components as suggested previously by
James *et al.* (1974). The 112 cm⁻¹ peak is associated with the NO$_3^-$ libration

about an axis perpendicular to the c axis. The softening of this band is believed to be associated with the flipping over of the NO_3^- group which is strongly coupled to the translational motion of the NO_3^- group, leading to the V – VI phase transition (Iqbal, 1976).

At high temperature the alkali metal nitrates, KNO_3 and $NaNO_3$, assume a NaCl-type structure. The Raman spectra of these crystals have been reported (Akiyama et al., 1980) and polarized Raman spectra of mixed single crystals of $(NH_4)_xK_{1-x}NO_3$ have shown the absence of phase IV (Akiyama et al., 1981a). Instead, Raman spectra of the mixed crystal are consistent with D_{2h}^{16} symmetry (orthorhombic, with $Z = 4$, which exists in NH_4NO_3 in the 32 – 80°C temperature range) (Akiyama et al., 1981b). The splitting of the NO_3^- asymmetric stretching mode, v_3, in the mixed crystal is also observed in phase III. This suggests that in the $NH_4NO_3(IV)$-type structure, hydrogen bonds are not formed between the NH_4^+ and NO_3^- ions as is observed in the case of NH_4NO_3 in phases IV and V. Apparently, in the NH_4NO_3-KNO_3 mixed crystal, NH_4NO_3 in the phase-III-type structure is converted directly to the phase V structure type around $-120°C$. At high temperatures, only one broad band in the region of 100 – 120 cm^{-1} is observed, assignable to the NO_3^- ion rotation in phase I or III (which is ferroelectric) of KNO_3.

The ionic radii of Rb^+ and Cs^+ are larger than that of K^+, and the nitrates of Rb^+ and Cs^+ assume a CsCl-type structure at high temperature as in NH_4NO_3. Both rubidium nitrate ($RbNO_3$) and cesium nitrate ($CsNO_3$) undergo a number of phase transitions above room temperature. $RbNO_3$ has a trigonal (phase IV) to cubic (CsCl, phase III) transition at 440 K, followed by a cubic to rhombohedral (phase II) transition at 561 K, and finally by a rhombohedral to a cubic (NaCl, phase I) transition at 586 K. $CsNO_3$ is isostructural with $RbNO_3$ and undergoes a similar series of phase transitions. The orientational order and the dynamics of the orientational state of the NO_3^- ion play an important role in these phase transitions. The onset of dynamic ordering of the NO_3^- ions is evidenced in the Raman spectra of the librational modes of this ion. Owens (1979) has studied the temperature-dependent Raman spectra of $RbNO_3$ and $CsNO_3$. At 300 K, the Raman spectra in the lattice mode region of $CsNO_3$ and $RbNO_3$ are almost identical. As the temperature increases, the frequency of the librational mode decreases and the linewidth increases rapidly. The Rayleigh wing also increases as the temperature is increased, similar to that observed in $(NH_4)_2SO_4$ due to increasing disorder (Iqbal and Christoe, 1976). The temperature-dependent behavior of the librational mode is quite similar to that of the NO_2^- librational mode in $NaNO_2$ (Andrade et al., 1973); the effect of which has been associated with the orientational fluctuation of the NO_2^- ion. Following Andrade et al. (1973), Owens (1979) fits the linewidth of the libration mode by the relation

$$\Gamma = a + bT + c\tau/(1 + \omega^2\tau^2), \qquad (3.14)$$

where τ is the orientational relaxation time which depends on temperature according to the equation

$$\tau = \tau_0 \exp(E/KT). \qquad (3.15)$$

The activation energy parameters E obtained for $CsNO_3$ and $RbNO_3$ are equal to 8.23 and 8.90 Kcal/mole, respectively, indicating that the NO_3^- ion reorientation barriers are quite similar in these two compounds. The frequency and the linewidth of the librational mode change continuously through the III → IV transition point, indicating that the phase transition is not first order. This is consistent with the results of the temperature-dependent Raman study of the internal ν_1 stretching mode of the NO_3^- ion in these materials (Karpow and Shultin, 1976).

4. Pyridinium Iodide

The order–disorder phase transition in pyridinium iodide at 247 K has also been studied by Raman scattering (Wong and Ripmeister, 1980). A large increase in the linewidth of the librational mode around T_c suggests that fluctuations in the out-of-plane orientation of the pyridinium ions exist in both the low and high temperature phases.

5. p-Terphenyl

The order disorder phase transition in para-terphenyl has been investigated by Raman scattering in the frequency range of 3–170 cm^{-1}. In contrast to the phase transition in biphenyl in which a soft phonon is observed, no underdamped soft mode is found in para-terphenyl (Girard et al., 1978). The phase transition in para-terphenyl occurs around 180 K and is believed to be of the continuous order–disorder type (Bree and Edelson, 1977).

6. Perovskite-layer compounds

The structural phase transitions in the $(C_nH_{2n+1}NH_3)_2MCl_4$ perovskite-type layer compounds with M = Cd, Mn, Fe, and n = 1, 2, 3, . . . , have received much attention in recent years. Research interest in these compounds has mainly arisen from the unusual two-dimensional properties and the dynamics of the reorientation of organic ions in connection with the phase transition. The structure of these compounds consists of corner sharing MCl_6 octahedra layers, with the molecular alkylammonium ions located between the layers. Both van der Waals and Coulombic interactions provide the main interlayer bonding. However, the interlayer interaction is weak compared with the interaction within the layer. Recent Raman studies of $(CH_3NH_3)_2CdCl_4$ and $(CH_3NH_3)_2MnCl_4$ have revealed a very broad Rayleigh wing spectrum extending from 0 to 50 cm^{-1} in the α_{xx}, α_{yy}, and α_{xy} polarization at room temperature (Couzi et al., 1977). Here the x and y axes are in the layer plane and the z axis is perpendicular to the layer. The α_{xx}, α_{yy}, and α_{xy} Rayleigh wing spectra display a remarkable temperature dependence, all of which narrow to become an elastic peak as the crystal is brought to the high temperature phase (D_{4h}^{17}), but they abruptly disappear when going into the monoclinic low temperature phase (C_{2h}^5). Similar results are obtained in the structural phase transitions in $(CH_3)_3NHCdCl_4$ (Mlik et al., 1980). These remarkable temperature-dependent Rayleigh wing spectra have been interpreted as the overdamped soft mode for the $D_{4h}^{17} \rightarrow D_{2h}^{18}$ phase transition (Dultz 1976; Chapius, 1977). However, as pointed out by Mokhlisse et al. (1982), this assignment is not consistent with group theory. These authors instead assign the Rayleigh wing spectra observed in the α_{xx}, α_{yy}, and α_{xy} polarizations to the $\mathbf{K} \sim 0$ rocking motion of the octahedra coupled to the reorientation of the organic ion. The broad NH_3 torsional mode at about 275 cm^{-1} in the D_{2h}^{18} phase is also not predicted by group theory. Since this mode also appears in the same polarizations and behaves in a similar manner as the Rayleigh wing spectra, it is consequently assumed to have the same dynamic origin.

Results of Brillouin scattering spectra of $(C_nH_{2n+1}NH_3)_2MnCl_4$, with $n = 1, 2$ have also been reported (Korajamaki et al., 1981). The acoustic phonon modes propagating within the layer are found to display anomalies near the phase transition temperatures, whereas the phonon propagating perpendicular to the layers behaves normally. Group-theoretical analysis shows that the soft mode associated with the $D_{4h}^{17} \rightarrow D_{2h}^{18}$ transition mainly involves the reorientational motion of the organic ion (Petzelt, 1975). Since the orientational frequency of the organic ion is in the microwave (10^9–10^{11} Hz) range, Brillouin scattering spectra are expected to provide useful information regarding the nature of the phase transition. Unfortunately, results of this Brillouin scattering experiment are still inconclusive. Additional experimental efforts coupled with theoretical analysis are needed to shed more light on the dynamic nature of this interesting class of molecular solids.

7. Miscellaneous Crystals

We next mention the Brillouin scattering study of 2-chloronaphthalene which undergoes an order–disorder phase transition at about 308 K (Rey-Lafon et al., 1979). This study shows that the frequency of the longitudinal acoustic phonon associated with C_{22} and the transverse acoustic phonon associated with C_{44} and C_{46} decrease rapidly as the phase transition temperature is approached. Again, the coupling of the strain and the order parameter is assumed to be the cause of the observed anomalies; however, the precise nature of the order parameter as well as the coupling scheme has not yet been elucidated.

The structural phase transition in octaflouronaphthalene, $C_{10}F_8$, takes place at 266.5 K on cooling and at 281 K on heating. Raman and neutron diffraction studies suggest only a unit cell doubling but no change of lattice symmetry, and that the lattice instability of a zone boundary acoustic phonon is responsible for the phase transition (Mackenzie et al., 1977). Additional studies using Brillouin and inelastic neutron scattering will be useful to verify this mechanism.

The study of the librational modes in NH_4Br below the 235-K order–disorder phase transition was repeated by Buhay, et al. (1978). They fit the peak frequency of the librational mode above 125 K to the equation $\omega^2 = A + B\eta$, where η is the order parameter. Since no quantitative calculations are given of the parameters A and B, they can at best be considered as fitting parameters. However, the experimental result is in good agreement with that reported previously by Wang and Wright (1972, 1973).

B. Transitions in the Displacive Limit

The observed anomalies in the elastic properties of crystals such as benzil are the consequence of bilinear coupling between some microscopic order parameter (the intermolecular optical mode of the E irreducible representation) and such macroscopic quantities as strains. One should contrast this type of phase transition with the phase transitions for which the role of the order parameter is played by strains. The type of solids for which the order parameter is a strain component and the soft mode is an acoustic phonon is known to undergo thermoelastic transitions (or ferroelastic if the solid becomes ferroelectric below T_c). Examples of this type of transitions are s-triazine $(C_3N_3H_3)$ (Raich and Berstein, 1980), sodium azide (NaN_3) (Iqbal and Christoe, 1975; Raich and Gillis, 1976). KCN and NaCN already discussed above also fall into this category but have sizeable order–disorder components and hence are classified in the order–disorder limit category.

1. NaN_3 and TlN_3

TlN_3 is quite similar to NaN_3 in which a shearing distortion of the CsCl tetragonal structure (space group $I4/mcm$) produces a monoclinic unit cell (Christoe and Iqbal, 1977). For the factor group D_{4h}, group theory predicts two Raman active internal modes (N_3^- symmetric stretching vibrations) of A_{1g} and B_{2g} symmetry which are observed (but unresolved) at 1323 cm^{-1} in TlN$_3$. The external modes are B_{1g} (libration), E_g (libration), and E_g (Tl$^+$ sublattice translation), with the positions at 173, 50, and 35 cm^{-1}, respectively. A quasielastic wing believed to be associated with the large amplitude librational motion of N_3^- is also observed in TlN$_3$ (Christoe and Iqbal, 1977). Pressure dependent studies (below 8 Kbar) in TlN$_3$ shows that the 10–60 cm^{-1} low frequency Raman spectral region displays an antiresonant lineshape. This is analyzed in terms of the coupling of the E_g N_3^- librational mode to the E_g Tl$^+$ sublattice translation, which is believed to be closely connected with the first-order phase transition induced by pressure in TlN$_3$ (Christoe and Iqbal, 1977)

2. s-Triazine

Raman scattering of s-triazine have been reported (Elliott and Iqbal, 1975; Daunt and Shurvell, 1975). In contrast to benzil, no Raman active optical lattice mode shows softening to near zero frequency near the phase transition temperature ($T_c = 198.8$ K), at which the crystal undergoes a phase transition from a high temperature trigonal phase (D_{3h}^6, $Z = 2$) to a low temperature monoclinic phase (C_{2h}^6, $Z = 2$). However, due to a change in the crystal environment of each molecule, a splitting of some intermolecular and intramolecular modes has been found. Raich and Bernstein (1980) have shown the splitting of the E_g rotary lattice mode to be associated with the lattice strain component e_{zx}. The temperature dependence of e_{zx} shows a small deviation from the simple mean field power law $(T_c - T)^{1/2}$. The deviation is due to the fact that the phase transition in s-triazine is not strictly second order. Brillouin scattering results show a strong temperature dependence in the elastic constants C_{44}, $\frac{1}{2}(C_{11} - C_{12})$, and C_{14} near the transition, with the elastic constant C_{44} developing the strongest temperature anomaly. This is qualitatively in agreement with the result of the Landau mean field calculation (Raich and Bernstein, 1980).

3. Benzil

The angular-dependent anisotropic forces which couple molecular orientation to translation usually play an important role in the phase transitions of molecular crystals. We now consider its effect on the benzil crystal. The phase transition of benzil ($C_6H_5COCOC_6H_5$) was found by birefringence studies at $T_c = 84$ K (Esherick and Kohler, 1973). The transition is first order, although only weakly so. The high temperature phase is determined to have a trigonal structure D_3^4 with three molecules per unit cell. The low temperature structure is monoclinic ($C2$), with the loss of the three fold axis (Toledano, 1979; Dworkin and Fuchs, 1977). Group-theoretical calculations give fifteen external modes ($2A_1 + 3A_2 + 5E$). The polar modes of E symmetry are expected to split into LO and TO components, but the experimental study shows only very weak LO–TO splitting. Raman measurements (using back-scattering geometry) of the external modes between 300 and 5 K show the existence of a soft mode for the phase transition (Sapriel *et al.*, 1979). The soft mode at the high temperature is of E symmetry, which splits into two modes ($A(x) + B(x)$) below the phase transition. The eigenvector of the soft mode has not been identified. Due to the small LO–TO splitting, the soft mode is likely to be associated with the rotational motion. The frequencies of the soft modes above and below T_c are plotted as a function of the temperature between 84 and 5 K (Fig. 7a). These lines merge at T_c. The square of the frequencies of the soft modes as well as their linewidths are plotted against the temperature in Fig. 7b. Over the temperature range between 45 and 80 K, the square of the frequency for the $A(x)$ mode decreases linearly with increasing temperature, and the frequency squared of the E mode above T_c also varies linearly with temperature. Except for a small cusp at 84 K, the linewidth of the soft mode shows a regular decrease from 3.5 to 0.6 cm^{-1} when the temperature is lowered from 300 to 5 K.

To support the Raman result that the soft E mode is clearly associated with the phase transition in benzil, Vacher and Boissier (1981) have carried out a Brillouin scattering experiment. In this work, the whole set of elastic constants is determined as a function of temperature (Fig. 8). Among them, the elastic constant C_{44} is most sensitive to the phase transition; it softens markedly as the phase transition is approached from both above and below (Fig. 9). Since the modulus of the transverse acoustic wave propagating along the c axis is proportional to C_{44}, the data indicate that this mode is a soft mode. The temperature-dependent data of the elastic constant $C = \frac{1}{2}\{(C_{44} + C_{66}) - [(C_{66} - C_{44})^2 + 4C_{14}^2]^{1/2}\}$ associated with the transverse acoustic mode propagating along the a axis and polarized along the c axis of the crystal are shown in Fig. 9 also. However, since C_{14} and C_{66} do not show an anomalous behavior, the softening of this acoustic mode is due chiefly to the elastic constant C_{44}. Thus, two soft transverse modes share a common origin of instability (the elastic constant C_{44}). In the case where the phase transition is induced by the zone center order parameter of E symmetry, as indicated by the Raman scattering result, the soft acoustic mode with zero velocity at T_c is expected to be that propagating along the a axis (assuming the transition to be second order). As seen in Fig. 8, the mode is very sensitive to temperature, but the elastic constant C_{44} intersects the temperature axis at about 64 K, rather than at $T_c = 84$ K. This deviation is probably a consequence of

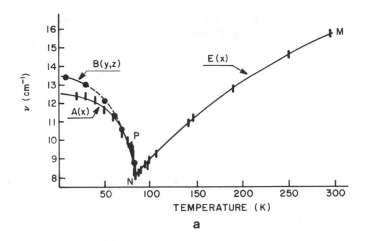

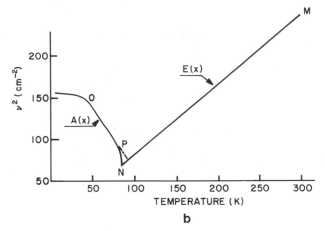

Fig. 7. (a) The frequencies of the soft modes of benzil ($C_6H_5COCOC_6H_5$) plotted as a function of temperature. (b) The square of the frequencies of the soft modes in benzil as well as their linewidths plotted as a function of temperature. (From Sapriel *et al.*, 1979. Used with the permission of the American Institute of Physics.)

the interaction of the order parameter (the optical mode of E symmetry) and the transverse acoustic mode.

Additional Brillouin data for the phase transition of benzil were also reported by Yoshihara, *et al.* (1982). These authors have discussed the experimental results using the Landau mean field theory. They show that the bilinear strain-order parameter coupling term can explain the transverse elastic anomalies observed for benzil. The elastic constant C_{11} (associated

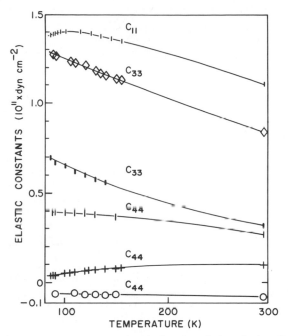

Fig. 8. Elastic constants versus temperature in the trigonal phase for benzil. (From Vacher and Boissier, 1981. Used with the permission of the American Institute of Physics.)

with the longitudinal acoustic phonon propagating along the a axis) also shows an anomaly near T_c. However, the same mean field theory cannot account for the anomalous behavior of the a axis longitudinal acoustic mode. It is suggested that the discrepancy is due to the existence of a nonmean field contribution as well as higher order coupling terms between the order parameter and strains.

4. Chloranil

A molecular crystal which displays an underdamped soft mode responsible for driving the continuous second-order phase transition is chloranil ($C_6Cl_4O_2$). Since the discovery of a phase transition of this crystal at $T_c = 90.3$ K, much attention has been paid to its study (Chihara et al., 1971; Chihara and Nakamura, 1973). The x-ray diffraction study shows that the transition changes from the monoclinic structure ($P2_1/a$, $Z = 2$) at room temperature to another monoclinic structure ($P2_1/n$, $Z = 4$) at high temperature. Both belong to C_{2v}^5 symmetry. The phase transition involves doubling of the unit cell parameter along the c axis.

From a crystallographic point of view, the phase transition occurs through

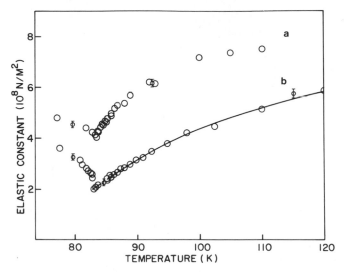

Fig. 9. Temperature dependence of the elastic constants in benzil. The elastic constants are (a) C_{44} and (b) $\frac{1}{2}[C_{66} + C_{44}) - \sqrt{(C_{66} - C_{44})^2 + 4C_{14}^2}]$ for T_c and T_a, respectively. Full line is calculated according to the method described in the text. C_{44} softening causes both temperature dependences. (From Yoshihara *et al.*, 1982. Used with the permission of the American Institute of Physics.)

a staggered rotation of the molecules about the axis perpendicular to the molecular planes. However, recent work has indicated that rotation about the molecular 0–0 axis also plays a role. The phase transition has been theoretically investigated by Toledano (1980) and it has been shown that the transition occurs at the A point $(0,0,\frac{1}{2})$ of the Brillouin zone. The motion responsible for the phase transition is a rotation belonging to the B_{2g} representation. Raman scattering studies have disclosed the existence of a soft mode (Hanson, 1975; Wada *et al.*, 1980) associated with the molecular rotation. Neutron scattering experiments above and below T_c have revealed a central peak which diverges at T_c (Ellenson and Kjems, 1977). From the super-structure reflection intensities, Ellenson and Kjems show an Ising-like critical behavior for the order parameter, with a critical exponent of $\beta = 0.33$. This result contrasts with the Raman scattering result which indicates a classical mean field result with the temperature variation $\omega^2 \propto (T_c - T)$ and $\eta \propto (T_c - T)^{1/2}$ (Fig. 10). No obvious explanation is proposed for this discrepancy. Clearly, the soft-mode behavior in the critical region is complex and requires additional studies.

A pressure-dependent study of the chloranil phase transition has been carried out using Raman scattering. When pressure is applied, the transition is linearly shifted to a higher temperature with a slope of 7.5 K/Kbar

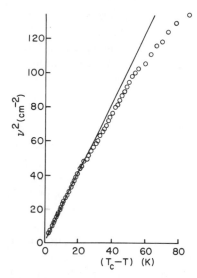

Fig. 10. Square of the soft-mode frequency of chloranil plotted against ($T_c - T$). Measurements with the grating spectrometer (O). Calculated with the experimental data in the temperature interval $2.5 < (T - T_c) < 23$ (———). (From Wada *et al.*, 1980. Used with the permission of the Office of the Physical Society of Japan.)

(Bandour *et al.*, 1981). Over the entire pressure range covered in this study (1–4.13 Kbar), the soft-mode temperature dependence is found to be in agreement with mean field theory down to a frequency of 2 cm^{-1} (Fig. 11). Thus, except for shifting the transition to a higher temperature, no notice-

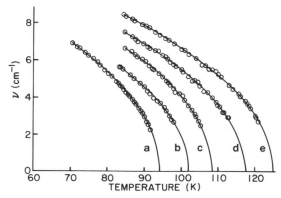

Fig. 11. The temperature shifts of the chloranil soft mode at several pressures (in bar): (a) 1; (b) 1040; (c) 2050; (d) 3100; (e) 4130. Measurements with the grating spectrometer (O), calculated values (———). (From Girard *et al.*, 1982. Used with the permission of the Institute of Physics.)

able change in the nature of the phase transition occurs on application of external pressure (Girard et al., 1982).

The soft mode below 2 cm^{-1} has also been followed using a Fabry–Perot interferometer. At 93.7 K, the soft mode appears as a shoulder on the overdamped Rayleigh wing, but it is completely covered at T = 94 K (Girard et al., 1982).

Brillouin scattering experiments of chloranil have also been carried out by Ecolivet (1981) using a multipass Fabry–Perot interferometer. The results show that the longitudinal acoustic mode propagating along the a axis displays a large anomaly, which involves a large frequency shift and line broadening at T_c. No significant anomaly is found in C_{44}, C_{66}, or C_{46}. However, intensity anomalies are observed with the disappearance of some Brillouin lines below T_c. The intensity study indicates that P_{12} vanishes (or becomes very small) below T_c.

Combining the Raman and Brillouin scattering results shows that the phase transition is associated with a three-phonon interaction process (of the type $\eta^2 S$), involving two soft optical modes at the zone boundary (at the A point of the first Brillouin zone) and one acoustic mode at the zone center. Since the coupling of two zone boundary phonons gives a totally symmetric representation A_g, this allows the coupling with the strain component e_{xx}. Such nonlinear coupling involving two soft modes (or two order parameters) and strain is different from the type found in benzyl, in which the soft mode is bilinearly coupled to the strain component e_{zx}. Despite the fact that the optical modes of both benzil and chloranil soften as the phase transition takes place, in benzil the frequency of the transverse acoustic mode associated with e_{zx} softens continuously with temperature and reaches a very small minimum value at T_c; whereas in chloranil, the frequency of the longitudinal acoustic mode associated with e_{xx} first increases with decreasing temperature, then displays a rapid decrease in the vicinity of T_c, and remains insensitive to temperature below T_c.

5. Malononitrile

Recent N^{14} pure quadrupole resonance studies have revealed in malononitrile (NCCH$_2$CN) a phase transition at $T_c = 294.7$ K (Zussman and Alexander, 1967). The quadrupole resonance splitting shows a temperature dependence of $(T - T_c)^{-1/2}$ near T_c. However, no heat capacity anomaly associated with this transition, is observed (Girdhar et al., 1968). For this reason the phase transition is probably of the displacive rather than order–disorder type. The crystal structure above the phase transition is monoclinic ($P2_1/c$, $Z = 4$). Two possible structures ($P2_1/m$ and $P2_1$) are consistent with the x ray data, but the IR and Raman results are consistent with the

$P2_1$, $Z = 4$ structure. Thus the transition from the upper to the lower temperature phase results in the disappearance of a glide plane and does not involve a doubling of the unit cell.

A comprehensive temperature-dependent Raman scattering study of a malonitrile single crystal does not show the presence of optical soft modes for the phase transition (Higashigaki and Wang, 1979). However, the line associated with the libration mode about the c axis (B_g) shows anomalies in both its frequency and linewidth and a CH_2 deformation band, $v_3(A_1)$, also shows a splitting below T_c. Rayleigh–Brillouin scattering data show effects of the phase transition on the Rayleigh intensity, and the frequency and the linewidth of the quasi-longitudinal and quasi-transverse modes. The lowest frequency quasi-transverse mode also softens as the phase transition is approached from above. Unfortunately, due to the lack of data on the precise crystal orientation with respect to the phonon propagation direction, the detailed nature of the phase transition in malononitrile could not be established from the existing Raman and Rayleigh–Brillouin results.

6. $(NH_4)_2SO_4$

Ammonium sulfate [$(NH_4)_2SO_4$] has been investigated by Raman (Unruh, 1980; Iqbal and Christoe, 1976) and by Brillouin scattering spectroscopy (Yoshihara et al., 1976). No underdamped soft mode has been observed in $(NH_4)_2SO_4$. The elastic constants C_{11}, C_{44}, and C_{55} display anomalies at the paraelectric–ferroelectric phase transition temperature ($T_c = -49.5°$), with C_{11} changed by the largest amount (about 70%). Although $(NH_4)_2SO_4$ becomes ferroelectric below $T_c = -49.5°C$, only a weak dielectric anomaly is found near T_c (Yoshihara et al., 1976). Thus, the observation of a large elastic anomaly and a weak dielectric one suggests that the phase transition of $(NH_4)_2SO_4$ is an improper ferroelectric phase transition. In the improper ferroelectric phase transition, the free energy starts from the quadratic term in the order parameter, and the order parameter weakly couples to polar modes but strongly couples to acoustic modes. On the basis of the EPR (Fujimoto et al., 1977) and x ray scattering data (Hasebe and Tanesaki, 1977; Hirotsu et al., 1982), the soft modes in $(NH_4)_2SO_4$ have been suggested to be the librational motion of the tetrahedra of NH_4^+ and SO_4^{-2} ions. This is consistent with the Raman study by Iqbal and Christoe (1975) who have interpreted the structureless background between 0–50 cm^{-1} to be due to the coupling of the lattice phonons to the reorientation of the NH_4^+ ions. The distortion of the SO_4^{-2} ion is proposed to account for the change in the linewidth and the frequency of the v_3 band of the SO_4^{-2} ion.

In the theoretical treatment of elastic anomalies associated with structural phase transitions, the symmetry of the order parameter and the strain plays an important role in determining the behavior of the anomaly near the phase transition temperature. Assuming that the anomaly in $(NH_4)_2SO_4$ is due to the coupling between the order parameter η (which belong to the B_{1u} representation of the paraelectric phase D_{2h}^{16}) and the strain $S_1(A_g)$, Yoshihara et al. (1976) have proposed for the interaction part, between the order parameter and the strain in the free energy expression, to be of the type $AS_1\eta^2 + BS_1^2\eta^2$, to account for the C_{11} anomaly. They have calculated the temperature dependence of C_{11} and obtained a qualitative agreement with the experiment.

Replacing NH_4^+ by Li^+ causes a large increase of T_c. In NH_4LiSO_4 the ferroelectric phase transition temperature is at $T_c = 186.5°C$, at which the structure changes from D_{2h}^{16}-$Pmcn$ ($Z = 4$) to C_{2v}^9-$P2_1cn$ ($Z = 4$). Brillouin scattering measurements show that elastic constants C_{11}, C_{22}, and C_{33} behave in a similar manner. They are nearly constant above T_c but show a monotonic increase below T_c. Similar to the case of $(NH_4)_2SO_4$, NH_4LiSO_4 is also an improper ferroelectric (Dvorak, 1974) with the symmetry of the order parameter belonging to the B_{3u} representation at the Γ point of the paraelectric D_{2h}^{16} phase. Similar to that found in $(NH_4)_2SO_4$, the low frequency Raman spectrum displays a structureless background, which is proposed to be due to dynamic disordering of the NH_4^+ ions in the lattice (Arthur et al., 1973). To account for the elastic anomaly the compressive strain must be of A_{1g} symmetry. Thus, the anomaly observed in C_{11}, C_{22}, and C_{33} is assumed to be due to terms of the form $S_1\eta^2$ and $S_1^2\eta^2$. However, since the discontinuous decrease in C_{11} is not observed at T_c, it suggests that either the third-order term $S_1\eta^2$ is small or the dispersion frequency of the order parameter η is low compared with the hypersonic frequency. It should be useful to study the elastic dispersion over a wide temperature and frequency range to determine the importance of the third-order coupling term (Arthur et al., 1973).

7. A_2MX_6 Crystals

The hexahalometallates of the general type A_2MX_6, with $A = K$, NH_4^+, . . . ; $M = Sn$, Re, . . . ; $X =$ halogen, crystallize (with some exceptions) in the cubic antifluorite structure of space group $Fm3m$ (O_h^5) and undergo successive phase transitions, accompanied by the softening of the rotary modes of MX_6^{2+} at the Γ or X points of the bcc – Brillouin zone (Pelzl et al., 1977; Lynn et al., 1978). Among the hexahalometallates, the phase transitions of K_2ReCl_6 and K_2SnCl_6 have been investigated most thoroughly. For K_2ReCl_6, the NQR (O'Leary and Wheeler, 1970) and neutron scattering (Henkel et al., 1980) studies have shown that the phase transition at $T_c = 109$ K which changes the crystal structure from cubic to tetragonal is of the displacive type, driven by soft rotary modes of $ReCl_4^{-2}$ at the Γ point. However, the situation is less clear for K_2SnCl_6. Raman scattering studies of K_2SnCl_6 show that the phase transition at $T_c = 262$ K is closely associated with the softening of the $SnCl_6^{-2}$ librational mode when T_c is approached from low temperature (Pelzl et al., 1977). The nature of the other phase transition at $T_c' = 255$ K remains unclear. Brillouin scattering studies (Henkel et al., 1980) of K_2SnCl_6 as a function of temperature show that as the phase transition temperature T_c is approached from above a pronounced softening of the mode associated with elastic constants $(C_{11} - C_{12})$ occurs, whereas the transverse mode associated with C_{44} shows no anomaly. On the basis of these light scattering results, a Landau-theoretical model based on the coupling of the elastic strain field to the quadratic functions of the fluctuations of the soft-mode coordinate involving the $SnCl_6^{-2}$ octahedra rotations at the X point has been proposed to analyze the nature of the phase transition in K_2SnCl_6. The result indicates that the order parameter related to the $SnCl_6^{-2}$ rotations at the X point which transforms as A_{2g} displays a strong anomaly for the mode associated with $(C_{11} - C_{12})$, while the mode associated with C_{44} does not show any anomaly. This is in agreement with experiment (Henkel et al., 1980).

Substitution of K^+ by NH_4^+ results in a lowering of T_c, accompanied by a gradual decrease of the transition enthalpy per mole (Regelsberger and Pelzl, 1978). This is considered to be due to a decrease of the rotational freedom of the $SnCl_6^{-2}$ octahedra caused by the NH_4^+ ions. The effect due to the presence of the ammonium ions is evidenced by the drastic increase of the linewidth of the ν_5 (F_{2g}) band, associated with the $SnCl_6^{-2}$ internal vibration, as the concentration of the NH_4^+ ions is increased. The concentration dependence of the linewidth of the ν_5 band is believed to originate from the static distortion of the lattice which lifts the three-fold degeneracy and the influence of the rotational motion of the NH_4^+ substituents.

Complete replacement of K^+ by NH_4^+ suppresses the phase transition. Raman scattering of $(NH_4)_2SnCl_6$ does not reveal any type of phase transition down to ~ 4 K (Regelsberger and Pelzl, 1978). However, in $(NH_4)_2SnBr_6$ two successive phase transitions at $T_c = 157$ K and $T_c' = 145$ K have been detected by NQR (Sasane et al., 1970) and heat capacity (Morfee et al., 1960) experiments. Recent Raman scattering experiments also show a strong softening of the $SnBr_6^{-2}$ librational mode as the phase transition temperature T_c is approached from below (Negita et al., 1980), similar to the behavior found in K_2SnCl_6 (Pelzl et al., 1977) and K_2SnBr_6 (Swanson, 1978). This suggests that the phase transition at T_c is of the displacive type. Another interesting feature in the Raman spectrum of

$(NH_4)_2SnBr_6$ is the splitting of the T_{2g} internal mode of $SnBr_6^{2-}$ below T'_c. This is probably due to the distortion of the $SnBr_6^{-2}$ ions. However, from the Raman data alone it is difficult to determine whether the softening of the rotary modes occurs at the Γ or at the X point of the cubic Brillouin zone. A temperature-dependent Brillouin scattering experiment of this compound should also be useful.

8. ABX_3 Crystals

Crystals of the ABX_3 (X is a halogen; A and B stand for an alkali and divalent metal ion, respectively) also undergo structural phase transitions from cubic at high temperature to tetragonal at low temperature (McMurdie et al., 1969). Further phase transitions to orthorhombic structures are also observed. For example, the crystal $RbCaCl_3$ transforms from cubic (O_h^1) to tetragonal (D_{4h}^5) at $T_c = 300°C$, and then to orthorhombic (D_{2h}^{16}) at $T'_c = 230°C$. While these structural phase transitions are due to a tilting of the $CaCl_6$ octahedra, the mechanism of the phase transitions in this type of crystal is still in debate. In general, if the phase transition is of the displacive type, we expect to observe at least one soft mode below the transition temperature by Raman scattering. Raman scattering studies of $RbCaCl_3$ have, however, detected no well-defined soft modes around either the cubic-tetragonal transition temperature at T_c or around the tetragonal–orthorhombic transition temperature at T'_c (Midorikawa et al., 1979), suggesting that the phase transitions in $RbCaCl_3$ may have considerable order–disorder character.

Although no Brillouin scattering work on $RbCaCl_3$ has been carried out, Brillouin scattering results on $CsPbCl_3$, however, suggest that the phase transition mechanism is of the displacive type (Midorikawa et al., 1980). $CsPbCl_3$ also belongs to the perovskite family and undergoes three phase transitions above room temperature (Hirotsu, 1971). On cooling it transforms from the cubic to tetragonal phase at $T_c = 47°C$, and then to the orthogonal phase at $T'_c = 42°C$, and finally to another orthorhombic phase at $T_c = 37°C$. Brillouin scattering studies indicate that as the phase transition temperature is approached from above, the elastic constant C_{11} decreases to a minimum and C_{12} increases to a maximum at T''_c, with no discontinuous change detected at T_c and T'_c. No anomaly is detected for C_{44}. This suggests that the contribution to the free energy density arising from the order parameter fluctuation is of the form $\phi \approx e_{xx}(\eta_1^2 + \eta_3^2)$, where e_{xx} is the compressional strain along the x axis and η_1, η_2, and η_3 are the rotation angles of the octahedra about the x, y, and z axes. A complete theoretical analysis, however, has not been provided for this system.

A significant pretransition effect is observed in C_{11} and C_{12} above T_c in CsPbCl$_3$. A similarly large pretransition effect (80 K above T_c) as well as an elastic anomaly near T_c are found in the longitudinal ($K \| (100)$) acoustic wave velocities and attenuation coefficients of TlCdF$_3$ and RbCaF$_3$ (Berger et al., 1968). In these fluoroperovskites, the order parameters are also the rotation angles of the CdF$_6$ or CaF$_6$ octahedra about the x, y, and z axes. The pretransition effect indicates that order parameter fluctuations are present above T_c. However, comparison of the elastic constant values obtained from Brillouin scattering with that obtained from ultrasonic measurements shows good agreement between the two values. This indicates that the dispersion in the ultrasonic–hypersonic frequency region is negligible, in contrast to that in order–disorder phase transitions of NH$_4$Cl and NH$_4$Br, in which both C_{11} and C_{12} exhibit significant dispersion above the structural phase transition points (Garland and Choo, 1973). The lack of dispersion in CsPbCl$_3$ indicates that the elastic relaxation time due to order parameter fluctuations is at least shorter than 10^{-11} s. This has an implication in elucidating the mechanism of the phase transition in CsPbCl$_3$ and other crystals of a similar perovskite structure.

In general, the order parameter fluctuation associated with an order–disorder phase transition occurs at lower than the lattice vibrational frequencies. In CsPbCl$_3$, the elastic relaxation time (which is $< 10^{-11}$ s) is much shorter than the values reported hitherto for most order–disorder systems. On the basis of this, it is suggested that the cubic-tetragonal transition in CsPbCl$_3$ has a displacive rather than order–disorder character, in contrast to the conclusion obtained previously from Raman scattering studies of RbCaCl$_3$, which suggests that the transition in RbCaCl$_3$ is of the order–disorder type. It appears that the soft modes in the structural phase transitions in this type of perovskite structure are associated with the instability of the phonons at the Brillouin zone boundary. Although it is clear that the order parameter is the rotation of the BX_6 octahedra, the question of whether the structural phase transition is of the displacive type is essentially semantic. However, the experimental data show that a high degree of dynamic disorder associated with large amplitude oscillations of the soft mode is present in these crystals. This is indicated by the large root mean square amplitude of the positions of Cl ions in the recent neutron scattering experiment (Hutton et al., 1969). Studies of the intensity of Raman and Brillouin spectral lines of RbMnCl$_3$ as a function of temperature have been initiated (Fjaer and Samuelsen, 1981). Such studies are expected to provide useful information about the structural behavior of the order parameter. Unfortunately, however, the work reported by Fjaer and Samuelsen (1968) is incomplete.

C. Incommensurate Phase Transitions

1. K_2SeO_4

In the preceding discussion, emphasis has been given to the study of structural phase transitions from soft modes either at the center or at the boundary of the Brillouin zone. Soft modes at the zone center $K \sim 0$ are allowed in first-order Raman scattering. Soft modes at the zone boundary are present in the light scattering spectrum due to combination with another mode of opposite K vector (see Chapter 1). A new type of phase transition which is driven by a soft mode located neither at the zone center nor at the zone boundary has also been found. K_2SeO_4 undergoes a series of phase transitions at $T_1 = 745.0$ K, $T_2 = 129.5$ K, and $T_3 = 93.0$ K. The phase transition occurring at T_2 is induced by the condensation of a soft mode polarized along the c axis with the wavevector $K = [(1 - \delta)/3a,0,0]$ where δ decreases slightly with decreasing temperature and vanishes discontinuously at T_2. The phase transition at T_2 is usually referred to as an incommensurate transition (Izumi *et al.*, 1977). Considerable interest, both experimental and theoretical, has been directed towards the incommensurate structural phase transitions in recent years (for a somewhat more detailed discussion see Chapter 2 and Petzelt, 1981).

A Raman scattering study of K_2SeO_4 covering the frequency range 0–900 cm^{-1} has been carried out over the temperature range of 77–300 K. One of the important results of this study is the observation of a temperature-dependent mode whose frequency decreases rapidly as the transition point T_2 is approached from below (Wada *et al.*, 1977). This temperature-dependent mode, observed only in the α_{aa} spectrum is now recognized as the soft mode for the incommensurate phase transition. Comparison of the polarization behavior with that expected for the $K \sim 0$ Raman selection rule shows that this mode does not correspond to one of the 24 predicted Raman active lattice modes ($7 A_g + 5B_{1g} + 5B_{2g} + 7B_{3g}$). The soft mode belongs to the A_1 representation. Fitting the temperature dependent soft-mode spectrum to Eq. (3.9), Wada *et al.*, (1977a,b,c) have obtained the peak frequency and the damping constant as a function of temperature (Fig. 12). The result shows the mean field temperature dependence of the peak frequency. However, the damping constant of the soft mode increases rapidly (and appears to diverge) as the transition temperature T_2 is approached, similar to that found in $SrTiO_3$ (Uwe and Sakudo, 1976).

Subsequent Raman scattering studies of K_2SeO_4 by Wada *et al.* (1977a,b,c) and by Unruh (1980) show, however, two soft modes, A_g/A_1 and B_1, below the commensurate–incommensurate phase transition at T_2 and the ferroelectric phase transition at T_3. The A_g/A_1 mode is known as the

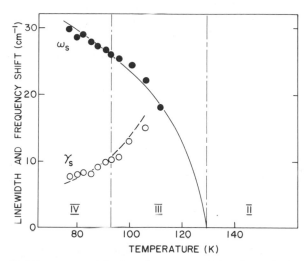

Fig. 12. The peak frequency and the damping constant of the soft amplitude mode of K_2SeO_4 plotted as a function of temperature. (The solid curve drawn through the peak frequency is calculated using mean field theory). (From Wada *et al.*, 1977. Used with the permission of the Office of the Physical Society of Japan.)

amplitude mode; its temperature dependence within the incommensurate phase is approximately given by $\omega_0^3 \sim (T_i - T)$. The B_1 mode is known as the phase mode and is obtained only in the low temperature commensurate phase. The temperature dependence of the phase mode follows a linear dependence given by $\omega_0' = a(T_i' - T)$, where $T_i' = 122$ K and $a = -0.12$ cm^{-1}/K (Fig. 13). These studies of the amplitude and phase modes have advanced our understanding of the incommensurate–commensurate phase transition.

Taking into account the dielectric anomaly, Unruh (1980) has pointed out that a coupling term of the type $\sim \eta^2 p^2$ included in the free energy expression would give a critical exponent of 0.37 and 0.38 along the crystallographic b and c axes, respectively (Unruh, 1980). This is qualitatively in agreement with experiment.

Brillouin scattering studies for K_2SeO_4 have been carried out (Yagi *et al.*, 1979, 1981; Cho and Yagi, 1981; Hauret and Benoit, 1982). Consistent with the assignment of the soft mode for the normal-incommensurate transition, the longitudinal acoustic phonon propagating along the (001) direction shows an anomalous temperature dependence near T_2. In the vicinity of T_2, C_{33} shows a pronounced variation (Fig. 14) and the corresponding linewidth (Γ) displays a maximum at T_2 (Fig. 15). Similar results are also found in the quasi-transverse phonons propagating along (101) or (011) and polarized in the planes (010) and (100), respectively. Apparently, the anom-

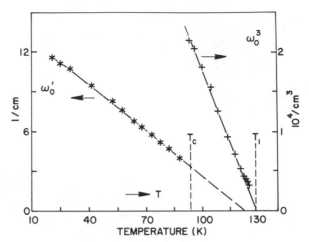

Fig. 13. Temperature dependence of the eigenfrequencies ω'_0 of the amplitude and phase mode of potassium selenate, K_2SeO_4. (From Unruh, 1981. Used with the permission of Gordon & Breach, Science Publications, Inc.)

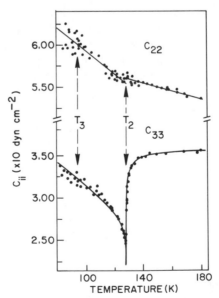

Fig. 14. Temperature dependence of C_{22} and C_{33} in K_2SeO_4. Results derived from Eqs. (3.17a) and (3.17b) (————). (From Cho and Yagi, 1980. Used with the permission of the Office of Physical Society of Japan.)

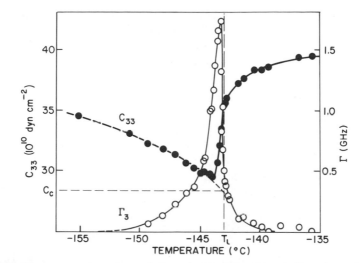

Fig. 15. Temperature dependence of C_{33} and of the full width at half maximum (FWHM), Γ_3, of the deconvoluted Brillouin peak corresponding to the acoustic wave propagating along (001) in K_2SeO_4. The best fit (---) to the power law $(T_i - T)$ with $\beta = 0.7$, extrapolated value $C_{33}(T_i) = 28.3 \pm 0.3 \times 10^{10}$ dyn cm^{-2}. (From Hauret and Benoit, 1982. Used with the permission of Gordon & Breach, Science Publication, Inc.)

alies present in the quasi-transverse phonons are due to admixture with the pure (001) longitudinal phonon. Over the 118–128 K temperature range, the elastic constant C_{33} varies with temperature as $a + (T_2 - T)^\beta$, $\beta = 0.7 \pm 0.1$ (Hauret and Benoit, 1982). While this result deviates from the simple mean field prediction, it is comparable with the neutron scattering intensity of Iizumi *et al.* (1977) ($\beta = 0.8 \pm 0.1$) and is in very good agreement with the value of $\beta = 0.7$ measured by Shiozaki *et al.* (1977) using a dilatometric method.

The qualitative feature of the elastic anomaly can be explained in terms of mean field theory by expanding the free energy density in a power series of the strain components (S_i) and the order parameter (η) associated with the soft optical mode, including the coupling between strains and the order parameter. Using the expression for the free energy density ϕ as

$$\phi = \tfrac{1}{2}\alpha\eta^2 + \tfrac{1}{4}\beta\eta^4 + \tfrac{1}{6}K\eta^6 + \tfrac{1}{2}C_{ii}S_i^2 + \gamma_i\eta^2 S_i \tag{3.16}$$
$$+ \epsilon_i\eta^2 S_i^2 + \delta_i\eta^4 S_i + \zeta(\nabla\eta)^2,$$

where $\alpha = \alpha_0(T - T_2)$; β, K, γ_i, ϵ_i, δ_i, ζ, and C_{ii} are constants, Cho and Yagi (1980) give for C_{33} the equations

$$C_{33} = C_{33}^0 - B(T - T_2)^{-1/2} \qquad \text{for } T > T_2 \tag{3.17a}$$
$$= C_{33}^0 - 2\gamma_3^2/\beta + A(T_2 - T) - B(T_2 - T)^{-1/2} \qquad \text{for } T < T_2, \tag{3.17b}$$

where $B_1 = \sqrt{2}\,\gamma_3^2 k T_2/(16\pi\zeta^{3/2}\alpha_0^{1/2})$; A is a function of the constants α_0, β, . . . , etc. The comparison of the experimental with the calculated data is shown in Fig. 14. It appears that the more general free energy density (Eq. (16)) gives good agreement with the experiment. We note from Eqs. (3.17a) and (3.17b), that the negative terms are due to the coupling term $\gamma_3\eta^2 S_3$. This term is linear in the strain and quadratic in the order parameter. Apparently, the incommensurate phase transition in K_2SeO_4 is triggered by the presence of this nonlinear three phonon coupling term.

Hauret and Benoit (1982) have provided an interpretation for the line-width maximum (Fig. 15) they observed. They suggested that below T_2 the longitudinal acoustic mode is coupled to an overdamped mode. Using this picture they have obtained

$$\Gamma \propto \frac{\tau}{1 + (\omega\tau)^2}, \tag{3.18}$$

where $\tau = \tau_0/(T_2 - T)$. Fitting the experimental data to Eq. (3.18) gives $\tau_0 = 2.6 \times 10^{-12}$ s K^{-1}. This suggests that very near T_2, a central component of the width of few cm^{-1} is present. This component has, however, not yet been observed.

Brillouin scattering studies of the phase transition at T_1 in K_2SeO_4, performed by Cho and Yagi (1980), show an anomaly in C_{11}. A mean field calculation indicates that the anomaly is caused by a coupling term of the form $\sim \eta^2 S_1^2$ in the free energy density. The soft mode associated with the order parameter η has not yet been observed. The low frequency Raman spectrum in the vicinity of T_1 shows a broad central line which may be attributed to the orientational fluctuations of the selenate ions (Unruh, 1980).

While $(NH_4)_2SO_4$ belongs to the general type of A_2BO_4 crystals, where $A = $ K, Na, Rb, Cs, Tl, or NH$_4^+$; $B = $ S or Se, it shows a very different phase transition behavior from that of K_2SeO_4. In general A_2BO_4 crystals are similar from the crystallographic point of view, but they show a variety of different structural transformations. As a matter of fact, except for K_2SeO_4 discussed above, other compounds of the A_2BO_4 type do not show incommensurate phase transitions.

2. Rb_2ZnCl_4 and $Rb_2Z_nBr_4$

Rb_2ZnCl_4 and Rb_2ZnBr_4 have attracted much attention because of transformation to incommensurate phases. The successive phase transition of these solids are quite similar to those of K_2SeO_4. Two phase transitions at 29 and $-83°$C in Rb_2ZnCl_4 and 73 and $-86°$C in Rb_2ZnBr_4 have been observed. The structure above the upper transition temperature is isomorphous with $\beta - K_2SO_4$ with space group symmetry $D_{2h}^{16} - Pmcn$ ($Z = 4$). In the intermediate phase, both crystals have incommensurate structures along the c axis characterized by the wavevector $\mathbf{K} = [h, k, l \pm (\frac{1}{3} - \delta)]$ (Gesi and Iizumi, 1978). The low temperature phase has a commensurate super-structure with the lattice parameter exactly tripled along the c axis of the prototypic phase. The low temperature phase is ferroelectric.

Raman scattering spectra of Rb_2ZnCl_4 were studied over the temperature range 77–350 K in the frequency range of 0–2000 cm^{-1} for various scatter-ing configurations by Wada *et al.* (1978a,b, 1979). No peaks with frequency shifts higher than 400 cm^{-1} were observed. In phase I, there are 81 funda-mental vibrational modes expected, with 42 Raman active modes (13 $A_g + 8B_{1g} + 8B_{2g} + 13B_{3g}$); however, only 24 modes are observed by Wada *et al.* (1978, 1979). The phonon mode which shows a strong temperature dependence is a low frequency mode at 26 cm^{-1} at 77 K observed in the $a(cc)b$ and $c(aa)b$ configurations. In addition, a nearly temperature-inde-pendent mode at lower frequency is also detected below 200 K. The spectra and the temperature dependence of both bands are shown in Figs. 16 and 17. We note the anti-crossing region around 230 K. Since both modes

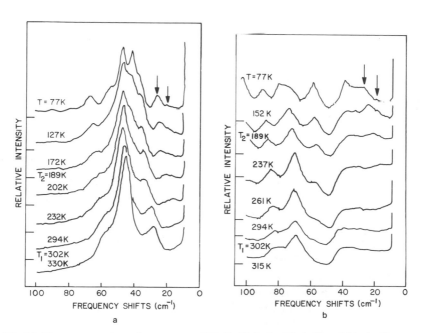

Fig. 16. Temperature-dependent spectra of Rb_2ZnCl_4 in the (a) $a(cc)b$ and (b) $c(aa)b$ scatter-ing configurations. (From Wada *et al.*, 1979. Used with the permission of the Office of Physical Society of Japan.)

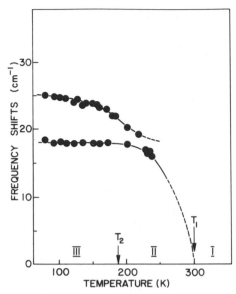

Fig. 17. Frequency shifts at peak intensity of the two low-lying modes in Rb_2ZnCl_4, belonging to the totally symmetric irreducible representation, as functions of the temperature. (From Wada *et al.*, 1979. Used with the permission of the Office of the Physical Society of Japan.)

belong to the same symmetric representation, only one of the two peaks corresponds to the amplitude mode which is the soft mode in the incommensurate phase.

In the commensurate phase of Rb_2ZnCl_4 below $T_2 = 189$ K, another soft mode (the phase mode) is expected to be observed in the spectrum with the Raman tensor α_{ac} belonging to the B_2 irreducible representation according to group-theoretical analysis (Wada *et al.*, 1978a,b,1979). The phase mode was not detected by Wada *et al.* in the temperature range above 77 K, but evidence for this mode in Rb_2ZnCl_4 has been found by Franke *et al.* (1980). In addition, these authors have observed another underdamped soft mode in the $a(cc)b$ scattering geometry at temperatures between 9 and 77 K with the frequency obeying the law: $\omega = A(T_3 - T)^{1/2}$, where $T_3 = 72$ K and $A = 2.2$ $cm^{-1} K^{-1/2}$. This new soft mode is assigned as a zone boundary mode of the ferroelectric phase. It would be useful to carry out Brillouin scattering experiments to verify the nature of this new soft mode.

Raman spectra of Rb_2ZnBr_4 were studied by Takashige *et al.* (1980a,b). The soft amplitude mode whose frequency decreases with increasing temperature toward the normal-incommensurate transition has been found in the $a(cc)b$ and $c(aa)b$ spectra. At about $-180°$C, the soft amplitude mode appears to display anti-crossing behavior with another mode at a higher frequency. However, no measurements at low temperatures have been carried out. Analogous to that found in K_2SeO_4, the frequency of the amplitude mode does not undergo a discontinuous change at the incommensurate–commensurate phase transition point (T_2). However, in contrast to K_2SeO_4, no rapid increase in the scattering intensity is observed as T_2 is approached from below. This indicates that the nature of the incommensurate–commensurate phase transition for this compound is not quite analogous to that of K_2SeO_4.

The phase mode is not observed below T_2; however, the shape of the Rayleigh wing seems to be different above and below T_2. It is possible that the phase mode is hidden under the Rayleigh wing. Further measurements of the spectral shape at low temperature using a multipass Fabry–Perot interferometer would be useful to locate the phase mode as well as to provide information about the acoustic waves in this solid. Combining the Raman and Brillouin results with the group-theoretical calculation should allow the nature of the phase transitions in Rb_2ZnBr_4 as well as in other Rb_2ZnCl_4 type of ferroelectrics to be clarified. Other Rb_2ZnCl_4 group ferroelectrics having the incommensurate–commensurate phase transition are: $N(CH_3)_4ZnCl_4$ (Takashigi et al., 1980a,b; Sawada et al., 1978a), $[N(CH_3)_4]_2CoCl_4$ (Sawada et al., 1978b), and K_2ZnCl_4 (Gesi, 1978). The soft amplitude mode has also been observed by Raman scattering in other types of solids such as thiourea, $SC(NH_2)_2$ (Wada, 1978a,b; Chapelle and Benoit, 1977), and biphenyl (Wada et al., 1977a,b,c).

3. Biphenyl

Biphenyl is especially interesting since it exhibits two incommensurate phases. The transition temperatures are at $T_1 = 40$ K and $T_2 = 16$ K. The space group above T_1 is $C_{2h}^5 - P2_1a$ ($Z = 2$). The intermediate phase between T_1 and T_2 is incommensurate with the characteristic wavevector $\mathbf{K} = \delta_a\mathbf{a} + \frac{1}{2}(1 - \delta_b)\mathbf{b}^*$. The low temperature phase below T_2 is also incommensurate with $\mathbf{K} = \frac{1}{2}(1 - \delta_b')\mathbf{b}^*$. The soft amplitude mode observed in the $x(zz)y$ scattering configuration (x and y are parallel to the a and b crystal axes, whereas z is perpendicular to the x-y plane), is located at 30 cm^{-1} at 4.5 K. The frequency of the soft mode decreases as the temperature increases, and at around 17.5 K anti-crossing takes place with a lower frequency mode. Another temperature insensitive low-lying mode at 11 cm^{-1} at 4.5 K becomes Raman-inactive above T_2. While this mode seems to be associated with the phase transition at T_2, the nature of this mode is yet to be clarified.

In the $z(yx)y$ spectrum, a temperature-dependent mode found at 33 cm^{-1} at 4.2 K was interpreted as the soft mode for the phase transition at T_1 by Bree and Edelson (1977). However, this interpretation has been questioned by Wada et al. (1977a,b,c).

4. $A_2B_2O_7$ Oxides and BaMnF$_4$

The recently discovered structural phase transitions in the $A_2B_2O_7$-type oxide compounds with a perovskite slab structure such as $Sr_2Nb_2O_7$ and $Sr_2Ta_2O_7$ have been studied by Raman spectroscopy (Kojima et al., 1979a,b; 1980). $Sr_2Nb_2O_7$ undergoes successive transitions at 1320 and $-156°C$ (Nanamatsu et al., 1975). At $T_c = 1320°C$, the structure changes from orthorhombic D_{2h} to orthorhombic C_{2v}. Below T_c, spontaneous polarization appears along the c axis. Subsequent elastic compliance measurements and dielectric measurements (Nanamatsu et al., 1975) as well as investigations using electron microscope techniques (Ohi et al., 1979) inferred that an incommensurate structure, modulated with a wavevector at $K = \pm(1 - \delta)a^*/2$ occurs below 220°C. Here a^* denotes a reciprocal lattice vector in the high temperature phase. In $Sr_2Nb_2O_7$, a soft optical phonon in the incommensurate phase has been observed in the $b(cc)b$ scattering geometry (Kojima et al., 1980). The level repulsion and the intensity transfer between the soft mode and another low frequency mode have also been observed. The uncoupled soft-mode frequency ω_s has been found to follow the relation: $\omega_s = A(T'_c - T)^\beta$, where $T'_c = 215°C$, $\beta = 0.38 \pm 0.2$. Pressure-dependent measurements have also been carried out, but no remarkable pressure effect has been found (Kojima and Nakamura, 1980). In the case of $Sr_2Ta_2O_7$, which undergoes a phase transition at $T_c = 170°C$ associated with a wavevector at $K = a^*/2$, the low frequency Raman spectrum in the $b(cc)a$ scattering geometry shows a temperature-dependent mode which softens with increasing temperature and vanishes near T_c (Yanamoto et al., 1979). The lineshapes of the mode at various temperatures were fitted by Eq. (3.7). The soft-mode frequency Ω was found to follow a temperature dependence according to $\Omega^2 = a(T_1 - T)$, where $T_1 = T''_c + 55°C$. The damping constant γ was found to increase rapidly with increasing temperature. The fact that the soft phonon frequency did not vanish at the phase transition temperature is likely to be due to the coupling of the soft mode with an acoustic phonon. However, the detailed coupling mechanism is unclear at present. Brillouin scattering studies of these types of compounds should be useful for elucidating the details of the coupling mechanisms. Brillouin scattering studies of such incommensurate transitions are scarce. An exception is the recent Rayleigh–Brillouin scattering study of BaMnF$_4$ by Lyons and Guggenheim (1979) near its incommensurate phase transition at $T_i = 247$ K that shows an anomalous dispersion ($\sim 4\%$) in the longitudinal acoustic mode for $K \parallel c$, in addition to a central peak with a width given by $\Gamma = D_1 q^2$, $D_1 = 0.14 \pm 0.02$ cm^2/s. This is identified as due to coupling between the LA phonon and the soft mode (the amplitude mode), where the latter contains a relaxing self-energy in accordance with a diffusion process.

This interpretation differs from that of Bechtle and Scott (1977) in which the incommensurate phase transition is explained in terms of the depolarized component of the light scattering spectrum.

D. Improper Ferroelectric Transitions

1. Hg_2Cl_2

Hg_2Cl_2 represents another type of improper ferroelastic phase transition. It undergoes a structural phase transition from tetragonal (D_{4h}^{17}) to ortho-rhombic at $T_c = 185$ K. The soft mode is not active in first-order Raman scattering above T_c, as indicated by its weak intensity. The weak tempera-ture-dependent Raman spectral line is associated with second-order scatter-ing from a transverse acoustic mode at the x-point of the first Brillouin zone in the tetragonal phase (Barta et $al.$, 1977a,b). Such an interpretation is confirmed by neutron scattering which displays a spectral line having a frequency about one-half of the Raman frequency (Benoit et $al.$, 1978). Brillouin scattering in Hg_2Cl_2 above and below T_c also supports the hypoth-esis that the transition is induced by the condensation of a transverse acous-tic mode at the Brillouin zone boundary. Using mean field theory and writing the free energy density as

$$\phi = \tfrac{1}{2}\alpha(\eta_1^2 + \eta_2^2) + \tfrac{1}{4}\beta_1(\eta_1^4 + \eta_2^4) + \tfrac{1}{4}\beta_2\eta_1^2\eta_2^2$$
$$+ \tfrac{1}{2}C_{11}(S_1^2 + S_2^2) + \tfrac{1}{2}C_{33}S_3^2 + C_{12}S_1S_2 + C_{13}(S_1 + S_2)S_3$$
$$+ \tfrac{1}{2}C_{66}S_6^2 + \tfrac{1}{2}C_{44}(S_4^2 + S_5^2)$$
$$+ [a(S_1 + S_2) + bS_3 + cS_6]\eta_1^2 + [a(S_1 + S_2) + bS_3 - cS_6]\eta_2^2. \quad (3.19)$$

An et $al.$ (1977) have calculated all of the static elastic constants above and below T_c as a function of temperature. In Eq. (3.19), η_1 and η_2 are the two order parameters associated with the transition. In the orthorhombic phase, only one of the two conditions $\eta_1 \neq 0$, $\eta_2 = 0$ or $\eta_1 = 0$, $\eta_2 \neq 0$ is realized. Although the calculated values are strictly valid at zero frequency, the results are in good agreement with experiments, thus indicating that the effect of dispersion is insignificant in Hg_2Cl_2.

2. Trissarcosine Calcium Chloride (TSCC) and Related Crystals

Another example of a second-order phase transition is observed in TSCC (trissarcosine calcium chloride) involving a transition from an orthorhom-bic paraelectric ($D_{2h}^{16} - Pnma$) to a monoclinic ($C_{2v}^9 - P2_1a$) ferroelectric phase at $T_c = 13 = $ K. Several aspects of the physical properties of this compound have been reviewed by Windsch (1976). Raman and Brillouin scattering studies of the phase transition in TSCC have been reported recently by Prokhorova *et al.* (1980). An oscillatory soft mode with $A_1(y)$ symmetry below T_c (y being the ferroelectric axis) was observed. The soft mode is inactive above T_c and becomes active below T_c because of a doubling of the unit cell. The spectra as well as the peak frequency and linewidth of the longitudinal (LO) and transverse optical (TO) components of the soft mode are shown in Fig. 18. The TO component is stronger in the $x(yy)\bar{x}$ than in the $x(zz)y$ geometry. We note that while far away from T_c the soft mode is clearly underdamped, strong damping occurs in the vicinity of the phase transition. The temperature dependence of the soft-mode frequency, ω in the temperature interval $0.6 \leq T/T_c \leq 0.85$ follows the relation: $\omega \propto (T_c - T)^{0.42}$. Brillouin scattering data show an anomaly in C_{11} and C_{22} on both sides of T_c; this result lends support to the interpretation that the interaction mechanism associated with the phase transition above T_c involves two soft modes at the Brillouin zone boundary and a longitudinal acoustic phonon (a three-phonon process) near the zone center.

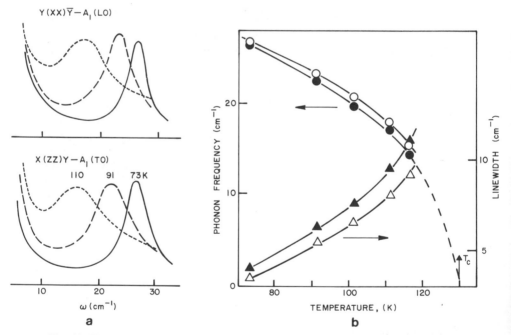

Fig. 18. The temperature dependence of the spectra (a) as well as the peak frequency and linewidth of the longitudinal ($\bigcirc$, $\triangle$) and the transverse ($\bullet$, $\blacktriangle$) optical components of the soft mode (b) in TSCC. (From Prokhorova *et al.,* 1980. Used with the permission of Gordon & Breach Science Publication, Inc.)

Raman scattering studies of TSCC have also been published by Brunel *et al.* (1980). In this work, in addition to the normal and deuterated TSCC crystals, the Raman spectra of a $TSCC_{1-x}Br_x$ mixed crystal have also been studied. They have demonstrated that the LO–TO splitting is present at 80 K and the splitting decreases with increasing temperature. At 95 K, it is less than 1.8 cm^{-1}, but it becomes undetectable around 100 K. For both normal TSCC and $TSCC_{1-x}Br_x$ ($x = 0.25$), the best fit of the soft-mode frequency ω is given by $\omega \sim [(T_c - T)/T_c]^{0.33}$. This result is in agreement with the dielectric constant measurement (Sorge and Straube, 1979). However, the authors have pointed out that due to the poor quality of the crystal in the temperature range ($T_c - 20$ K), they do not have confidence in the value of the critical exponent extracted from the data.

It should be pointed out that Prokhorova *et al.* (1980) have explicitly stated that the phase transition in TSCC is of the order–disorder type. However, since the transition clearly displays an underdamped soft mode below T_c, this designation does not correspond to the generally accepted classification (see discussion in Chapter 1).

The paraelectric–ferroelectric phase transitions in dicalcium strontium propionate (DSP) $[Ca_2Sr(C_2H_5CO_2)_6]$ and dicalcium lead propionate (DLP) $[Ca_2Pb(C_2H_5CO_2)_6]$ have also attracted much attention because of their interesting physical properties (Sorge and Straube, 1979). Three phases (designated I, II, and III in order of decreasing temperature) are observed in these crystals: I, space group D_4^4; II, C_4^2; III, C_4^2. For DSP the phase transition temperature for I and II is 8°C and for II and III, −170°C; whereas for DLP, the corresponding transition temperatures are at 60 and −81°C. Phases II and III are isomorphous with no change in the space group. Raman scattering studies by Nagae *et al.* (1976) have indicated that the phase transition between phase I and II is of the order–disorder type. These authors have challenged the earlier assignment of the 48 cm^{-1} band as the soft mode for the transition (Quilichini and Poulet, 1972). The Raman spectra of DSP and DLP do not show unusual changes across the phase transitions. It is likely that the phase transitions in these compounds involve zone boundary phonons, but no neutron scattering experiments are as yet available to verify this hypothesis.

3. BiVO₄

The phase transition from a tetragonal C_{4h}^6 ($I4_1/a$) to a monoclinic C_{2h}^6 ($I2_1/b$) structure in $BiVO_4$ was recently discovered by Bierlein and Sleight (1975). Raman scattering experiments have revealed a temperature-dependent low frequency zone-center optical mode with B_g symmetry in the high temperature phase and A_g symmetry in the low temperature phase. It is thus suggested that the transition is driven by a B_g zone-center soft mode which is linearly coupled to a soft acoustic mode (Bierlein and Sleight, 1975).

Dudnik *et al.* (1979) have proposed, however, that the phase transition in $BiVO_4$ involves cell doubling. This would make it an improper ferroelastic transition, similar to Hg_2Cl_2 and TSCC previously discussed. This would be the case if the VO_4 group at the center of the unit cell is slightly rotated or translated relative to the VO_4 groups at the cell corners, a situation which is very difficult to establish by structural analysis alone. Benyuan *et al.* (1981) have studied the Brillouin and Raman spectra of $BiVO_4$ as a function of temperature. They have shown that in the high temperature phase, the doubly degenerate E_g mode splits into two B_g components at low temperature. The coupling of the E_g optical mode with an acoustic mode characteristic of a proper ferroelastic phase transition (similar to the case of benzil discussed previously) is believed to drive the phase transition. In both substances, the order parameter manifests itself as an acoustic mode. Unfortunately, no detailed Brillouin scattering studies to allow the determination of the elastic constants, were carried out by Benyuan *et al.* (1981).

E. Miscellaneous Transitions

1. PbHPO₄

Lavrencic *et al.* (1978) have made Brillouin and Raman scattering studies of the ferroelectric transition in $PbHPO_4$, which occurs at $T_c = 310$ K. The phase transition involves proton ordering in a double well potential as indicated by the large isotopic effect on T_c on replacing hydrogen by deuterium. A broad Rayleigh wing appears in the Raman spectrum which becomes underdamped below 230 K. The scattering maximum decreases in frequency on raising the temperature from above 100 cm^{-1} at 80 K to 60 cm^{-1} at 230 K. This was first thought to be the soft mode involving proton tunneling, but further Brillouin and IR measurements failed to confirm this interpretation. Brillouin scattering shows an anomaly in the hypersonic velocity involving C_{22}. Using the Landau theory which includes a term corresponding to the coupling of the order parameter with the strain $S_{yy}(S_2)$ having a form given by $\eta^2 S_{yy}$, they were able to duplicate the experimental result satisfactorily, provided that a diffusive soft mode with a relaxation time $\tau = \tau_0/(T_c - T)$ was also assumed (Lavrencic *et al.*, 1978). It is proposed that the diffusive soft mode is associated with a very low-lying OH-bending mode, but this is not completely certain. Further studies of this very novel second-order phase transition system would be useful. Qualitatively, the temperature dependence of C_{22} below T_c is similar to that of chloranil, which also involves a coupling term of the $\eta^2 S$ type.

2. Inorganic Phosphates

Preliminary measurements of the elastic constant by Brillouin scattering for aluminum phosphate (AlPO$_4$) as a function of temperature have been performed by Ecolivet and Poignant (1981). The structure of AlPO$_4$ is isomorphic with quartz and similar physical properties have been found in these two crystals. Similar to quartz, the α-phase of AlPO$_4$, which is stable at room temperature, is piezoelectric. The $\alpha \rightarrow \beta$ phase transition for AlPO$_4$ occurs at 588°C, in contrast to 573°C for quartz. The elastic constant C_{33} shows an anomaly at T_c. It is interesting to note that the reduced plot of $C_{33}(T)/C_{33}$ (294 K) versus T/T_c for AlPO$_4$ can be superimposed on that for quartz, indicating that the phase transition mechanism in AlPO$_4$ is similar to that in quartz. Combining the Brillouin result with the Raman data (Scott, 1974) it can be concluded that one of the important mechanisms driving the phase transition in AlPO$_4$ also involves an interaction term of the $\eta^2 S_{zz}$ type.

The rare-earth pentaphosphates, RP_5O_{14} (where R represents one of the rare earths from lanthanum to terbium) crystallize with a monoclinic unit cell ($P2_1/c$), which with increasing temperature undergoes a continuous phase transition to an orthorhombic structure ($T_c = 174$°C for the terbium compound). A soft mode associated with the phase transition is Raman active in both the high and low temperature phases (Fox et al., 1976,1978). In RP_5O_{14}, the soft modes are active both above and below T_c. On both sides of T_c, the squares of the frequencies are proportional to $|T - T_c|$, but the frequencies do not vanish at T_c (Fox et al., 1976,1978). This is due to a strong soft mode- (or order parameter-) strain interaction which keeps the soft-mode frequency large at T_c, a situation quite similar to that of BiVO$_4$ (Kobayashi et al., 1971). No Brillouin scattering study has been carried out for RP_5O_{14}; neither has the mechanism of the phase transition been clarified.

3. Sb$_5$O$_7$I

Penta-antimony-hepta-oxide-iodate (Sb$_5$O$_7$I) displays very interesting properties in that all known polytypes of this crystal family undergo structural phase transitions with transition temperatures T_c ranging between 438 and 481 K and they are all ferroelastic in the low temperature phase. Depending on the stacking sequence and the orientation of successive slabs consisting of antimony and oxygen atoms, centric and acentric polytypes result. The centric crystals are ferroelastic and the acentric ones are both ferroelastic and ferroelectric. The centric two-slab polytype (also called α-Sb$_5$O$_7$I) is abbreviated as 2MC-Sb$_5$O$_7$I (M stands for monoclinic symmetry and C for centric stacking) and the acentric two-slab polytype (also called β-Sb$_5$O$_7$I) is abbreviated as 2MA-Sb$_5$O$_7$I (A for acentric). The mechanism for the phase transition is the same for both the α and β forms. In the high temperature phase, the unit cell contains two formula units of Sb$_5$O$_7$I with the two I atoms located along the hexagonal axis. Below T_c two equivalent I atoms in neighboring unit cells translate alternately in opposite directions normal to the hexagonal axis. The iodine displacements in the oxygen sublattice result in a doubling of the unit cell and yield a monoclinic low temperature structure. The order parameter of the phase transition is expected to transform according to the threefold star at the M point in the Brillouin zone. Thus, the order parameter will have three components and is expected to couple quadratically to the elastic strain, thereby yielding a ferroelastic low temperature structure. In addition, in the 2MA-polytype, due to the lack of inversion symmetry of the hexagonal phase, coupling of the order parameter to the electric polarization is allowed by symmetry, thereby yielding the ferro-electric properties of these crystals.

Temperature-dependent Raman scattering measurements of β-Sb$_5$O$_7$I do not show any evidence for a soft mode (Prettl *et al.*, 1979), in contrast with the case of the α form, in which a heavily damped soft mode is observed near T_c. However, in both the α and β forms, the phase transition is accompanied by a strongly temperature-dependent quasielastic scattering whose intensity reaches a maximum around T_c and decreases above T_c (Prettl *et al.*, 1975; Prettl and Rieder, 1976) due to decreasing order parameter–elastic strain coupling.

The phase transition temperature in all Sb$_5$O$_7$I-prototype crystals is very sensitive to the presence of arsenic. Substitution of Sb by As lowers T_c by 50 – 100 K (Nitsche *et al.*, 1977). The reason for this effect is not known at present.

The intensities of some low frequency Raman bands are sensitive to temperature variations. The relation between the intensity of Raman lines activated by the phase transition and the order parameter can be deduced from the Landau theory. The intensity of zone boundary modes behaves like η^2, the intensity of the Γ-point phonon which is inactive in Raman scattering but activated by the phase transition goes like η^4. These results for β-Sb$_5$O$_7$I are in agreement with experiment. A doubly degenerate E' mode at the Γ point of the hexagonal structure above T_c splits into two A' modes below the transition temperature. The frequency of the splitting is found to be proportional to the square of the order parameter. No Brillouin scattering experiments have been carried out in this system.

4. Boracites

Structural and magnetic transitions in nickel iodine boracite ($Ni_3B_7O_{13}I$) have been investigated with the Raman scattering technique by Murray and Lockwood (1978). Most of the boracites which are paraelectric at room temperature and have the formula $M_3B_7O_{13}X$ (M being a divalent metal and X is a halogen) undergo a first-order phase transition to become ferroelectric on cooling. Many transition metal boracites also become antiferromagnetic at temperatures below T_c. Because the electric and magnetic properties are coupled, there is considerable interest in possible device applications for the boracites. An excellent review of boracite properties is given by Nelmes (1974). The primary order parameter in the high temperature cubic phase is associated with a zone boundary X-point doubly degenerate mode. In $Ni_3B_7O_{13}I$ (abbreviated as Ni-I), the ferroelectric and magnetic phase transition temperature are coincident at $T_c = 68$ K (Nelmes, 1974). Below T_c the structure is orthorhombic ($C_{2v}^5 - Pca2_1$). A further transition to a monoclinic structure ($C_s^2 - Pa$) at 10 K has been postulated (Al'shin and Betrurov, 1976). Raman spectra of paraelectric Ni-I have been reported previously by Murray and Lockwood (1978a). Results of temperature-dependent light scattering studies have been reported by the same authors in a subsequent paper (Murray and Lockwood, 1978b). This paper provides evidence for the 68 K transition and confirms the structural phase transition at 10K. Below T_c, the order parameter associated with the X-point zone boundary mode splits to produce two critical modes of A_1 and A_2 symmetries. Since the unit cell doubles below T_c, in the new folded Brillouin zone these become $\mathbf{K} = 0$ modes and appear in the $\alpha_{x'x'}$ and $\alpha_{y'x'}$ spectra as low frequency bands ($\omega < 250$ cm^{-1}) with a marked temperature dependence below and close to T_c. Here x' is along the [110] direction of the crystal. Such modes have been observed in $Cr_3B_7O_{13}Cl$ at 149.5 cm^{-1} (A_1) and 91 cm^{-1} (A_2) (Lockwood, 1976), and in $Ca_3B_7O_{13}Cl$ at 136.0 cm^{-1} (A_1) and 67 cm^{-1} (A_2) (Lockwood and Syme, 1978). In $Ni_3B_7O_{13}Cl$, tentative assignments for the A_1 critical mode is at about 194 cm^{-1} on the side of the 120 cm^{-1} line and the A_2 soft mode cannot be clearly identified due to the spectral complexity in the low frequency range, but is probably in the 40–80 cm^{-1} region.

The phase transition near 10 K also affects the Raman spectrum. In addition to the complex and dramatic changes occurring in the $\alpha_{x'z}$ and $\alpha_{y'z}$ spectra, which are totally different from those observed in the orthorhombic phase, an apparent antiresonance dip at 135 cm^{-1} in the $\alpha_{y'z}$ spectrum is also present. However, due to the complexity in the line profile, detailed analysis of the spectral feature in this region is difficult.

In Ni-I, at temperatures above T_c (about 130 K) there are anomalies in the magnetic properties of Ni-I (Will and Morche, 1977). This has been attributed to short-range magnetic ordering (Quezel and Schmid, 1968). No evidence of long-range magnetic ordering in the form of a new excitation has been detected, thus suggesting that the one-magnon energy is very low in this system.

5. Mixed Crystal Systems

Raman studies of rare earth aluminate compounds (e.g., LaAlO$_3$, EuAlO$_3$, and SmAlO$_3$) have been previously carried out by Scott and co-workers (see, e.g., Scott and Remeika, 1970). Alain et al. (1975,1977) have recently taken up further Raman studies of this type of materials including the mixed crystal Sm$_{0.8}$La$_{0.2}$AlO$_3$ (Alain et al., 1979). Raman spectra at high temperature have been analyzed in terms of the first-order phase transition from the orthorhombic D_{2h}^{16} phase to the rhombohedral D_{3d}^6 phase. The study has provided evidence for the A_{1g} and B_{3g} soft modes observed in the low temperature phase of SmAlO$_3$ and EuAlO$_3$; however, due to a strong background near the low frequency region, conclusive results have not been obtained. The mixed crystal Raman data support the phase transformation from orthorhombic to rhombohedral, and then to cubic. Combining the results of earlier studies with that of the mixed compound shows that the A_g and B_{3g} modes in the low temperature phase have the properties of the soft E_g mode in the high temperature phase, whereas the A_g soft mode at 266 cm^{-1} can be correlated with the A_g mode below T_c. The result of the recent studies has thus corrected the assignments made in the previous work (Scott and Remeika, 1970). However, additional studies are still needed to resolve the complexity of the low frequency Raman spectra of this class of compounds.

The vanadium doped lead phosphate compounds Pb$_3$(P$_x$V$_{1-x}$O$_4$)$_2$ undergo a phase transition from a rhombohedral to a monoclinic phase. The critical temperature and the latent heat are strongly dependent on the amount of vanadium (Torres et al., 1980). The critical temperature and the latent heat of Pb$_3$(P$_x$V$_{1-x}$O$_4$)$_2$ as a function of x for $1 \leq x \leq 0.723$ are shown in Table I. With increasing amount of vanadium, the first-order character of the transition in pure Pb$_3$(PO$_4$)$_2$ transforms gradually to second order. This behavior suggests the existence of a tricritical point near $x = 0.7$. Qualitatively, the effect of vanadium substitution is similar to the effect of applying pressure, which also depresses the transition temperature (Decker et al., 1979). Brillouin scattering measurements performed above and below T_c of Pb$_3$(PO$_4$)$_2$ show a significant anomaly in C_{11} and C_{22} in the vicinity of T_c. However, similar experiments have not been carried out for the mixed compounds. At the present time, there is no clear idea about the phase transition mechanism in this system.

The effects of impurities on phase transitions and the behavior of soft

TABLE I

THE DEPENDENCE OF THE CRITICAL TEMPERATURE AND
LATENT HEAT ON THE VANADIUM CONCENTRATION FOR
$Pb_3(P_xV_{1-x}O_4)_2$

Composition	Temperature of transition (°C)	Transition heat (cal/g)
$Pb_3(PO_4)_2$	180	0.17
$Pb_3(P_{0963} V_{0037} O_4)_2$	163	0.075
$Pb_3(P_{0921} V_{0079} O_4)_2$	133	0.052
$Pb_3(P_{084} V_{016} O_4)_2$	61	0.037
$Pb_3(P_{0797} V_{0216} O_4)_2$	38	
$Pb_3(P_{0747} V_{0253} O_4)_2$	− 36.5	0.002
$Pb_3(P_{0733} V_{0267} O_4)_2$	− 45.5	
$Pb_3(P_{0723} V_{0277} O_4)_2$	− 47.5	

modes have received considerable recent interest. A recent review of the dynamics of phase transitions by Halperin and Varma (1976) has also dealt with this topic. Detailed Raman scattering studies of the effects of Nb and Li on the $KTaO_3Nb$ and $KTaO_3Li$ systems were recently reported by Prater et al. (1981,1982). Replacement of Ta by Nb in the $KTa_{1-x}Nb_xO_3$ system for $x \leq 0.05$ depresses the transition temperature. For example, for $KTa_{0.98}Nb_{0.02}O_3$, when the temperature is lowered below T_c (about 28 K in this sample), an intense peak appears. This peak is at about 20 cm^{-1} at 16.5 K and it increases in intensity and moves up in frequency as the temperature is decreased below T_c. For the sample containing 3 at. % Nb, this line splits into two peaks when the temperature is lowered below 4.2 K. The peaks correspond to the Raman-active transverse optical modes in the rhombohedral symmetry ferroelectric phase. As has been discussed several times before, in an ideal soft-mode induced phase transition, the Raman-active soft-mode frequency should approach zero as the temperature approaches T_c from below. In all samples containing Nb as impurities, the square of the frequency of this temperature-dependent low frequency TO mode cannot be extrapolated linearly to zero at T_c. In the cubic paraelectric phase, first-order Raman scattering is symmetry forbidden and these features disappear as expected.

While the soft zone-center TO mode decreases in frequency as the Nb concentration increases; as far as the TO branch energy region is concerned, the presence of Nb shows no evidence of causing symmetry-breaking. Disorder-induced scattering is observed from the coupled TA and TO branches. This mechanism has been proposed to account for the temperature-dependent low frequency features which have been attributed in the past to an impurity resonance mode and two-phonon scattering.

Replacement of K by Li also produces interesting effects. First the transition temperature increases rapidly with increasing Li concentration and reaches a value of $T_c = 70$ K at $x = 0.054$. The intensities of the disorder-induced scattering features observed for pure $KTaO_3$ also increases as the Li concentration increases. In particular, a low frequency feature, which was previously associated with a Li resonance mode appears to be scattering from the coupled TA and TO branches due to disorder induced by the lithium impurity. Finally, the presence of Li impurities stiffens the TO branch at the zone center, and the ferroelectric phase results from an order–disorder transition of the off-center lithium ions.

6. Pressure-Induced Transitions

Barium sodium niobate (BNN) $(Ba_2NaNb_5O_{15})$ undergoes successive phase transitions at about 560, 300, and $-168°C$ (Prater *et al.*, 1982). Both phases above 300 and below $-168°C$ have the same space group $C_{4v}^2 - P4bm$, and the intermediate phase (III) between 300 and $-168°C$ has the structure with the point group $C_{2v} - mm2$ and is ferroelastic. The crystals known to have such an intermediate phase are Rochelle salt and terbium-gadolinium vanadate (Jora and Shirane, 1962). Raman spectra of BNN crystals under pressure up to 35 kbar, using a diamond anvil device, have been studied by Kojima *et al.* (1979a,b). The most interesting features related to the pressure-induced effects is the coupled mode behavior connected with the deformation of the NbO_6 octahedrons under pressure, and the anomalous hardening and intensity decrease of the 32 cm^{-1} B_2 mode with increasing pressure. However, whether or not these pressure-induced spectral changes can be correlated with the disappearance of ferroelasticity at high pressure (above 22 kbar) of BNN at room temperature (Kojima *et al.*, 1978) remains unclear.

The pressure-induced phase transition in $K_2Hg(CN)_4$ has been investigated by Raman scattering (Wong, 1981). In the 0–5 Kbar pressure range, three pressure effects on the Raman spectrum are observed:

(1) Splitting of the CN stretching band;
(2) A large pressure-induced shift of the internal C—Hg—C bending mode;
(3) Softening of the lattice mode at 44 cm^{-1}.

These effects are considered to be associated with the distortion of the $Hg(CN)_4^{2-}$ tetrahedra. The spectral changes below 5 Kbar are continuous, but drastic changes occur at 5 and 12 Kbar. This indicates that phase transitions occur at these pressures. A phase change takes place at room temperature at ~ 1.5 Kbar. The spectral change is similar to that observed in the I–II transition at 1 bar and at 110.5 K, which appears to be a pseudo-second-order phase transition (Bolton and Prasad, 1978).

At low pressure and 0 K para-hydrogen and ortho-deuterium are in spherically symmetric states. At very high pressure, it is predicted that the anisotropic interactions deform the molecular distribution so that the molecules spontaneously enter an orientationally ordered state. By means of high pressure Raman scattering in a diamond anvil cell, a phase transition in which the molecules, which are spherically symmetric at low pressure, go into an orientationally ordered state has been observed in $O - D_2$ at 278 ± 5 Kbar. Line broadening of the roton bands for $p \gtrsim 200$ Kbar is interpreted as a precursor of this transition (Silvera and Wijngaarden, 1981).

7. $C_6H_5NH_3Br$

The ferroelectric phase transition in the $C_6H_5NH_3Br$ crystal at $T_c = 27°C$ has been studied by Raman scattering (Hattori et al., 1980). No $K = 0$ soft optical phonon is observed in this experiment. This result does not favor the proposed mechanism that the phase transition is due to the instability of the transverse optical B_{2g} phonon coupled to the S_5 (S_{zx}) strain component of the same symmetry (Terauchi et al., 1980). It is possible that the phase transition is associated with the orientational order–disorder of the NH_3^+ ionic group, as proposed by Suga (1961).

8. Metal-Insulator and Magnetic Transitions

Raman scattering measurements of phase transitions of V_2O_3 and of Cr-doped V_2O_3 have been performed by Kuroda and Fan (1977) and Tatsuyama and Fan (1980). In V_2O_3, a metal-to-insulator, crystallographic- and antiferromagnetic-ordering transitions take place concurrently at $T_c \sim 150$ K. In addition to the frequency shift and splitting of the spectral lines due to the change of crystallographic structure (from D_{3d} to C_{2h} symmetry below T_c), a magnon excitation peak located at about 440 cm^{-1} is observed below T_c. The intensity of this peak decreases strongly with increasing temperature and vanishes near T_c. This peak is probably associated with the dynamics of antiferromagnetic ordering and is worthy of additional investigation. Doping by Cr affects the electrical resistivity, but it does not cause significant change in the frequencies of the phonons and the magnon-Raman spectra. The temperature dependence of the frequency shift of each line of Cr-doped V_2O_3 is slightly different from pure V_2O_3. This is probably related to the slight change in the structure and lattice dimensions of the material.

V. CONCLUDING REMARKS

To conclude this chapter, it should be emphasized that despite the fact that the materials for this review were selected mostly from publications which appeared since 1977, due to space limitation as well as the personal interest of the author, several interesting yet important papers have been left out. Most of the discussion presented in this chapter is centered on the low frequency lattice modes with special emphasis on the soft modes. However, it should be pointed out that in the course of the last few years, it has been discovered that in several systems which undergo continuous phase transitions, the complete vanishing of the soft phonon frequency is preempted by the appearance of an additional central peak which grows rapidly in intensity as T_c is approached (cf. discussion in Chapter 1). The appearance of the central peak is reflected by the formation of precursor order which is closely associated with the hard modes induced by the ordering of the soft-mode coordinates (Bruce et al., 1980). The central peak displays a higher degree of temporal and spatial coherence than that associated with the soft mode (Bruce et al., 1980). Molecular dynamics studies of a simple model system show that the central peak effect is intrinsic to the ideal dynamics of a displacive system near its critical point (Schneider and Stoll, 1976; Bruce, 1978). Bruce et al. (1980) have provided detailed experimental studies in $KMnF_3$ and $RbCaF_3$ and have demonstrated in these systems the connection of the precursor order and the central peak as well as phonon sidebands of the soft-mode spectral function. The precursor order, dominant near the phase transition, is responsible for the persistence of quasi-first-order hard-mode features above the transition temperature in many solids undergoing displacive phase transitions. Clearly, the technique of Raman and Rayleigh–Brillouin light scattering from the fluctuations in both soft and hard modes has demonstrated itself to be an invaluable tool for the study of the dynamics of structural phase transitions in solids.

ACKNOWLEDGMENT

This chapter was prepared by the author during a part of his stay as Chevron Visiting Professor in the Division of Chemistry and Chemical Engineering at the California Institute of Technology.

REFERENCES

Akiyama, K., Morioka, Y., and Nakagawa, I. (1980). *J. Phys. Soc. Jpn.* **48,** 898.
Akiyama, K., Morioka, Y., and Nakagawa, I. (1981a). *Bull. Chem. Soc. Jpn.* **54,** 1662.
Akiyama, K., Morioka, Y., and Nakagawa, I. (1981b). *Bull. Chem. Soc. Jpn.* **54,** 1667.
Alain, P., and Piriou, B., (1975). *Solid State Commun.* **10,** 35.

Alain, P., and Piriou, B., (1977). *J. Phys. (Paris)* **38**, 17–389.
Alain, P., and Contures, J. P., and Piriou, B. (1979). *J. Raman Spect.* **8**, 89.
Al'shin, B. I., and Baturov, L. N. (1976). *Sov. Phys. Solid State (Eng. Transl.)* **18**, 2062.
An, C. X., Hauret, G., and Chapelle, J. P. (1977). *Solid State Commun.* **24**, 443.
Andrade, P. da R., Prasad Rao, A. O., Katiyar, R. S., and Porto, S. P. S. (1973). *Solid State Commun.* **12**, 847.
Arthur, J. W., Lockwood, D. J., and Taylor, W. (1973). *In* "Advances in Raman Spectroscopy" (J. Mathieu, ed.), Chap. 17. Hyeden, London.
Bandour, J. L., Delugeard, Y., Cailleau, H., Sanquer, M., and Zeyen, C. M. E. (1981). *Acta Crystallogr.* **B34**, 1553.
Barta, C., Zadokhin, B. S., Kaplianskii, A. A., and Markov, Yu. F. (1977a). *Pis'ma Zh. Eksp. Teor. Fiz.* **26**, 480.
Barta, C., Zadokhin, B. S., Kaplianskii, A. A., and Markov, Yu. F. (1977b). *Pis'ma Zh. Eksp. Teor. Fiz.* **26**, 347.
Bechtle, D. W., and Scott, J. F. (1977). *J. Phys. C Solid State Phys.* **10**, L209.
Benoit, J. P., An, C. X., Luspin, Y., Chapelle, I. P., and Lefebre, J. (1978). *J. Phys. C* **11**, L721.
Benyuan, G., Copic, M., and Cummins, H. Z. (1981). *Phys. Rev.* **B24**, 4098.
Berger, J., Hauret, G., and Rousseau, M. (1978). *Solid State Commun.* **25**, 569.
Bierlein, J. D., and Sleight, A. W. (1975). *Solid State Commun.* **16**, 69.
Boissier, M., Vacher, R., Fontaine, D., and Pick, R. M. (1978). *J. Phys. (Paris)* **39**, 205.
Bolton, B. A., and Prasad, P. N. (1978). *Chem. Phys.* **35**, 331.
Born, M., and Huang, K. (1962). *In* "Dynamical Theory of Crystal Lattices". Univ. Press, London.
Bree, A., and Edelson, M. (1977). *Chem. Phys. Lett.* **46**, 500.
Bruce, A. D. (1978). *In* "Solitons and Condensed Matter Physics" (A. R. Bishop and T. Schneider, eds.), pp. 116–134. Springer-Verlag, Berlin.
Bruce, A. D., Taylor, W., and Murray, A. F. (1980). *J. Phys. C: Solid State Phys.* **13**, 483.
Brunel, L. C., Bureau, J. C., Wartewig, S., and Windsch, W. (1980). *Chem. Phys. Lett.* **72**, 119.
Buhay, H., Sokoloff, J. B., and Perry, C. H. (1978). *J. Chem. Phys.* **68**, 5139.
Burns, G., and Scott, G. F. (1970). *Phys. Rev. Lett.* **25**, 167.
Chapelle, J. P., and Benoit, J. P. (1977). *J. Phys. C: Solid State Phys.* **10**, 145.
Chapuis, G. (1977). *Phys. Status Solidi* **A43**, 203.
Chihara, H., and Nakamura, N. (1973). *J. Chem. Phys.* **59**, 5392.
Chihara, H., Nakamura, N., and Tachiki, M. (1971). *J. Chem. Phys.* **54**, 3640.
Chihara, H., Nakamura, N., and Tachiki, M. (1973). *J. Chem. Phys.* **59**, 5389.
Cho, M., and Yagi, T. (1980). *J. Phys. Soc. Jpn.* **49**, 429.
Cho, M., and Yagi, T. (1981). *J. Phys. Soc. Jpn.* **50**, 543.
Christoe, C. W., and Iqbal, Z. (1977). *J. Phys. Chem. Solids* **3**, 1391.
Coogan, C. G., and Gutowsky, H. S. (1964). *J. Chem. Phys.* **40**, 3419.
Couzi, M., Daoud, A., and Perset, R. (1977). *Phys. Status Solidi* **A41**, 271.
Daubert, J., Knorr, K., Dultz, W., Jex, H., and Currat, R. (1976). *J. Phys. C* **9**, L389.
Daunt, S. J., and Shurvell, M. F. (1975). *J. Raman Spectrosc.* **4**, 205.
Decker, D. L., Petersen, S., Debray, D., and Lampert, M. (1979). *Phys. Rev.* **B19**, 3552.
Dudnik, E. F., Gene, V. V., and Maushkina, I. E. (1979). *Bull. Acad. Sci. USSR, Phys. Ser.* **43**, 149.
Dultz, W. (1974). *Solid State Commun.* **15**, 595.
Dultz, W. (1976). *In* "Molecular Spectroscopy of Dense Phases," p. 211. Elsevier, Amsterdam.
Dultz, W., Durand, D., and Luty, F. (1977). *Ferroelectrics* **16**, 205.
Dvorak, V. (1974). *Ferroelectrics* **7**, 1.

Dworkin, A., and Fuchs, A. (1977). *J. Chem. Phys.* **67**, 1789.
Ecolivet, C. (1981). *Solid State Commun.* **40**, 503.
Ecolivet, C., and Poignant, H. (1981). *Phys. Status Solidi A* **63**, K107.
Ellenson, W. D., and Kjems, J. K. (1977). J. Chem. Phys. **67**, 3619.
Elliott, G. R., and Iqbal, Z. (1975). *J. Chem. Phys.* **63**, 1914.
Esherick, P., and Kohler, B. E. (1973). *J. Chem. Phys.* **59**, 6681.
Fjaer, E., and Samuelsen, E. J. (1981). *Ferroelectrics* **36**, 459.
Fjaer, E., Grip, J., and Samuelsen, E. J. (1980). *Ferroelectrics* **25**, 347.
Fox, D. L., Scott, J. F., and Bridenbaugh, P. M. (1976). *Solid State Commun.* **18**, 111.
Fox, D. L., Scott, J. F., Bridenbaugh, P. M., and Pierce, J. W. (1978). *J. Raman Spectroscopy* **7**, 41.
Franke, E., Le Postollec, M., Mathieu, J. P., and Poulet, H. (1980). *Solid State Commun.* **33**, 155.
Fujimoto, M., Dressel, L. A., and Yu, T. J. (1977). *J. Phys. Chem. Solids* **38**, 97.
Garland, C. W., and Choo, C. K. (1973). *Phys. Rev.* **B8**, 5143.
Geisel, T., and Keller, J. (1975). *J. Chem. Phys.* **62**, 3777.
Gesi, K. (1978). *J. Phys. Soc. Jpn.* **45**, 1431.
Gesi, K., and Iizumi, M. (1978). *J. Phys. Soc. Jpn.* **45**, 1777.
Girard, A., Cailleau, H., Marqueton, Y., and Ecolivet, C. (1978). *Chem. Phys. Lett.* **54**, 479.
Girard, A., Delugeard, Y., Ecolivet, C., and Cailleau, H. (1982). *J. Phys. C.* **15**, 2127.
Girdhar, H. L., Westrum, Jr., E. F., and Wulff, C. A. (1968). *J. Chem. Eng. Data* **13**, 239.
Halperin, B. I., and Varma, C. H. (1976). *Phys. Rev.* **B14**, 4030.
Hanson, D. M. (1975). *J. Chem. Phys.* **63**, 5046.
Harley, R. T., *et al.* (1974). *J. Phys.* **67**, 3145.
Hasebe, K., and Tanisaki, S. (1977). *J. Phys. Soc. Jpn.* **42**, 568.
Hattori, A., Wada, M., Sawada, A., and Ishibashi, Y. (1980). *J. Phys. Soc. Jpn.* **49**, 624.
Hauret, G., and Benoit, J. P. (1982). *Ferroelectrics* **40**, 1.
Haussuhl, S. (1973). *Solid State Commun.* **13**, 147.
Henkel, W., Pelzl, J., Hock, K.-H., and Thomas, H. (1980). *Z. Phys.* **B37**, 321.
Higashigaki, Y., and Wang, C. H. (1979). *J. Chem. Phys.* **79**, 3813.
Hirotsu, S. (1971). *J. Phys. Soc. Jpn.* **31**, 552.
Hirotsu, S., Kunii, J., Yauramoto, I., Miyamota, M., and Mitsui, T. (1982). *J. Phys. Soc. Jpn.* **50**, 3392.
Hollander, F., Semmingson, D., and Koetzle, T. F. (19770. *J. Chem. Phys.* **67**, 4825.
Hosea, T. J., Lockwood, D. J., and Taylor, W. (1979). *J. Phys. C* **12**, 387.
Hutton, J., Nelmes, R. J., Meyer, G. M., and Eiriksson, V. R. (1979). *J. Phys. C* **12**, 5393.
Iizumi, M., Axe, J. D., and Shirane, G. (1977). *Phys. Rev.* **B15**, 4392.
Iqbal, Z. (1976). *Chem. Phys. Lett.* **40**, 41.
Iqbal, Z., and Christoe, C. W. (1975). *Solid State Commun.* **17**, 71.
Iqbal, Z., and Christoe, C. W. (1976). *Ferroelectrics* **12**, 177.
James, D.W., Carrick, T., and Leong, W. H. (1974). *Chem. Phys. Lett.* **28**, 117.
Jona, F., and Shirane, G. (1962). "Ferroelectric Crystals." Pergamon, New York.
Karajamaki, E., Laiho, R., Levola, T., Kleeman, W., and Schafer, F. J. (1981). *Physica* **111B**, 24.
Karpow, S. V., and Shultin, H. A. (1976). *Sov. Phys. Solid State* **17**, 1915.
Kobayashi, J., Bouillot, J., and Kinoshita, K. (1971). *Phys. Status Solidi B* **47**, 619.
Kojima, S., and Nakamura, T. (1980). *Ferroelectrics* **25**, 589.
Kojima, S., Asaumi, K., Nakamura, T., and Minomura, S. (1978). *J. Phys. Soc. Jpn.* **45**, 1433.
Kojima, S., NaKamura, T., Asaumi, K., Takashige, M., and Minomura, (1979a). *Solid State Comm.* **29**, 779.

Kojima, S., Ohi, K., Takashige, M., Nakamura, T., and Kakinuma, H. (1979b). *Solid State Commun.* **31**, 755.

Kojima, S., Ohi, K., and Nakamura, T. (1980). *Solid State Commun.* **35**, 79.

Krasser, W., Buchenau, U., and Haussuhl, S. (1976). *Solid State Commun.* **18**, 287.

Kruger, K., Maier, H.-D., Petersson, J., and Unruh, H. G. (1980). *Ferroelectrics* **25**, 621.

Kuroda, N., and Fan, H. Y. (1977). *Phys. Rev.* **B16**, 5003.

Landau, L. O. and Liftshitz, E. M. (1970). "Statistical Physics." 2nd Ed. Addison-Wesley, Reading, Mass. p. 424.

Lavrencic, B. B., Copic, M., and Zgonik, M. (1978). *Ferroelectrics* **21**, 325.

Lockwood, D. J. (1976). *Solid State Commun.* **18**, 115.

Lockwood, D. J., and Syme, R. W. G. (1978). "Proceedings of the 4th International Meeting on Ferroelectricity," Leningrad.

Lockwood, D. J., and Torrie, B. H. (1978). *J. Phys. C: Solid State Phys.* **7**, 2729.

Lynn, J. W., Patterson, H. H., Shirange, G., and Wheeler, R. G. (1978). *Solid State Commun.* **27**, 859.

Lyons, K. B., and Guggenheim, H. J. (1979). *Solid State Commun.* **31**, 285.

Mackenzie, G. A., Arthur, J. W., and Pawley, G. S. (1977). *J. Phys. C: Solid State Phys.* **10**, 1133.

McMurdie, H. F., de Groot, J., Moris, M., and Swanson, H. E. (1969). *J. Res. Natl. Bur. Stand. Sect. A.* **73**, 621.

Matsuo, T., Suga, H., and Seki, S., (1968). *Bull. Chem. Soc. Jpn.* **41**, 583.

Michel, K. H., and Naudts, J. (1977a). *J. Chem. Phys.* **67**, 547.

Michel, K. H., and Naudts, J. (1977b). *Phys. Rev. Lett.* **39**, 212.

Michel, K. H., and Rowe, J. M. (1980). *Phys. Rev.* **B22**, 1417.

Midorikawa, M., Ishibashi, Y., and Takagi, Y. (1979). *J. Phys. Soc. Jpn.* **46**, 1240.

Midorikawa, M., Sawada, A., and Ishibashi, Y. (1980). *J. Phys. Soc. Jpn.* **48**, 1202.

Mlik, Y., Daoud, A., and Couzi, M. (1980). *J. Phys. Status Solidi* **59**, 183.

Mokhlisse, R., Couzi, M., and Wang, C. H. (1982). *J. Chem. Phys.* **77**, 1138.

Morfee, R. G. S., Staveley, L. A. K., Walters, S. T., and Wigley, D. L. (1960). *J. Phys. Chem. Solids* **13**, 132.

Murray, A. F., and Lockwood, D. J. (1978a). *J. Phys. C: Solid State Phys.* **11**, 2349.

Murray, A. F., and Lockwood, D. J. (1978b). *J. Phys. C: Solid State Phys.* **11**, 4651.

Nagae, Y., Wada, M., Ishibashi, Y., and Takagi, Y. (1976). *J. Phys. Soc. Jpn.* **41**, 1659.

Nakashina, S., and Balkanski, M. (1976). *Solid State Commun.* **19**, 1225.

Nanamatsu, S., Kimura, M., and Kawamura, T. (1975). *J. Phys. Soc. Jpn.* **38**, 817.

Negita, K., Nakamara, N., and Chihara, H. (1980). *Solid State Commun.* **34**, 949.

Nelmes, R. J. (1974). *J. Phys. C: Solid State Phys.* **7**, 3840.

Nitsche, R., Kramer, V., Schuhmacher, M., and Bussmann, A. (1977). *J. Cryst. Growth* **42**, 549.

Ohi, K., Kimura, M., Ishida H., and Kakinuma, H. (1979). *J. Phys. Soc. Jpn.* **46**, 1387.

O'Leary, G. P., and Wheeler, R. G. (1970). *Phys. Rev.* **B1**, 4409.

O'Reilly, D. E., Peterson, E. M., Scheie, C. E., and Kadaba, P. K. (1973). *J. Chem. Phys.* **58**, 3018.

Owens, F. J. (1979). *Chem. Phys. Lett.* **64**, 116.

Pelzl, J., Engels, P., and Florian, R. (1977). *Phys. Status Solidi* **82**, 145.

Petzelt, J. (1975). *J. Phys. Chem. Solids* **36**, 1005.

Petzelt, J. (1981). *Phase Transitions* **2**, 155.

Pinczuk, A., Burns, G., and Dacol, F. H. (1977). *Solid State Commun.* **24**, 163.

Pinczuk, A., Welber, B., and Dacol, F. H. (1979). *Solid State Commun.* **29**, 515.

Prater, R. L., Chase, L. L., and Boatner, L. A. (1981). *Phys. Rev.* **B23**, 221.

Prater, R. L., Chase, L. L., and Boatner, L. A. (1982). *Phys. Rev.* **B23**, 5904.

Prettl, W., and Rieder, K. H. (1976). *Phys. Rev.* **B14**, 2171.

Prettl, W., Rieder, K. H., and Nitsche, R. N. (1975). *Z. Phys.* **B22**, 49.

Prettl, W., Rieder, K. H., and Nitsche, R. N. (1979). *Z. Phys.* **B32**, 215.

Price, D. L., Rush, J. M., Hinks, D. G., and Susman, S. (1972). *J. Chem. Phys.* **56**, 3697.

Prokhorova, S. D., Smolensky, G. A., Siny, I. G., Kuzminov, E. G., and Mikvabia, V. O. (1980). *Ferroelectrics* **25**, 629.

Quezel, G., and Schmid, H. (1968). *Solid State Commun.* **6**, 447.

Quilichini, M., and Poulet, H. (1972). *Solid State Commun.* **10**, 239.

Raich, J. C., and Bernstein, E. R. (1980). *J. Chem. Phys.* **73**, 1955.

Raich, J. C., and Gillis, N. S. (1976). *J. Chem. Phys.* **65**, 2088.

Regelsberger, M., and Pelzl, J. (1978). *Solid State Commun.* **28**, 783.

Rey-Lafon, M., Loyance, P. L., Boissier, M., and Vacher, R. (1979). *Solid State Commun.* **31**, 69.

Rowe, J. M., Hinks, D G., Price, D. L., Susman, S., and Rush, J. J. (1973). *J. Chem. Phys.* **58**, 2039.

Rowe, J. M. *et al.* (1975). *J. Chem. Phys.* **62**, 4551.

Samuelsen, E. J., and Semmingsen, D. (1977). *J. Phys. Chem. Solids* **38**, 1275.

Samuelsen, E. J., Fjoe, E., and Semmingsen, D. (1979). *J. Phys. C: Solid State Phys.* **12**, 2007.

Sandercock, J. (1971). *In* "Light Scattering in Solids," pp. 9–12. Flammarion, Paris.

Sapriel, J., Boudou, A., and Perigaud, A. (1979). *Phys. Rev.* **B19**, 1484.

Sasane, A., Nakamura, D., and Kubo, M., (1970). *J. Magn. Reson.* **3**, 76.

Satija, S., and Cowley, R. A. (1982). *Phys. Rev.* **B25**, 6765.

Satija, S. K., and Wang, C. H. (1977). *J. Chem. Phys.* **66**, 2221.

Satija, S. K., and Wang, C. H. (1978). *Solid State Commun.* **28**, 617.

Sawada, S., Shiroishi, Y., Yamamoto, A., Takashige, M., and Matsuo, M. (1978a). *J. Phys. Soc. Jpn.* **44**, 687.

Sawada, S., Shiroishi, Y., Yamamoto, Takoshige, M., and Matsuo, M. (1978b). *Phys. Lett.* **67A**, 56.

Schneck, J., Primot, J., Von der Muhll, R., and Ravez, J. (1977). *Solid State Commun.* **27**, 57.

Schneider, T., and Stoll, E. (1976). *Phys. Rev.* **B13**, 1216.

Scott, J. F. (1974). *Rev. Mod. Phys.* **46**, 83.

Semingsen, D. (1973). *Acta Chem. Scand.* **27**, 3961.

Semingsen, D. (1975). *Acta Chem. Scand.* **A29**, 470.

Shiozoki, S., Sawada, A., Ishibashi, Y., and Takagi, Y. (1977). *J. Phys. Soc. Jpn.* **42**, 1229.

Silvera, I. F., and Wijngaarden, (1981). *Phys. Rev. Lett.* **47**, 39.

Sorge, G., and Straube, U. (1979). *Phys. Status Solidi* **519**, 117.

Suga, H. (1961). *Bull. Chem. Soc. Jpn.* **34**, 426.

Swanson, B. I. (1978). *Phys. Status. Solidi A* **47**, K95.

Takashige, M., Nakamura, T., and Sawada, S. (1980a). *Ferroelectrics* **24**, 143.

Takashige, M., *et al.* (1980b). *J. Phys. Soc. Jpn* **48**, 150.

Tang, H. C., and Torrie, B. H. (1978). *J. Phys. Chem. Solids* **39**, 845.

Tatsuyama, C., and Fan, H. Y. (1980). *Phys. Rev.* **B21**, 2977.

Terauchi, H., Sakai, T., and Yamada, Y. (1980). *J. Phys. Soc. Jpn.* **48**, 177.

Toledano, J. C. (1979). *Phys. Rev.* **B20**, 1147.

Toledano, P. (1980. *Ferroelectrics* **25**, 403.

Torres, J., Primot, J., Pougnet, A. M., and Aubree, J. (1980). *Ferroelectrics* **26**, 689.

Unruh, H.-G. (1980). *Ferroelectrics* **25**, 507.

Uwe, H., and Sakudo, T. (1976). *Phys. Rev.* **B13**, 271.

Vacher, R., and Boissier, M. (1981). *Phys. Rev.* **B23**, 215.

Vacher, R., and Boyer, L. (1972). *Phys. Rev.* **B6,** 639.
Wada, M., Sawada, A., Ishibashi, Y., and Takagi, Y. (1977a). *J. Phys. Soc. Jpn.* **42,** 1229.
Wada, M., *et al.* (1977b). *J. Phys. Soc. Jpn.* **43,** 544.
Wada, M., Swada, A., and Ishibashi, Y. (1977c). *J. Phys. Soc. Jpn.* **50,** 737.
Wada, M., Swada, A., and Ishibashi, Y. (1978a). *J. Phys. Soc. Jpn.* **45,** 1429.
Wada, M., Swada, A., Ishibashi, Y., and Takagi, Y. (1978b). *J. Phys. Soc. Jpn.* **45,** 1905.
Wada, M., Swada, A., and Ishibashi, Y. (1979). *J. Phys. Soc. Jpn.* **47,** 1185.
Wada, M., Shichi, H., Sawada, A., and Ishibashi, Y. (1980). *J. Phys. Soc. Jpn.* **49,** 1892.
Wang, C. H., and Satija, S. K. (1977). *J. Chem. Phys.* **67,** 851.
Wang, C. H., and Wright, R. B. (1972). *J. Chem. Phys.* **56,** 2124.
Wang, C. H., and Wright, R. B. (1973). *J. Chem. Phys.* **58,** 2934.
Wang, C. H., Satija, S. K., and Luty, F. (1982). *Chem. Phys. Lett.* **90,** 397.
Will, G., and Morche, H. *J. Phys. C: Solid State Phys.* **10,** 1389.
Windsch, W. (1976). *Ferroelectrics* **12,** 48.
Wong, P. T. T. (1981). *Phys. Rev.* **B23,** 375.
Wong, P. T. T., and Ripmeister, J. A. (1980). *Chem. Phys. Lett.* **72,** 122.
Yacoby, Y. (1976). *Phys. Rev.* **B13,** 4132.
Yacoby, Y., Cowley, R. A., Hosea, T. J., Lockwood, D. J., and Taylor, W. (1978). *J. Phys. C: Solid State Phys.* **11,** 5065.
Yagi, T., Cho, M., and Hidaka, Y. (1979). *J. Phys. Soc. Jpn.* **46,** 1957.
Yagi, T., Cho, M., and Hidaka, Y. (1981). *Ferroelectrics* **36,** 367.
Yanamoto, N., Yagi, K., Honjo, G., Kimura, M., and Kawamura, T. (1979). *J. Phys. Soc. Jpn.* **48,** 1387.
Yoshihara, A., Fujimura, T., and Kamiyoshi, K. (1976). *Phys. Status Solidi A* **34,** 369.
Yoshihara, A., Wilker, W. D., Bernstein, E. R., and Raich, J. C. (1982). *J. Chem. Phys.* **76,** 2064.
Zussman, A., and Alexander, S. (1967). *Solid State Commun.* **5,** 259.

4

Raman and Infrared Spectroscopy of Phase and Conformational Transitions in Biological Systems

Z. IQBAL*

Institute of Inorganic Chemistry
University of Zürich, CH-8057 Zürich, Switzerland

E. WEIDEKAMM

F. Hoffmann-La Roche & Co. Ltd.
Biological Pharmaceutical Research Division
F. Hoffmann-La Roche & Co. Ltd., CH-4002 Basle, Switzerland

* Present address: Corporate Research Center, Allied Corporation, Morristown, New Jersey 07960.

I. INTRODUCTION

This chapter is divided into four principal sections. The first deals with general concepts regarding the structure and architecture of molecular–biological systems, the basic principles, and some new illustrative results of cooperative transitions in such systems. In the latter subsection we also discuss recent ideas and results of transitions in biological systems under nonequilibrium conditions. In the following three sections we then proceed to selectively review Raman and infrared spectroscopic investigations of phase and conformational transitions in lipid (biomembrane), polypeptide (protein), and nucleotide (nucleic acid) ensembles. Although the primary aim of the chapter is to review and pinpoint recent developments, we will also attempt to strike a pedagogical note in some of the discussions.

The techniques of spontaneous and resonance Raman scattering and infrared (both grating and fourier transform) spectroscopy are now well established and documented (cf. Chapter 1 and references therein). However, some developments that are applicable to the study of biological systems are worth pointing out in this Introduction. The reader seeking further details and references should consult the excellent review by Wallach *et al.* (1979).

It is well known that the Raman spectra of the biologically active component in water-containing samples are easier to obtain than the corresponding infrared spectra, simply because of the relatively smaller Raman cross sections of the H_2O-vibrational modes. However, Raman spectra below ~ 150 cm^{-1} from water-containing samples are still difficult to obtain because of the large contribution of inelastic scattering due to the reorientation of water molecules. Furthermore, because this background is large, its time-dependent fluctuation in the laser beam can simulate Raman bands. A differentiation system due to Yacoby and Linz (1974) has been shown to be consistently reliable in reducing this background. In this method the background contribution is decreased by obtaining the derivative of the scattered intensity with respect to the energy displacement. Since the background scattered intensity varies much less with energy than the Raman intensity, the noise associated with the background is reduced with respect to the Raman signal.

Two further problems facing Raman scattering studies of biological samples are laser-induced luminescence and light-induced sample damage and/or modification during data acquisition. One simple and relatively economical method of avoiding the former is to couple the exciting ion-laser with a dye-laser and to use the latter as the scattering source at a frequency removed from the region of luminescence excitation in the biological system concerned. A more sophisticated approach is to use a nonlinear Raman process such as coherent anti-Stokes Raman spectroscopy (CARS) (Nibler and Knighten, 1977) to spatially remove the luminescent contribution.

The problem of sample modification in the laser beam can be minimized in a straightforward manner by the use of a sample flow system (Drissler, 1981; Callender *et al.*, 1976) that can in principle reduce the irradiation time of scattering particles to values below 2 msec. A more sophisticated approach is to excite with either a chopped Argon ion-laser or a pulsed-laser and detect the Raman signal with an optical multichannel analyzer coupled to direct reading Vidicon (Bridoux and Delhaye, 1970). This kind of optical detection is analogous to the photographic plate since it records intensities of over 500 frequency intervals (resolution elements) simultaneously, thus increasing the signal-to-noise ratio. Fourier transform spectroscopy (using an interferometric optical-pass system), now increasingly used in biological studies, is the absorption analogue of multichannel (or multiplex) Raman techniques.

II. BASIC CONCEPTS

A. Structure of Representative Biomolecules

A living cell is a composite of biomolecules which at a submacroscopic level consists of a boundary which confines the interior of the cell and separates it from the external environment. The boundary is referred to as the *membrane*. The interior of the cell is further compartmentalized into nucleus, mitochondria, etc.— each compartment being surrounded also by a membrane. Biological membranes are essentially composed of lipids, proteins, and carbohydrates, the relative proportion of each varying with the function of the membrane in question. Lipids, which are subdivided into several categories, e.g., phospholipids, triglycerides, cholesterol, etc., occur most abundantly in membranes, with phospholipids heading the list. Molecular formulae of some of the lipids displayed in Fig. 1 shows structures consisting of two segments:

   (i)   a short polar chain (usually referred to as the head group) and

   (ii)   two long (consisting of usually 14–18 carbon atoms) hydrocarbon chains, attached to a glycerol moiety. In biological membranes, the lipids form a bilayer matrix and the proteins are embedded in it as discrete particles. A schematic drawing of such a membrane structure is shown in Fig. 2, in which the hydrophobic segment remains buried inside the membrane and the polar head groups form the walls which are hydrophilic (Danielli and Davson, 1935; Tredgold, 1977 and references therein).

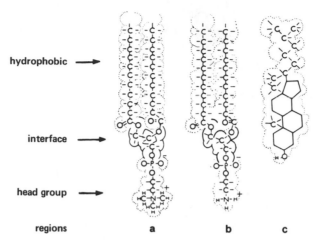

Fig. 1. The structures of some common membrane components. Spatial extent ($\cdots$) of the H atoms in the structures. (a) Dipalmitoyl-phosphatidyl choline, (b) Dipalmitoyl-phosphatityl ethanolamine, (c) Cholesterol (from Tredgold, 1977).

Biological molecules such as proteins are polymers formed by the linear condensation of monomeric units such as amino acids. As shown schematically in Fig. 3, these polymers consist of a repeating unit (B) and variable side chains (R_i). The sequence of the R_i groupings determines the primary structure of the macromolecule. Important structural parameters are the side chain angles (X_i), and backbone torsion angles $\{\phi_i\}$ as indicated in Fig. 3.

Three conformational types of such structures can be identified:

(1) Helical. When the values of ϕ_i are independent of R_i and each residue in the chain acquires the same set of values, the polymer assumes a helical conformation. Clearly such a structure is relatively symmetrical and is generally stabilized by intra- or interchain hydrogen bonds.

(2) Intermediate order. When the torsion angles ϕ_i depend on R_i but do not fluctuate with time as in the case of globular proteins and enzymes, the three-dimensional structures are several orders of magnitude more complex

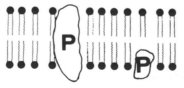

Fig. 2. Schematic diagram of membrane bilayer; the lipid head group (●) and the hydrocarbon chains (ı). The proteins (P) are shown embedded in the bilayers.

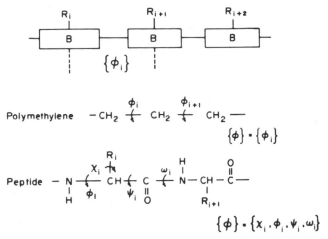

Fig. 3. Schematic representation of linear biopolymers; backbone (B), the side chains (R), and the set of torsion angles (ϕ_i) which determine the conformation of the ith unit (from Govil and Hosur, 1982).

than helical structures.   For our purposes we will refer to these structures as those having intermediate order.

(3)   Random.   Under the influence of heat or chemical perturbations the ordered structures *melt* into disordered structures such as random coils.   In a random coil the structure no longer has spatial significance since it fluctuates both in space and in time.   However, short range order would be present and the properties can be defined by time and space averages.

Two kinds of nucleic acids, deoxyribonucleic acid (DNA) and ribonucleic acid (RNA), are responsible for the storage, propagation, and expression of the genetic information of a cell.   While DNA carries the genetic information and serves as a template of its own replication, the RNA molecules transcribe and translate the DNA information into the amino acid language of the proteins.

DNA and RNA are polymers of nucleotide-subunits and each of these nucleotides consists of a purine or pyrimidine base, a 5-carbon cyclic sugar and a phosphate.   As shown in Fig. 4 the backbone of a nucleic acid polymer is formed by a -[phosphate-5′sugar 3′]$_n$-chain.

The possible conformations which can be assumed by the nucleic acid backbone are mainly limited to the rotational freedom of the N-glycosydic linkage of base to sugar and the two O—P bonds in the phosphodiester linkage of phosphate to sugar (cf. Fig. 4).

Hydrogen bonding between the amino and keto groups of the purine and pyrimidine bases can lead to the pairing of two nucleic acid chains and to the

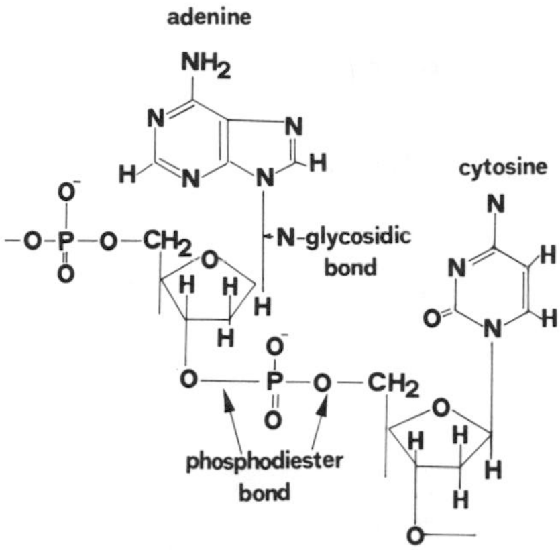

Fig. 4. Schematic representation of the backbone of a nucleic acid polymer.

formation of strongly stabilized (helical) duplices. These complexes are further stabilized by hydrophobic interactions between the flat aromatic ring surfaces of their bases (*base stacking*).

The wide range of different structures reflects the conformational flexibility and molecular dynamics of the nucleic acids and they are important prerequisites of the manifold functions or molecular interactions of both DNA and RNA.

In Table I the different known-helical-type DNA structural characteristics are summarized. However, theoretical calculations show that other stable structures could exist and therefore this table might well be extended during the next few years (Robson, 1977; Gupta *et al.,* 1980).

B. Theoretical and Structural Considerations

Cooperative processs in biological systems can take place in a three-dimensional ensemble, such as the lipid bilayer of a biomembrane or at the localized level of a polypeptide chain, under particular conditions of temperature, chemical environment, and external fields. The onset of the phenomenon of cooperativity is the result of increasing *communication* or interaction among individual subunits of a system, leading, for example, to a phase or conformational transition. Most transitions involve a change in the three-dimensional spatial structure of the system coupled with a change in local conformation. Purely conformational transitions essentially involve one-dimensional finite range interactions and hence are not phase transitions in the strict thermodynamic sense (cf. Chapter 1). However, a discussion of purely conformational transitions is included in this chapter primarily because of their importance in biology and the sensitivity of infrared and

TABLE I

Structural Characteristics of DNA Helices[a]

Helix type	bp per turn	Rotation per bp[b]	Vertical rise per bp (Å)	Approximate diameter (Å)
A	11	32.7°	2.56	23
B	10	36.0°	3.38	19
C	9⅓	38.6°	3.32	19
D	8	45.0°	3.04	—
E	7½	48.0°	3.25	—
Z	12	−30.0°	3.71	18

[a] From Cantor (1981).
[b] bp = base pair.

Raman spectroscopy to such changes. In what follows in this subsection we treat, first, some basic concepts and results of *conventional*, i.e., near-equilibrium phase transitions in biological systems and, second, phase transitions in such systems that occur far away from thermodynamic equilibrium, i.e., nonlinear transitions.

1. Order–Disorder Transitions

Biological molecules consist of polymeric chains which undergo large amplitude thermal motions even at relatively low temperatures. In lipid bilayers the motionally disordered phospholipid molecules pack in a distorted hexagonal lattice (Tardieu *et al.*, 1973) with extended chains that are aligned and tilted at an angle of ~ 30° to the normal to the bilayer plane. As the temperature is raised through the lower transition point T_1 (usually referred to as the pretransition) the packing becomes monoclinic and is coupled with an increase of the motional disorder of the chains and the appearance of ripples caused by a sinusoidal modulation of the chains normal to the bilayer plane (Pearce and Scott, 1982). Above the main melting transition T_m the chains disorder via *gauche* rotations (see Fig. 5).

Two facts are worth noting:

(a) The hydrocarbon chains locally undergo a transition from a more rigid, extended conformation in the low temperature phase to a shortened conformation in the high temperature phase, leading to a substantial change in volume of the bilayer upon the transition.

(b) The main *melting* transition of the bilayer is largely first order, as indicated by fact (a) and a large transition enthalpy. However, reduced dimensionality in such bilayer systems may introduce second-order charac-

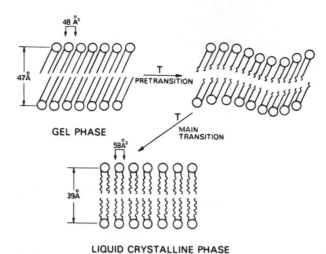

LIQUID CRYSTALLINE PHASE

Fig. 5. The different lipid bilayer phases (from Levin, 1980). Reprinted with permission from North-Holland Publishing Company.

teristics such as criticality, similar to that observed in smectic-type liquid crystals (cf. Chapter 1, also Nagle and Scott, 1978, and discussion below).

The transition can be described in terms of an order–disorder model for which we can write the effective Hamiltonian

$$H = H_{attr} + H_{steric} + H_{rot}, \tag{1}$$

where H_{attr} is the sum of attractive interactions holding the bilayer, H_{steric} represents a repulsive term that prevents two molecular units from coming closer together than their van der Waals or hard core radii, and H_{rot} describes terms which allow only the *trans* conformation with energy zero and two *gauche* conformations with energy 0.5 kcal mol^{-1}.

A macroscopic, phenomenological order parameter for a lipid monolayer *precursor* can be defined in terms of the results of Hui *et al.* (1975) and the theoretical calculations of Marcelja (1974). One motivation for using monolayers is that they provide two experimentally controllable thermodynamic parameters: namely, the area per lipid molecule (A) and the surface or lateral pressure (Π) which correspond to the volume and pressure, respectively, in a three-dimensional system. Theoretical Π versus A isotherms, which are in excellent agreement with experiment for such a system, and are similar to P-V curves for a liquid, are shown in Fig. 6 (Marcelja, 1974; Hui *et al.,* 1975).

From Fig. 5 it is evident that a critical point exists at a critical temperature T_c. As in the case of the density fluctuation in a fluid, the area change ΔA

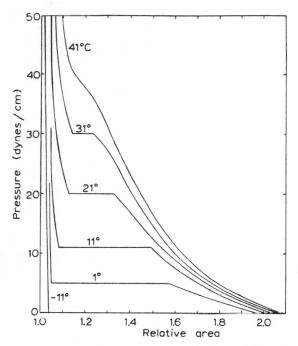

Fig. 6. Calculated lateral pressure (π) versus area per polar head (A) for surface monolayers at different temperatures (from Marcelja, 1974).

across the two phase region goes to zero at the critical point, thus behaving like a typical Landau order parameter. In bulk lipids, however, the three-dimensional pressure and volume are not analogous to π and A in mono-layers, but the estimated critical pressure of ~ 50 dynes/cm is close to that for a lipid monolayer (Hui *et al.*, 1975 and Fig. 6). This suggests that bulk bilayer systems near the phase transition are also at a critical point (Nagle and Scott, 1978). Critical fluctuations would then be expected to occur near T_c and this is indeed supported by the observation of an anomalous maximum in the permeability of sodium ions across a model membrane at T_c (Papahadjopoulos *et al.*, 1973).

2. Nonlinear Transitions

Unlike usual crystalline and noncrystalline material, biological systems in the active or *living* state are in some respects far from thermodynamic equilibrium and are maintained as so-called dissipative structures by means of energy and matter exchange with their environment. Active biological systems thus behave like lasers and should in principle display collective effects such as coherent excitation. Some fifteen years ago Fröhlich (1968) conjectured that a strong coherent excitation of a nonlinear mode of excitation can indeed occur in a biological system provided that the rate of energy supply S exceeds a critical value S_o. A unit biological system in Fröhlich's model consists of biomolecules surrounded by water and ions. Such a configuration can lead to the existence of internal electric fields as high as 10^5 V cm^{-1}, for example, in cell membranes. Oscillations of parts of such a system would give rise to corresponding electric vibrations which have been estimated to be in the $10^{11} - 10^{12}$ Hz ($\sim 3 - 30$ cm^{-1}) range. Fröhlich showed that if this system is supplied with energy, then a nonlinear mode–mode coupling would occur leading to the channeling of the energy into a single coherent mode. This phenomenon resembles the condensation of a Bose gas and hence the passage from the nonactive to the active state of a biological system can be described as a nonlinear phase transition.

Raman scattering provides a unique method of exploring this phase transition because we can obtain the thermal population factor by measuring the ratio r of the intensity of the anti-Stokes to Stokes scattering lines. For a system at thermal equilibrium at a measured Raman frequency ν and temperature T,

$$r = r_T = e^{h\nu/RT}. \tag{2}$$

With the onset of nonlinear coherent excitation, thermal population enhancement above the thermal equilibrum level of certain polar modes of vibration (which have the necessary long interaction range) would occur (cf. Fröhlich, 1981). Such population enhancements have indeed been observed in Raman experiments on a number of systems. For example, as evident from the Stokes and anti-Stokes Raman scattering of active cells of *Escherichia coli* shown in Fig. 7, and intensity ratio r $\approx$ 1 of the Raman line at ~ 125 cm^{-1} (minus a factor of ~ 2 above the thermal value of 0.55) is observed (Webb *et al.,* 1977). Suspensions of living cells of the green monocellular algae *chlorella pyrenoidosa* also show 30–160% population enhancement of the Raman lines associated with the carotenoid molecules, compared to thermal equilibrium (Drissler and Macfarlane, 1979). As pointed out by Drissler (1981) in all Raman experiments of this nature on biological systems, the influence of the laser radiation on the system being examined has to be carefully considered. To avoid experimental artifacts experiments should be carried out using rapid flow sampling or preferably pulsed Raman measurements.

Two further experimental results are worth pointing out because they demonstrate the potential application of Raman scattering in monitoring the dynamics of such nonlinear phase transitions. Stokes Raman spectra of *E. coli* in the metabolic-active (*B*) and -inactive (*A*) states displayed in Fig. 8

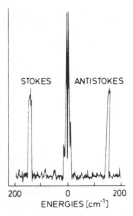

Fig. 7. Comparison of Stokes and anti-Stokes Raman intensities from *E. coli* bacteria at room temperature (from Webb *et al.*, 1977).

from the work of Webb and Stoneham (1977) clearly demonstrate the onset of sharp transitions below 200 cm^{-1} as the system enters the metabolic-active state. More controlled experimentation may allow a closer insight into the evolution of the cross section and life times of these modes as the system undergoes the phase transition.

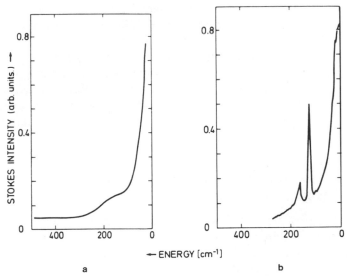

Fig. 8. Stokes Raman spectra at room temperature from "living" *E. coli* bacteria in the metabolic inactive (a) and active (b) states (from Webb *et al.*, 1977).

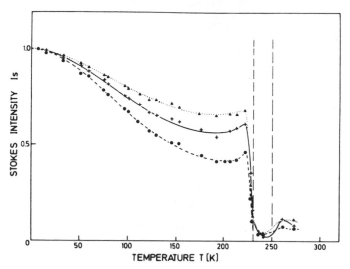

Fig. 9. Resonance Raman line intensities of carotenoid segment of algae as a function of temperature (from Drissler, 1981). 1006 cm^{-1} (●--●), 1530 cm^{-1} (▲ ··· ▲), and 1157 cm^{-1} (+ —— +).

The second example involves temperature-dependent measurements of the resonance Raman enhanced carotenoid vibrations of living (near room temperature) and frozen algae (Drissler, 1980). The plot of the Raman intensities versus temperature (cf. Fig. 9) shows a sharp drop in the intensities of the carotenoid vibrations to zero at 225 K, followed by a weaker reappearance of the lines above 261 K. The behavior of the Raman intensity is reminiscent of that of a dynamic order parameter near a phase transition. Naively, we can picture the transition as involving the onset of coherent oscillations that in turn disrupts, via biopolymer chain fluctuations, the electron–phonon coupling process of resonance Raman enhancement. Similar resonance Raman effects have been observed with the onset of the disordered phase in model biomembranes (cf. Section III.C).

III. PHASE TRANSITIONS IN PHOSPHOLIPIDS AND BIOMEMBRANES

Raman spectroscopy provides a sensitive method of investigating molecular interactions in biomembranes and the dynamics associated with the order–disorder phase transition in phospholipid layers, both in model and real systems. Important structural information is also obtained using polarized infrared spectroscopic techniques particularly on specially prepared thin film samples (Fringeli, 1977).

In what follows in this subsection, we will discuss data obtained mainly by Raman spectroscopy in different phospholipids and biomembranes. Wallach *et al.* (1979) have recently written a rather exhaustive review on the vibrational spectroscopy of such systems. We will, however, restrict ourselves here to selected examples that provide an insight into the nature and the dynamics of cooperative phase transitions in these systems.

A. Spectral Details and the Order Parameter

The Raman spectrum in the crystalline solid phase, of the model phospholipid (DPC, cf. Fig. 1a), can be assigned to vibrations localized at different regions of the molecule (cf. Fig. 10). Of importance in the study of lipid state transitions are the lines in the $2700-3100$ cm^{-1} and $1050-1150$ cm^{-1} spectral ranges, which are assignable to CH stretching and skeletal C—C stretching modes, respectively (Gaber and Peticolas, 1977; Bunow and Levin, 1977). The line at 2850 cm^{-1} is assigned to the symmetric —CH$_2$ stretching modes of the hydrocarbon chain, while the sharp line near 2890 cm^{-1} is associated largely with the —CH$_2$ asymmetric stretching mode. The lines above 2900 cm^{-1} can be assigned to the stretching modes of the —CH$_3$ and —N—CH$_3$ moieties located at the chain end and head group regions, respectively. Of the skeletal C—C stretching modes, the lines at 1064 and 1133 cm^{-1} are characteristic of the *trans* chain segments, while the component at 1090 cm^{-1}, superimposed in phospholipids on the O—P—O stretching line, arises from chain segments containing the *gauche* configuration. The interface region of the phospholipid bilayer can be monitored by observing the stretching vibrations of the inequivalent C=O groups (cf. Fig. 1a). These modes are relatively weak in the Raman spectrum but appear with much greater intensity in the infrared spectrum (Fringeli, 1977).

With the onset of the phospholipid bilayer order–disorder phase transition important changes in the Raman spectra between 900 and 3000 cm^{-1} occur, as can be seen from Fig. 11, for distearoyl phosphatidylcholine-water multilayers. The most sensitive indicator of the transition is the drop in intensity of the line at 2890 cm^{-1} with respect to the line at 2850 cm^{-1}, in the disordered phase. This is coupled with an increase in intensity of the scattering at 2936 cm^{-1}. At first it is surprising that the localized —CH$_2$ asymmetric stretching mode at 2890 cm^{-1} is sensitive to the delocalized dynamics associated with the hydrocarbon chain disorder. However, as pointed out by Synder *et al.* (1978), the 2890 cm^{-1} line overlaps with the 2-phonon scattering corresponding to the —CH$_2$ bending modes in the 1440 to 1460 cm^{-1} region (cf. Fig. 10). The 2-phonon scattering is expected to gain intensity via Fermi resonance with the symmetric stretching mode at 2850 cm^{-1} (since the 2-phonon state is totally symmetric it cannot interact with

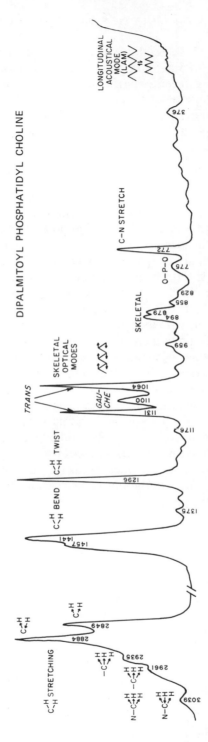

Fig. 10. Raman spectrum of solid dipalmitoyl phosphatidylcholine. Recorded at 50 cm^{-1}/in./min; time constant, 1 sec, gain 10^6 count/sec; slits 250 μm; power at laser head, 900 MW; excitation wavelength, 5145 Å (from Gaber and Peticolas, 1977).

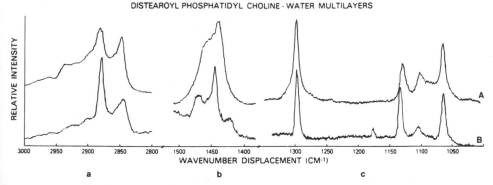

DISTEAROYL PHOSPHATIDYL CHOLINE - WATER MULTILAYERS

Fig. 11. Raman spectra of distearoyl phosphatidylcholine-water multilayers in the C—H stretching (a), CH$_2$ deformation (b), and the C—C skeletal (c) regions at 39°C (A) and -180°C (B) (from Yellin and Levin, 1977).

the asymmetric stretching mode). The drop in intensity of the 2890 cm^{-1} line can in the disordered phase therefore be interpreted as due, in part, to the loss of the interchain correlation that gives rise to the Fermi resonance. Consistent with this interpretation, the infrared band intensities are not sensitive to the order–disorder transition (Asher and Levin, 1977) since the 2-phonon state is not expected to be IR-active because of symmetry reasons.

With the onset of the disordered phase, the hydrocarbon chains also undergo chain shortening due to gauche rotations (cf. Section II.B). This would result in frequency dispersion effects, particularly in the Raman spectrum, leading to line broadening and hence to a decrease in the peak intensity. Gaber and Peticolas (1977) conjectured that half the intensity drop of the 2890 cm^{-1} Raman line is due to each of the above two effects since both have been observed to be equal in magnitude in hexadecane. A lateral order parameter S_{Lat} can then be defined as

$$S_{Lat} = \frac{r(\text{sample}) - r(\text{liq. hexadecane})}{r(\text{cryst. hexadecane}) - r(\text{liq. hexadecane})}, \qquad (3)$$

where $r = I_{2890}/I_{2850}$ (I_{2890} and I_{2850} represent the peak intensities of the 2890 and 2850 cm^{-1} lines, respectively). From Eq. (3) $S_{Lat} = 1$ for chains in the ordered state and $S_{Lat} = 0$ for chains in the disordered state, with intermediate values expected (and found, see Subsection IV.C) for other cases.

The intensity increase of —CH$_3$ stretching mode at 2936 cm^{-1} in the disordered phase is interesting in that it can be used to monitor the phase transition at the hydrocarbon chain end position. However, the intensity increase is also probably associated with the effects of lateral and chain-shortening disorder discussed above with regard to the intensity decrease of the $-CH_2$ line at 2890 cm^{-1}. Thus it is unlikely that the intensity of the 2936 cm^{-1} line monitors events localized at the terminal $-CH_3$ position alone. A better way of monitoring motional order at the chain-end and comparing it to the dynamics at the $-CH_2$ positions further up the chain is to use the linewidth (Γ) increase of the modes as a function of temperature, on selectively deuterated phospholipids. The increase of Γ in the disordered phase is induced by the onset of large amplitude atomic fluctuations and is a reflection of the decreased phonon lifetime in the fluctuation regime (cf. Iqbal and Christoe, 1975 and Chapter 3).

In one such study (Mendelsohn et al., 1982), both deuterium magnetic resonance (^{2}H-NMR) and Raman spectroscopy were used to investigate the fluidity at the terminal $-CH_3$ and $-CH_2$ positions in DPC multilayers. The phase transition was sensed in the ^{2}H-NMR experiment using $16d_6$-DPC multilayers as a reduction in the quadrupole splitting (from 14 kHz to $\sim$ 3 kHz) due to an enhancement of the motional averaging in the disordered phase, induced by *trans* $\rightarrow$ *gauche* rotations (cf. Section II.A) taking place in the time scale of $10^9 - 10^{10}$ Hz. In the Raman experiment the phase transition is evident as an increase in the linewidth (full width at half intensity) of the CD$_2$ stretching mode in $10d_2$-DPC but not in that of the terminal CD$_3$ mode in $16d_6$-DPC.

The NMR and Raman data can be reconciled as follows (Mendelsohn et al., 1982): The NMR response is sensitive to order both at the terminal position and further up the hydrocarbon chain. Since disorder at the latter position sets in suddenly above T_c via *trans* $\rightarrow$ *gauche* rotations, the NMR response shows a sizable change at the transition point. By contrast, the Raman response senses only the localized CD$_3$ stretching vibrations that remain unaffected by the onset of disorder further up the chain at T_c. This result also indicates that the degree of disorder at the terminal CD$_3$ position remains unchanged at T_c. The above example points to the need for taking the characteristics time of the measurement into account when comparing results obtained by different spectroscopic techniques.

Gaber and Peticolas (1977) define what they call a *trans* order parameter based on the relative intensity of the line at 1134 cm^{-1}, assigned to the C—C stretching mode of a *trans* hydrocarbon chain. The order parameter S_{Trans} is given by

$$S_{\text{Trans}} = \frac{[I_{1133}/I_{\text{ref}}]_{\text{obs}}}{[I_{1133}/I_{\text{ref}}]_{\text{DPL, solid}}}, \tag{4}$$

where I_{ref} is the intensity of the *gauche* component at 1090 cm^{-1}. For accurate work I_{ref} is taken to be that of the choline CN stretching mode at 722 cm^{-1} (cf. Fig. 10) which remains constant in intensity through the phase transition.

S_{Lat} and S_{Trans} represent empirical semi-quantitative measures of the degree of lateral *inter-chain* order and localized *intra-chain* conformational order, respectively. These quantities do not intrinsically go to zero at T_c as the transition is approached from the ordered phase and hence cannot be correlated with the canonical Landau order parameter (cf. Chapter 1).

Low frequency vibrations associated with the longitudinal acoustic vibrations of extended chains are Raman active (cf. Fig. 10) in the ordered state. Since these modes are collective in nature at the localized chain and nearest-neighbor *inter-chain* level, they would be expected to be extremely sensitive to chain order and display a drop to near zero intensity at T_c. Therefore, in principle, the scattering intensity of such a mode would be proportional to the canonical order parameter of the phospholipid phase transition. A review of results in the low frequency range in phospholipid systems, is given by Wallach *et al.* (1979). However, no quantitative measurements have been reported so far because of the perturbing influence of H_2O vibrations in the low frequency range.

B. Studies in Model Systems

The effect of the order–disorder transition on the Raman line intensities as a function of temperature, monitoring the lateral (S_{Lat}) and trans (S_{Trans}) order parameters (Eqs. 3 and 4 and Section III.A) are shown in Figs. 12a and b from the data of Gaber and Peticolas (1977). Both the pretransition and the main order–disorder transition are evident from the displayed profiles of multilayers. Similarly, by monitoring the intensity of the 2936 cm^{-1} Raman line relative to the 2890 cm^{-1} line (represented as $I_{disordered}/I_{ordered}$) both the pretransition and the main transition can be observed in multilayers of DPC and POPC (1-palmitoyl-2-oleoyl phosphatidylcholine) as shown in Fig. 13 taken from the data of Levin (1980). In contrast, it is evident that in vesicles the transition is somewhat broadened and the pretransition is not reflected in the data. From these results it can be concluded that the modulation (similar to that in the incommensurate phases in crystals discussed in the previous chapters) occurring in the pretransition regime involves a change in S_{Trans} and S_{Lat} as in the main transition. However, due to the surface curvature in the vesicles the modulated phase is not stabilized. This supports the theoretical model of Cevc *et al.* (1981) where the modulated or rippled structure is initiated by water-mediated interlamellar coupling that is less likely to occur in the vesicle geometry.

Cholesterol (CHOL, cf. Fig. 1c) has a profound effect on the lipid bilayer structure via the probable formation of a CHOL-lipid complex which dramatically reduces the cooperativity of the phase transition. This is reflected in a broadened temperature profile that does not show the pretransition

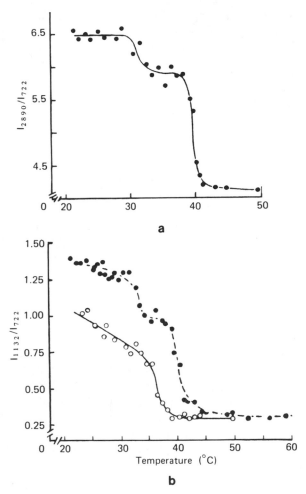

Fig. 12. Temperature profiles of dipalmitoyl phosphatidylcholine (DPL). (a) Lateral order curve for DPL multilayer, (b) trans order curve for DPL multilayer (●) and vesicles (○) (from Gaber and Peticolas, 1977).

structure (cf. Fig. 13b). The effect of another sterol, designated LAN in Fig. 13b), was also investigated by Levin (1980). LAN closely resembles CHOL except for three additional CH_3 groups. One of the methyl groups of LAN projects from the α-face of the sterol ring (cf. Fig. 1c), thus making LAN relatively more bulky. This is reflected in the increased perturbing effect of LAN on the lipid phase transition (Fig. 13b).

Cholesterol affects the cooperativity of the order–disorder (gel to liquid crystal) transition in phospholipids at sterol/phospholipid molar ratios greater than 0.2. However, peptides such as gramicidin A that form ion-per-

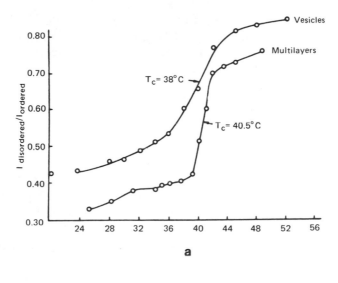

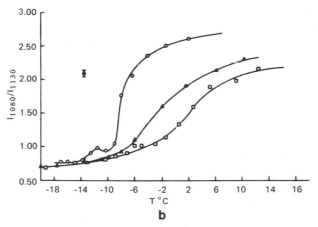

Fig. 13. (a) Temperature profile of dipalmitoyl phosphatidylcholine vesicles and multilayers in the C—H stretching region and (b) temperature profile of cholesterol (CHOL) and lanosterol (LAN) in 1-palmitoyl-2-oleoyl phosphatidylcholine (POPC) in the C—C streching region. POPC (○), POPC/CHOL (□) POPC/LAN (▲) (from Levin, 1980).

meable pores or channels across the phospholipid bilayers, affect the transition cooperatively at a molar ratio of 0.0015 (Weidekamm *et al.,* 1977). Weidekamm *et al.* followed the relative intensities of both the —CH$_2$ and CH$_3$ stretching modes and found that at a gramicidin A/DPC molar ration of 1:650, the transition monitored using I_{2890} was eliminated but that using I_{2936} was unaffected.

This result is rather interesting and needs further investigation because as discussed previously it is probably not correct to assume that I_{2936} monitors *only* the dynamics at the terminal —CH$_3$ position. In contrast with cholesterol, it appears that the effect of gramicidin A on the hydrocarbon chain involves long range effects, imposed through interaction with the apolar amino acid side chains of the peptide. It is worth noting here that at least in a relatively high concentration regime accessible to Raman studies, the gramicidin A maintains its stable crystal state conformation (Iqbal and Weidekamm, 1980).

More detailed studies of the interactions localized at the channel-forming component can be carried out if it contains a conjugated polyene segment which gives rise to resonance-enhanced Raman scattering. This is the case for amphotericin B (Bunow and Levin, 1977) and nystatin (Iqbal and Weidekamm, 1979), both of which are polyene-containing antibiotics which form channels in the presence of cholesterol. In amphotericin B containing liposomes, Bunow and Levin (1977) did not observe any conformational change at the antibiotic site but a drastic reduction in the resonance-enhanced —C≡C— band intensity was observed with the onset of the broadened transition in cholesterol-DPC liposomes. This suggests the onset of long-range interactions in the disordered liquid crystal phase which perturbs the polyene charge density. In the case of nystatin, sizable spectral changes involving the relative intensities of the resonance-enhanced C≡O and C≡C stretching modes indicate that a conformational change of the antibiotic in cholesterol-containing liposomes occurs. However, unlike amphotericin B, the resonance-enhanced band intensities remain constant through the transition. More detailed studies of these effects would be important to shed further light on the role of long-range interactions near the phase transition in biomembrane systems.

One interesting and potentially useful application of IR-spectroscopy in membrane studies, demonstrated by the work of Akutsu *et al.* (1975), is worth bringing up here. These authors obtained very specific conformational details of built-up films of dipalymitoyl phosphatidylethanolamine by obtaining directions of selected vibrational transition moments using polarized infrared spectroscopy. From the evaluated dichroic ratios of CH$_2$, C≡O, PO$_2^-$, and C—C—N$^+$ modes, they came to the following conclusions:

(a)   The moments of the C≡O stretching, and the PO$_2^-$ and C—C—N$^+$ asymmetric stretching modes are oriented parallel to each other and deviate less than 20° from the film plane, thus indicating that the polar head group is essentially aligned along the film surface.

(b)   The hydrocarbon chain axes are tilted at about 75° to the film plane. Such studies when carried out in the presence of other membrane components and under conditions of varying temperature should provide extremely important information regarding specific conformational changes near T_c.

C. Studies in Naturally Occurring Biomembranes

Plasma membranes isolated as small, sealed vesicles and intact erythrocyte ghosts have proved useful as real biological membrane systems amenable to Raman spectroscopic investigations. These systems show phase transition phenomena similar to those observed in the model systems. However, there are a few new and interesting features which are worth noting here.

For example, in a study of the CH stretching region of erythrocyte ghosts by Raman scattering as a function of temperature and pH, Verma and Wallach (1976) observed three strong lines at 2930, 2880, and 2850 cm^{-1}. The line at 2930 cm^{-1} was assigned as largely (>60%) due to penetrating protein residues, while the lines at 2880 and 2850 cm^{-1} could be assigned to the hydrocarbon chain of the lipid component (cf. Section III.B. As evident in Fig. 14, I_{2930}/I_{2850} showed a sharp increase at a particular temperature, indicating the occurrence of an order–disorder phase transition (cf. Section III.B). However, it was observed that the transition temperature T_c was very sensitive to the pH in the 6.0–7.4 range. At pH = 6.0, $T = 0-7°C$, and it increases to ~28–38°C at pH values of 6.5 and 7.4, respectively (cf. Fig. 14). The results indicate that the phase transition is more complex than in

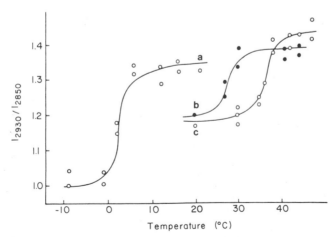

Fig. 14. Variation of $[I_{2930}/I_{2850}]$ of erythrocyte ghosts with temperature at pH = 6.0 (a), 6.5 (b), and 7.4 (c) (from Verma and Wallach, 1976).

model systems and that it involves a cooperative change in the hydrocarbon chain order and conformation of the protein incorporated into the membrane bilayer interior. The extreme sensitivity of the transition to pH in the 6.0 – 7.5 range is a reflection of the low dielectric constant of the membrane core — an environment where small changes in charge flux could cause cooperative conformational changes in the protein. It is well known that the next-to-protein layer forms a rigid *annulus* of lipids with ordered hydrocarbon chains (see, e.g., Schröder, 1977). Changes in the rigidity of the *annulus* occur with the conformational change in the protein, resulting in the extreme pH sensitivity of T_c. More quantitative studies of this phenomenon in real biomembranes are, however, necessary to indicate the biological implications of such molecular processes.

Rhodopsin extracted from the eyes of vertebrates and invertebrates, as well as bacteriorhodopsin, provide an interesting system for investigations using resonance-enhanced Raman (RR) scattering (see, e.g., Lewis, 1976 and references therein; Iqbal *et al.*, 1979). Animal rhodopsin consists of 11-*cis* retinal (consisting of a 12-atom polyene grouping which gives rise to RR scattering) attached to a matrix of sugar, lipid, and protein called opsin, and is a component of the rod-cell membrane of the retina. On photon absorption the polyene grouping undergoes a *cis* to *trans* conformational transition which is the critical first step in the visual process of animals. In the Raman spectrum we can monitor this transition by observing the drop in frequency from 1545 cm^{-1} in the *cis* state to 1530 cm^{-1} in the *trans* state. The decrease in frequency occurs as a result of the increased electron delocalization in the *trans* conformation. Temperature and pH induced motional dynamics, which have not been studied so far, and the vibrations associated with the opsin segment, could provide interesting information with biological implications.

In addition to the study of vertebrate rhodopsin by RR spectroscopy (e.g., Lewis, 1976), the deprotonation dynamics of the bacteriorhodopsin Schiff base by kinetic RR spectroscopy (Marcus and Lewis, 177) have been described. Using a variable-speed continuous flow method the authors were able to probe the molecular dynamics of isolated sites in bacteriorhodopsin and they obtained evidence from the time-related intensity changes of the C=C and C=N bands, that the deprotonation of the Schiff base could occur considerbly earlier than the ejection of a proton on the outer side of the membrane.

RR spectra (obtained with pulsed laser radiation) of the lowest energy excited triplet state of all-trans-retinal are discussed by Atkinson *et al.* (1981). The detection of the excited and ground electronic state conformations of specific isomeric retinal forms by this kind of spectroscopy should enable us to set up experiments which could correlate isomerization pathways with the excited electronic states of the particular isomer.

Low temperature RR spectra of the L intermediate of bacteriorhodopsin were obtained by Narva *et al.* (1981). The photostationary state spectra of the L + L' form were generated by computer substraction and discussed in the light of their contribution to the photoreactive scheme of bacteriorhodopsin.

A 14–22 μsec light-induced and bacteriorhodopsin-mediated membrane potential change could be detected in reconstituted phospholipid-bacteriorhodopsin vesicles using β-carotene as a probe in kinetic RR spectroscopy (Johnson *et al.*, 1981).

IV. TRANSITIONS IN POLYPEPTIDES AND PROTEINS

A. General Spectral and Conformational Considerations

The function and activity of proteins are generally based on their characteristic folding and on the specific interactions of adjacent polypeptide chains (cf. Fig. 3 and Section II.A).

Due to its partial double bond character the peptide ($-CO-NH-$) moiety assumes a planar conformation, thus allowing for the possibility of obtaining a trans- or cis-configuration. This conformation then determines the backbone structure of the polypeptide and is reflected in characteristic Raman and IR-active bands and in their relative intensities.

While Raman spectra can be used to distinguish between the ordered structures (e.g., α-helix, β-sheet) and the disordered *random coil,* it is difficult to resolve α-helical and disordered polypeptide regions using IR-spectroscopy. However, in many cases IR-spectroscopy can be used to monitor parallel or antiparallel β-sheet conformations.

Elliot and Ambrose (1950), for example, found that the IR-active $C=O$ absorption bands in α-helical polypeptides are about 25 cm^{-1} higher than in β-sheet polypeptides—the first time that vibrational spectra were used to study these two conformations in polypeptides. Later Miyazawa (1960) provided the theoretical basis for this observation by taking into account the intrachain (α-helix) and interchain (β-sheet) hydrogen interactions.

The *α-helices* consist of 18 amino acid residues per 5 turns and therefore the helical rotation angle per residue translation (Ψ) is $5 \times 360°/18 = 100°$. Classically, most L-amino acids will form a right-handed helix, while the screw-sense of D-amino acids is left handed.

Other helical conformations, such as the 3_1-helix are observed in polypeptides (e.g., polyglycine) and fibrous proteins (e.g., collagen). In this case the helix rotation angle Ψ for a repeat unit is 120°.

In the parallel or antiparallel *β-sheet* conformation the peptide chains are nearly fully extended to enable intermolecular hydrogen bonding. Characteristic of the β-sheet vibrational spectrum is the splitting of the amide I modes (cf. Table I for description of amide vibrations) in the infrared spectra into a strong band near 1630 cm^{-1}, polarized orthogonal to the chain axis, and a weak band near 1690 cm^{-1}, polarized parallel to the chain. Usually, in Raman scattering a very strong amide I band near 1670 cm^{-1} is observed (cf. Table II). The amide I and II mode splittings are clearly associated with the transition dipole–dipole coupling, as indicated by the force-field calculations of Moore and Krimm (1976) on poly-L-alanine.

In disordered conformations or random coils of polymers in solution, the mean end-to-end distances are statistically determined from the possible rotation angles (Ψ) about the backbone bonds. In this kind of polymer chains, the Ψ values are not equally probable and are governed by the conformational energy. In addition, so-called reverse-turn structures (type I β-turn and type II β-turn) have been found to constitute important conformational components of protein structure (Chou and Fasman, 1977; Bandekar and Krimm, 1979). The utility of Raman spectroscopy in analyzing the amide bands of these β-turns has been recently discussed by Fox et al. (1981), and a correlation between the frequencies of the various amide bands and the polypeptide–protein conformation is given in Table II.

Detailed assignments of polypeptide conformations to amide mode frequencies and tables of observed and calculated frequencies have been published and discussed (e.g., by Baron et al., 1979; Sugawara et al., 1978; Frushour et al., 1976).

Williams and Dunker (1981) made a valuable contribution to a dependable theoretical basis for the correlation of spectra with conformational properties. In their approach the broad amide I band of a complex protein is resolved into six components representing the following types of secondary order: ordered or dihydrogen-bonded helix, disordered or monohydrogen-bonded helix, antiparallel β-sheet, parallel β-sheet, reverse β-turn, and disordered. Normalized reference Raman spectra which represented the amide I band of a polypeptide with 100% of a single type of structure were computed from the solvent-substracted Raman spectra of proteins and polypeptides with known secondary structure using least-squares solution of the overdetermined system of equations. Each amide I spectrum was computed of 15 equally spaced wavenumbers from 1630–1700 cm^{-1}. According to statistical tests the authors obtained a significant discrimination between monohydrogen-bonded and dihydrogen-bonded helices as well as between parallel and antiparallel β-sheets, while no such discrimination was possible between random structures and turns.

The amide IV modes which provide valuable information concerning the polypeptide conformation appear only weakly in the infrared spectra of polypeptides and furthermore, there are interferences from the strongly

TABLE II

RAMAN FREQUENCIES OF POLYPEPTIDES AND PROTEIN AMIDE GROUPS[a]

Amide	α-Helix	β-Sheet parallel	β-Sheet antiparallel	Disordered (random coil)
I. Primarily C=O stretching	1639s[c] 1660s[f,k] 1641[g] 1662[f] 1647vs[c] 1650[h] 1652[d] 1655[i]	1655[h] 1673[f]	1631vs[c] 1672vs[c] 1673[k] 1674[f]	1653vs[c] 1655[k] 1656[c] 1665vs[c,f] 1683vs[c] 1685[f,k]
II. Primarily N—H in-plane bending with a C—N stretching contribution	1517w[c] 1537m[c]		1511w[c] 1535w[c]	1521m[c] 1547[c] 1565[c]
III. Primarily C—N stretching with N—H in-plane bending (coupling phases are opposite to Amide II)	1264s[f,k] 1270[f,l] 1275[h,m]	1227[f] 1230–1235[e] 1235[h] 1240[n] 1252[f] 1260[m]	1227–1240[h] 1230[l] 1234s[f] 1240[l]	1235[k] 1239[f] 1245[h,n] 1248[f] 1243–1249[b]
IV. O=C—N in-plane bending		~630w		
V. N—H out-of-plane bending		~730w		
VI. C=O out-of-plane bending		~600w		
VII. Internal rotation about C—N related to the barrier hindering internal rotation		~200w		
A. N—H stretching in Fermi resonance		~3300		
B. Amide II first overtone		~3100		

[a] Correlation between frequency position and peptide conformation.   Relative intensities: s, strong; vs, very strong; m, medium; w, weak.

[b] Frushour and Koenig (1974b).

[c] Wallach et al. (1970).

[d] Yu et al. (1973).

[e] Koenig (1972).

[f] Yu et al. (1972).

[g] Williams and Dunker (1981).

[h] Prescott et al. (1976).

[i] Fasman et al. (1978).

[j] Painter and Koenig (1976).

[k] Yu and East (1975).

[l] Frushour and Koenig (1974a).

[m] Bellocq et al. (1972).

[n] Pézolet et al. (1976).

IR-active vibrations of the methyl and methylene groups. These modes, however, appear clearly and without interference in the Raman spectra of polypeptides. Differences exist between Raman-active ($1665-1670$ cm^{-1}) and the IR-active (~ 1650 cm^{-1}) amide I mode frequencies of disordered polypeptides and proteins, which can be explained in terms of sequences of amide groups disposing of similar ϕ and Ψ angles (Painter and Coleman, 1978).

B. Conformational Transitions in Model Polypeptides

1. pH-Induced Order-to-Disorder Transitions

The amino acid residues of poly-L-lysine and poly-L-glutamic acid contain terminal amino and carboxyl groups, respectively. In aqueous solutions both polypeptides assume the α-helical conformation in the non-ionized state. Near pH $= 7$ the side chains become ionized and as a consequence the α-helix becomes unstable and converts to a random coil. This transition occurs over a narrow pH interval and is strictly cooperative (Yu *et al.*, 1973); Koenig and Frushour, 1972). At pH $= 11.4$ poly-L-glutamic acid is in the ionized random coil conformation and converts to the α-helical conformation at pH values < 4.85. This transition to the α-helix is accompanied by a decrease in intensity of the amide III band at 1249 cm^{-1} and a downward frequency shift to 1238 cm^{-1}; in addition the intense line at 949 cm^{-1} [ν(C-C)] is shifted to 931 cm^{-1} upon conversion. The midpoint of conversion at pH $= 3.5$ (at $T = 20°C$) is in good agreement with the ORD measurements of Fasman *et al.* (1964). The cooperative pH-induced random coil-to α-helix transition of poly-L-lysine is shown in Fig. 15, where the normalized intensity of the amide III mode at 1243 cm^{-1} is plotted against pH. This band shows strong intensity in the ionized random coil conformation but decreases drastically upon conversion to the α-helical conformation (Yu *et al.*, 1973). Concomitantly the skeletal vibration of the random coil poly-L-lysine at 958 cm^{-1} shifts to 954 cm^{-1} in the α-helix. The midpoint of conversion was found to be near pH $= 10.1$ under the conditions used.

2. Temperature-Induced Transitions

a. α-Helix to Random Coil

With increasing temperature the α-helical poly-L-glumatic acid is denatured to a random coil conformation. In Fig. 16 the normalized amide III band intensity at 1238 cm^{-1} of poly-L-glutamic acid is plotted as a function

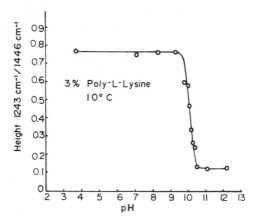

Fig. 15. Plot of the relative height of the 1243 cm^{-1} amide III band of poly-*L*-lysine to the 1446 cm^{-1} band at 10°C, 3% in H_2O versus pH, showing ionized $\leftrightarrows \alpha$ transition (from Yu *et al.*, 1973).

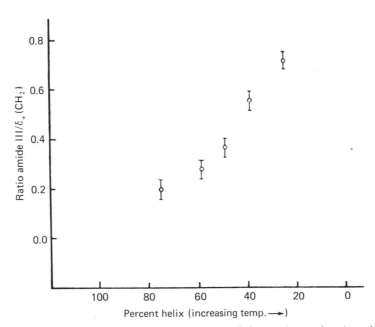

Fig. 16. Intensity ratio of amide III to methylene twisting mode as a function of percent helix. Both the ratio and the percent helix are functions of temperature (2% PGA (O), 0.2 N NaCl at pH-4.85) (from Koenig and Frushour, 1972).

of percent helical content, which can be directly correlated to temperature (Koenig and Frushour, 1972). In contrast with the pH-induced transition this thermally induced α-helix to random coil transformation is noncooperative. Furthermore, since the amide III and the skeletal mode frequencies do not shift with increasing temperature the authors suggest that the two random coils might have different local conformations.

b. α-Helix to β-Sheet

At pH = 11.8 poly-L-lysine is non-ionized and forms an α-helix (Yu *et al.*, 1973). When the temperature is raised this helical polypeptide precipitates in the β-sheet conformation. During the course of this conversion the amide I band shifts from 1645 to 1670 cm^{-1}, and in the amide III region an intense band evolves at 1240 cm^{-1}. In addition the skeletal vibration at 945 cm^{-1} in the α-helix is shifted to 1021 cm^{-1} with the onset of the transition.

In Fig. 17 the cooperativity of the α-helix to β-sheet transition can be seen by plotting the intensity of the normalized amide III line at 1240 cm^{-1} versus temperature. Similar frequency shifts of the amide III mode were observed in thermally induced left-handed α-helix to antiparallel β-sheet conversion of poly-β-benzyl-L-aspartate (Frushour and Koenig, 1975), although this region was dominated by benzyl side chain scattering. Infrared spectra,

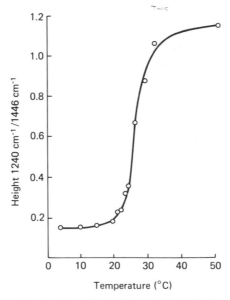

Fig. 17. Plot of the relative height of the 1240 cm^{-1} amide III band of poly-L-lysine (3%, pH-10.96) to the 1446 cm^{-1} band at pH-10.96 versus temperature, showing the cooperative $\alpha \rightarrow \beta$ transition (from Yu *et al.*, 1973).

however, showed distinct bands at 1237 and 1216 cm^{-1} assignable to amide III vibrations of the antiparallel β-sheet conformation. In the amide I mode region, Raman spectroscopy revealed a clear frequency shift from 1663 to 1679 cm^{-1}.

3. Mechanically Induced Transitions

The mechanical deformation of α-helical poly-L-alanine by rolling (or stretching) into the antiparallel β-sheet conformation was studied by Frushour and Koenig (1974a) using Raman spectroscopy. The observed frequency changes concerned the amide I band, which shifted from 1656 cm^{-1} in the α-helix to 1669 cm^{-1} in the β-sheet conformation, and three weak amide III bands near 1274 cm^{-1}, which disappeared during deformation while two prominent bands evolved at 1243 and 1231 cm^{-1}. These new bands were assigned to the presence of both β-sheet and disordered conformations. Other spectral changes which accompany this α-helix $\rightarrow$ β-sheet transition were observed in the backbone and side chain vibrational region (frequency shift of the sharp band at 1069–1098 cm^{-1}; intensity decrease of the intense band at 909 cm^{-1}) and disappearance of the carbonyl band at 531 cm^{-1}, which could be used as a measure of the helical content of poly-L-alanine.

4. Chemically Induced Transitions

Sederel et al. (1980) investigated the solid-state conformation of β-benzyl-L-aspartate copolymers with L-alanine, L-leucine, L-valine, etc., by IR spectroscopy. The incorporation of these amino acid residues into the polypeptide chain induced a change from the left-handed to the right-handed α-helix as revealed by the IR-spectra in the amide I-, amide II-, and 250–700 cm^{-1}-regions. This reversal of the helical sense has been defined as conformational induction by Klug and Applequist (1974).

Raman spectral changes induced by side chain interactions in mixtures of right- and left-handed α-helical enantiomers of poly-γ-benzyl glutamate have been reported by Wilser and Fitchen (1974). These changes, which consisted of frequency shifts in the amide I–amide III region and intensity alterations predominantly of the side chain bands, were discussed in terms of side chain interactions of right- and left-handed helices in racemic mixtures.

The specific effect of salts on the conformation of poly-L-lysine has been studied by Yu et al. (1973) and Tang and Albrecht (1974) using Raman and IR spectroscopy. The binding of NaClO$_4$ to poly-L-lysine induced the formation of the α-helix as revealed by the amide I band shift from 1646 to 1638 cm^{-1}. In contrast, the addition of NaCl or CaCl$_2$ produced a shift of the amide I band to slightly higher frequency positions, indicating the conversion to a disordered conformation.

The influence of organic acids on polypeptides has been described by Wilsèr and Fitchen (1974) and by Bonora and Toniolo (1981). Wilser and Fitchen found that after using computerized solvent substraction, the amide III band at 1291 cm^{-1} of poly-γ-benzyl-L-glutamate is removed by dichloracetic acid and that a broad peak near 1254 cm^{-1} appeared. This spectral change was interpreted as a transition from the α-helical to the disordered polypeptide conformation. Bonora and Toniolo (1981) used IR spectroscopy to investigate the interaction between trifluoroacetic acid, dichloroacetic acid, formic acid, acetic acid, and L-homo-oligopeptides. To distinguish between hydrogen-bonding interactions or protonation of the peptide groups, these authors investigated the spectral region of the amide I and amide II bands (1500 – 1700 cm^{-1}).

In all oligopeptides studied, hydrogen-bonding interactions were revealed by the shift of the amide I bands at 1665 – 1685 cm^{-1} to lower frequencies. No change in frequency and intensity of the amide II bands could be detected. Only in the case of the methionine-oligopeptide at very high trifluoroacetic acid concentrations the disappearance of the amide II band and the replacement of the amide I by the solvent carboxylate band at 1600 – 1620 cm^{-1} pointed to a protonation of the peptide group.

The observed decrease of intensity of the amide III bands during the random coil → α-helix transition and the increase during the random coil → anti-parallel β-sheet transition, were called hypo- and hyperchromism, respectively, by analogy with similar effects occurring in the UV spectra of polypeptides. This relationship between Raman and UV spectra is based on the dependence of the Raman scattering intensity upon a summation over all pairs of excited electronic energy levels. Therefore, the Raman intensities are sensitive to changes in the intensity of the UV bands. These problems were reviewed and summarized by Tang and Albrecht (1974) and Frushour et al. (1976).

C. Conformational Transitions in Naturally Occurring Polypeptides and Proteins

The above detailed correlations between the conformation of synthetic peptides and their amide band positions and intensities can be extended to conformational studies of naturally occurring polypeptides and proteins. Much progress concerning the elucidation of the structure-activity relationship in proteins has been due to the detailed information obtained via Raman and IR spectroscopy.

Using Raman spectroscopy, Yu et al. (1972) were able to reveal multiple spectral changes accompanying the heat denaturation of insulin at low pH. During this denaturation reversible globular-fibrous transitions occur and might well parallel the observed reversibility of the biological activity of this protein.

In the amide I region the strong band at 1662 cm⁻¹ with a shoulder near 1680 cm⁻¹, which has been assigned to the α-helical and random coil structure, was shifted on heating at 100°C, for 45 min, to 1673 cm⁻¹ and increased in intensity (see Fig. 18). Intense Raman bands at 1673 cm⁻¹ are indicative of the β-sheet structure as derived from model polypeptides. The spectral shift to higher frequencies could be explained in terms of a weaken-

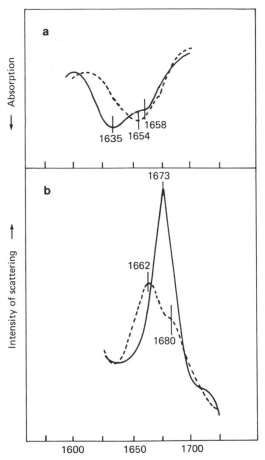

Fig. 18. Comparison of infrared (a) and Raman (b) amide I frequencies of insulin; native (---), denatured (———) (from Yu *et al.*, 1972).

ing of the hydrogen bonding with increasing temperature, and the corresponding decrease in line width of the amide I band as a reflection of the greater uniformity in the hydrogen bonding. In addition, intra- and interchain coupling between adjacent peptide units could also be responsible for the observed frequency shift.

The amide III band at $1270 \, \text{cm}^{-1}$ (with a shoulder at $1288 \, \text{cm}^{-1}$) shifts on heating to $1239 \, \text{cm}^{-1}$ indicating a transition from the α-helical conformation to both, the random-coil and β-sheet structure. Additional changes occur in the skeletal C—C and C—N stretching region ($800-1200 \, \text{cm}^{-1}$) and in the skeletal bending region ($<800 \, \text{cm}^{-1}$), indicating an extensive unfolding of the protein backbone and a transition to the β-sheet conformation.

Disulfide-bridges (—C—S—S—C—) play an important role in determining the tertiary and quaterniary structure of proteins and in modifying the biological activity of many polypeptides and proteins. In native insulin three disulfide bridges exist, showing frequencies at $515 \, \text{cm}^{-1}$ (S—S stretching) and at $668-678 \, \text{cm}^{-1}$ (C—S stretching). Upon heat denaturation of insulin the intensity of the S—S stretching vibration increases while that of the C—S stretching vibration at $668 \, \text{cm}^{-1}$ decreases. Concomitantly, a shift of the $668 \, \text{cm}^{-1}$ band to $657 \, \text{cm}^{-1}$ was observed. In contrast with this, the intensity of the band at $678 \, \text{cm}^{-1}$ did not change and showed only a small shift to $680 \, \text{cm}^{-1}$. These observations were explained by involving different geometries for the two interchain disulfide bridges, and by the resistance of the intrachain bridge to conformational changes upon denaturation. No significant changes in the amide I and III mode regions of aqueous insulin solutions were observed when the pH was increased from 2.4 to 8.3.

A Raman spectroscopic study of the reversible thermal unfolding of bovine pancreatic ribonuclease A (pH-5 in 0.1 M NaCl) was published by Chen and Lord (1976). The thermal denaturation of this enzyme over the temperature range from $32-70\,°\text{C}$ was followed by spectral changes in the amide I and III mode regions. During the unfolding process the amide III line at $1250 \, \text{cm}^{-1}$ increases considerably in intensity (see Fig. 19), while the lines at 1235 and $1265 \, \text{cm}^{-1}$ decrease in intensity. The melting point (T_m) obtained from the plot of the intensity at $1250 \, \text{cm}^{-1}$ versus temperature (Fig. 19) was about $60\,°\text{C}$, which is in good agreement with the T_m obtained by other techniques (Garel and Baldwin, 1973; Winchester et al., 1970). The authors suggest that the noncooperative shape of the melting curve reflects a multiple process with signs of *premelting* below $60\,°\text{C}$ in which the residues of the peptide backbone convert continuously from their ordered native helical or β-sheet conformations to some intermediate geometry, and that even at temperatures near $70\,°\text{C}$ considerable amounts of helical and β-sheet conformations are present. Concomitantly, the amide I line at $1668 \, \text{cm}^{-1}$ shifts to

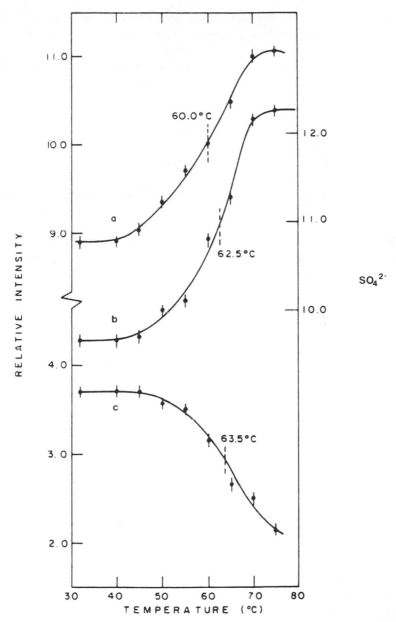

Fig. 19. Thermal transition curves of 7% R Nase A as monitored by (a) the amide III vibration at 1250 cm^{-1}, (b) SO$_4^{2-}$ stretching at 982 cm^{-1}, (c) C$_\alpha$—C stretching at 937 cm^{-1} (from Chen and Lord, 1976).

1671 cm^{-1} and the linewidth increases by about 10 cm^{-1} upon denaturation, indicating a more disordered structure. Similar melting curves with T_m at $62 - 63\,°C$ were obtained when the intensities or the intensity ratio of the tyrosyl bands at $830 - 850$ cm^{-1} are plotted versus temperature. These changes reflect the strength of the hydrogen bonding in the tyrosyl residues and might be regarded as a change from a *buried* to a more *exposed* structure. In addition, changes in the geometry of the disulfide bridges during the thermal unfolding of ribonuclease A were followed by measurements of the frequency and linewidth of the Raman lines near 510 cm^{-1} (S—S stretching) and 657 cm^{-1} (C—S stretching). Figure 20 shows the curves obtained from the frequency shift and linewidth increase of the S—S stretching band at 516 cm^{-1}, as well as of the relative intensity of the C—S stretching line at 657 cm^{-1} as a function of temperature. The melting or transition points obtained from these curves were found to lie between 60 and $62\,°C$.

The information derived from this Raman spectroscopic study is compatible with the model of ribonuclease A unfolding in six sharply defined intermediate stages as proposed by Burgess and Scheraga (1975).

The conformational changes of the major protein components in egg white, occurring during thermal denaturation and aggregation has been studied by Painter and Koenig (1976b) using Raman spectroscopy. As revealed by the spectral shifts of the amide I and III lines, lyophylized ovalbumin is predominantly present in a disordered conformation mixed in with small amounts of the β-sheet structure. Upon thermal denaturation at $70\,°C$ for 10 min the amide I line shifts from 1667 to 1672 cm^{-1} and an intense amide III band at 1236 cm^{-1} evolves. These spectral changes suggest the formation of extensive regions of the antiparallel β-sheet conformation in ovalbumin.

From the broad and structureless amide III band and the amide I band at 1667 cm^{-1} it can be estimated that conalbumin has about 50% α-helical and 50% unordered regions in the native state. After coagulation the amide I band shifts to 1672 cm^{-1} and a distinct amide III band at 1239 cm^{-1} is observed, demonstrating the formation of extensive intermolecular β-sheet structures.

Chen *et al.* (1973) investigated the Raman spectra of aqueous lysozyme in the temperature range from $32 - 76\,°C$ and found that the native structure of this enzyme including the geometry of the disulfide bridges, was practically unchanged up to $76\,°C$. However, thermal denaturation of lysozyme at $100\,°C$ for 2 hr produced irreversible changes in the peptide backbone as revealed by the amide I and III frequencies and led to geometrical alterations of the disulfide bonds.

A comparison of the lysozyme structure in crystals and in solution by Raman spectroscopy indicated only small spectral differences which were

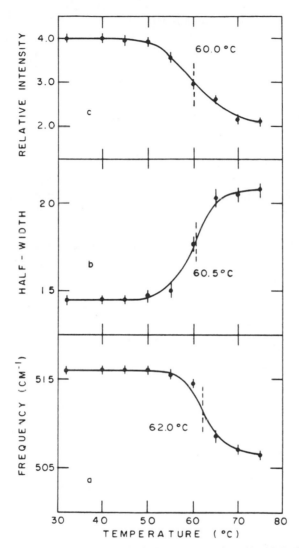

Fig. 20. Thermal transition curves of 7% R Nase A as monitored by (a) the frequency of the S—S stretching line, (b) the half-width of the S—S stretching line, (c) the relative intensity (peak height) of the C—S stretching line at 657 cm^{-1} (from Chen and Lord, 1976).

interpreted in terms of side chain conformational changes (Yu and Jo, 1973).

The effect of pH on the conformation of proteins has been extensively investigated and elucidated using the potentialities of Raman spectroscopy. The pH denaturation of tropomyosin, a water-soluble muscle protein, has been studied by Frushour and Koenig (1974b). In the native state the polypeptide chains of this protein are arranged in a two-stranded α-helical coil. Based on the ORD data of Lowey (1965) the α-helical content near pH-7 amounts to about 90%, but decreases drastically when the pH is raised above 9.5. The strong amide I band of native tropomyosin appeared at 1655 cm^{-1}, while the amide III region around 1250 cm^{-1} was weak. In addition a medium-intensity line at 940 cm^{-1} (skeletal stretching) was observed. In the pH-denaturated state (above pH-9.5) a strong amide III line appeared at 1254 cm^{-1} and the intensity of the line at 940 cm^{-1} decreased. These intensity changes clearly reflect the transition of the α-helical conformation to a predominantly disordered state. The pH-dependence of the above-mentioned Raman line intensities and of the calculated α-helix content are shown in Fig. 21 from the data of Frushour and Koenig (1974b). Based on the same spectral parameters, Pézolet et al. (1976) followed the pH-denaturation of human immunoglobulin G (IGG). In the native state at pH-7, the β-structure content of this protein was evaluated to be about 37%. When IGG was denatured at pH-11, the intensity variations and changes of the amide I and III regions and of the skeletal stretching modes (991 and 1078 cm^{-1}), indicated a decrease of the amount of β-structure and a transition toward a more disordered conformation.

Conformational changes of calf thymus histones (H1, H2A, H2B) which are the major constituents of the chromosomal proteins were described by Guillot et al. (1977). On raising the pH from 3 to 5, or increasing the NaCl concentration to 1 M in aqueous histone solutions, the same frequency shift of the amide III region were induced and were interpreted as a transition toward a more compact or globular structure with a helical content of about 20%.

Raman spectra of native feather keratin revealed that this protein contained 64% of the antiparallel pleated sheet structure and 36% of a disordered component. After dissolution the structure was 100% unordered (Hsu et al., 1976). To obtain a quantitative measure of the different conformational contributions, the authors used Gaussian or a combination of Gaussian – Lorentzian functions to resolve the overlapping bands involved. In addition arguments for the superiority of the amide I region to the amide III region in characterizing disordered polypeptide structures were discussed.

Recently Shelnutt et al. (1981) developed a Raman difference spectroscopic technique which allows reliable detection of frequency differences down to $\simeq 0.01$ cm^{-1}. This technique was applied to study details of protein – heme interactions in cytochrome C of 24 species. Systematic frequency differences (0.02 – 2 cm^{-1}) which arose from the different amino acid sequences of the porphyrin ring could be classified into three groups of structural variations:

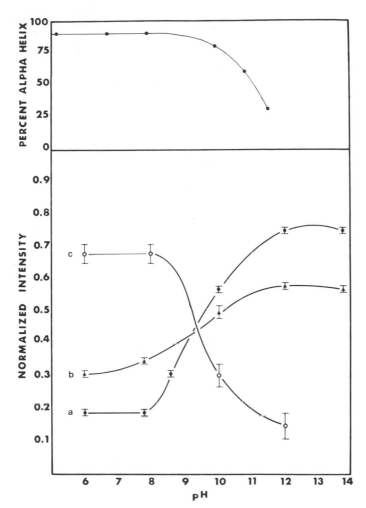

Fig. 21. Intensities of several conformationally sensitive lines in the Raman spectrum of tropomyosin plotted as a function of pH. The intensities were measured as peak heights and normalized to the 1451 cm^{-1} line; (a) amide III mode, 1254 cm^{-1}, (b) $v_s(COO^-)$, 1402 cm^{-1}, (c) skeletal vibration, 940 cm^{-1} (from Frushour and Koenig, 1974b).

    1.   Direct interaction between near-heme residues and porphyrin which influence the electron density in the porphyrin π-orbitals,

    2.   species-specific differences in the amino acid sequence at residue 92 (far-heme position) which influence the conformation of this region, and

    3.   the conformation near cysteine-14 which might affect the substituent sensitive mode at 1313 cm^{-1}.

Conformational transitions localized in the region of C—S and S—S bonds can be studied using Raman spectroscopy. The origin of C—S and S—S stretching vibrations were investigated by Sugeta *et al.* (1972, 1973) using normal coordinate analyses of dialkyl disulfides. These results show that the S—S stretching frequencies depend on the internal rotation about the C—S bonds.

As shown in Fig. 22 frequency positions can be related to distinct C—C—S—S—C—C conformations. Tu *et al.* (1976) studied the conformation of sea snake venom (type I) with respect to the C—S and S—S frequency region. The sharp and symmetrical peak at 512 cm^{-1} (S—S stretching assigned to the gauche–gauche–gauche form) indicated that the 4 disulfide bonds in the native toxin have a similar geometry. After heat treatment at 100°C for 30 min, the major peak at 512 cm^{-1} remained practically unchanged but a new shoulder at 546 cm^{-1} appeared, pointing to the

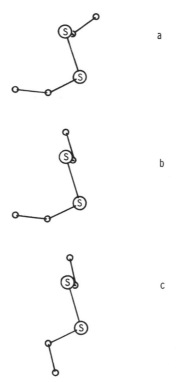

Fig. 22. Dependence of the S—S stretching frequency on the internal-rotation [trans (t) or gauche (g)] about the C—S bonds, (a) gauche–gauche–gauche form, v(S—S)-510 cm^{-1}, (b) gauche–gauche–trans form, 525 cm^{-1} (c) trans–gauche–trans form, 540 cm^{-1} (from Tu *et al.*, 1976).

existence of a new type of S—S stretching vibration which could be assigned to the trans–gauche–trans form of at least one disulfide bridge.

The C—S stretching frequencies depend on the molecular conformation about the C—C bonds adjacent to the C—S bonds (Sugeta et al., 1972). If a hydrogen atom is trans with respect to the C—S bond, the respective vibrations are in the 630–670 cm^{-1} region. For this reason Tu et al. (1976) assumed that the C—S stretching band at 658 cm^{-1} in the native toxin indicate that the conformation about the C—C bond is mostly in the P_H form. This band was not significantly affected by heat denaturation.

The Raman spectrum of sea snake toxin B in relation to its structure and neurotoxicity was investigated by Takamatsu et al. (1976). The intensity ratio of the 510 cm^{-1} band (gauche–gauche–gauche form) to the 523 cm^{-1} band (gauche–gauche–trans form) was found to be about (1.25, indicating that 3 out of 5 disulfide bridges in the toxin possess a gauche–gauche–gauche structure, while the remaining 2 were of the gauche–gauche–trans form. The strong band at 662 cm^{-1} was assigned to the C—S stretching in the trans form and the weak band at 705 cm^{-1} to the C—S stretching in the gauche form.

In a similar study Prescott et al. (1976) investigated the Raman spectrum of aqueous solutions of sea anemone toxin II and assigned the intense band at 509 cm^{-1} to the gauche–gauche–gauche form arising from all three disulfide bridges.

In water soluble bovine lens protein fractions (β_1, β_2, β_3) a band at 512 cm^{-1} revealed the presence of disulfide bridges (Yu and East, 1975). In addition a strong S—H band at 2582 cm^{-1} could be observed. Denaturation of the lens proteins by heating at 100°C for 1 hr did not affect this sulfhydryl band, indicating that ocular lens opacification does not necessarily involve the oxidation of S—H groups or other conformational changes.

V. TRANSITIONS IN NUCLEOSIDES, NUCLEOTIDES, AND NUCLEIC ACIDS

A. General Spectral Considerations

The molecular vibrations of nucleosides (base + sugar) and nucleotides (base + sugar + phosphate) can be assigned to the modes associated with the bases or to the sugar-phosphate backbone and lie in the spectral region between 200–3000 cm^{-1}. The intensity and frequency of many Raman bands are sensitive to the conformation of the macromolecules and are, therefore, well suited to monitor phase transitions and local structural perturbations.

The Raman scattering intensity depends mainly on the first few UV-absorption bands which are associated with electronic transitions localized on the bases. Therefore, in contrast to the strong skeletal ring vibrations of the bases, relatively weak or no intensity changes are associated with the backbone phosphate or ribose vibrations (Painter and Koenig, 1976a; Lord and Thomas, 1967).

The information obtained from these intensity and frequency changes can be correlated with the cooperative (and noncooperative) melting behavior of polynucleotides, the conformational changes caused by hydrogen bonding, base stacking, gel formation, the effects of protonation, relative humidity, acylation, interaction with ions, proteins, etc., the intercalation with certain drugs and dyes, and the kinetics of deuterium exchange and hydrolysis of nucleic acids.

In UV spectroscopy a decrease of the molar absorptivity of the nucleic acid bases is observed as a consequence of vertical base stacking interactions and lateral interactions (De Voe and Tinoco, 1962). This decrease has been called hypochromism and correspondingly the decrease of the Raman intensities of certain vibrational bands of the aromatic bases is referred to as Raman hypochromism (Tomlinson and Peticolas, 1970; Pézolet et al., 1975).

The Raman spectra of bases, nucleosides, and nucleotides have been extensively studied by Lord and Thomas (1967) in the solid state and in solution. Qualitative vibrational assignments were made and the intensity and frequency changes observed at different pH values were correlated with structural perturbations in oligo- and polynucleotides (Erfurth et al., 1972; Tsuboi et al., 1971; Tsuboi, 1974; Koenig, 1973).

B. Conformational Transition Studies in Nucleosides

Aqueous solutions (50 mM) of cytidine and uridine ribonucleosides were investigated in the protonated and unprotonated state by O'Connor et al. (1976a). Both bases are protonated at the $N-3$ position, the pK values being 4.1 and 9.2, respectively. The observed intensity changes of the nucleoside bands were grouped into three classes:

1. bands, which are diagnostic of the concentration of the species in solution (state of protonation) and of the pK value,

2. bands, whose intensity is independent of pH, and

3. bands, which are sensitive to pH, but the intensity change does not parallel the concentration of the species in solution. Both nucleosides exhibited only two intensity invariant bands at 784 and 865 cm^{-1}. Six diagnostic bands (or band envelopes) were detected in the cytidine spectrum and five in the uridine spectrum.

The cytidine band at 1254 cm^{-1} (ring vibration $C-NH_2$ stretch) was the most intense band in acid solution. Its intensity decreased significantly as a function of deprotonation and was split into two well-defined bands at 1241 and 1290 cm^{-1}. This spectral range represented best the qualitative and quantitative indicator of protonation for cytidine.

The information derived from these pH-diagnostic bands of cytidine extended markedly the understanding of processes occurring at specific pH values in poly (C), for example, the cooperative structural transition producing a double helix.

In the uridine spectrum the most intense band at low pH was located at 1230 cm^{-1} (assignment as above) and showed the greatest intensity reduction as deprotonation occurred and three weaker bands at 1199, 1234, and 1293 cm^{-1} appeared. In addition the intensity of the carbonyl band at 1670 cm^{-1} was pH-dependent and shifted to lower frequency when the pH was raised.

Delabar and Guschlbauer (1979) studied ^{2}H and ^{15}N substituted guanosines by Raman spectroscopy in neutral, acidic, and basic solutions. When 0.02 M guanosine solutions at pH-7 are cooled to 10°C, a gel starts to form below the melting point of 27–30°C. This gel consists of tetramers which are stabilized by stacking interactions, horizontal base–base hydrogen bonds, and vertical base–sugar bonds (Chantot *et al.*, 1974).

The process of gel-formation which is not observed with other nucleosides is spectroscopically reflected in frequency and intensity changes. The observed frequency shifts were tentatively attributed to hydrogen bond formation between two nucleosides. These base–water bonds which exist in solution above the melting point become essentially base–base or base–sugar bonds in the gel state.

The carbonyl stretching vibration band peaking at 1671 cm^{-1} in guanosine-d_4 solutions at 60°C, evolves into two bands with maxima at 1700 and 1665 cm^{-1}, in the gel state. Both maxima were tentatively assigned to hydrogen bonded C=O group vibrations, the first is located in the hydrophobic environment of the stacked tetramers and the second one is localized in a region accessible to water. At low temperatures the relative intensity of the ribose C—O stretching vibrations at 1080 cm^{-1} decreased in comparison with that at 1030 cm^{-1}. This observation was explained in terms of the reduced mobility of the ribosyl group in the gel state. In addition, the intensity of several ring vibrations (e.g., at 1577, 1490, 1368, and 1323 cm^{-1}) decreased during gel formation by more than 50%.

C. Conformational Transition Studies in Nucleotides

Aqueous solutions of 5'-GMP (guanosine mono-phosphate) at pH-5 form a clear viscous gel upon cooling which consists of continuous helices stabilized by hydrogen bonding and stacking interactions. This secondary structure is clearly different from that of the 3′-GMP under the same conditions which form square planar tetramers (Gellert *et al.,* 1962).

Raman spectroscopic studies concerning these differences have been performed by Small and Peticolas (1971). These authors observed a number of new bands in the 5′-GMP spectrum at 0°C. The most prominent lines were the conformation-dependent —O—P—O— symmetric stretching mode of the dihydroxy species at 814 cm^{-1} (Brown and Peticolas, 1975) and the guanine ring stretching mode at 670 cm^{-1}. It was suggested that the structure of the 5′-isomer is stabilized by hydrogen bonding between the phosphate groups and guanine amino- or 2′OH ribose-groups. The Raman data presented by Thomas and Hartman (1973) showed that the highly localized vibration of the O—P—O group at 814 cm^{-1} in ordered mononucleotides (such as in the helical 5′-GMP at pH-5) requires for its generation a covalent structure which contains the sequence 5′C—O—P—O—3′C or 5′C—O—P—O—H and a highly specific geometry of the —O—P—O— linkages. Melting curves of 5′-GMP and 3′-GMP revealed a larger hypochromism of the 1490 cm^{-1} band (guanine ring stretching) in the 5′-isomer than in the 3′-isomer.

Raman spectra of 5′-GMP at pH-7.5 have also been studied by Gramlich *et al.* (1976). The splitting of the C=O stretching mode at 1670 cm^{-1} and the Raman hypochromism of the 1487 cm^{-1} band which was caused by decreasing the temperature from 40 to 0°C showed that the carbonyl group and the N − 7 position are involved in the protonation of the ordered 5′-GMP at neutral pH. The 814 cm^{-1} band which is indicative of helix formation in 5′-GMP at pH-5 was not observed under these conditions (see above). A plot of the intensity of the 1487 cm^{-1} band versus temperature (Fig. 23) revealed a typical co-operative transition curve.

Based on the similarities concerning the spectral characteristics and cooperative phase transitions of 5′-GMP at pH-7.5 and 3′-GMP at acidic pH these authors also suggested for the structure of the 5′-isomer square planar tetramers stacked upon each other, with the ribose and phosphate residues protruding into the solvent. This model is in good agreement with earlier findings of Miles and Frazier (1972) using IR spectroscopy.

Raman pH-profiles of 5′-GMP and 5′-AMP (adenosine monophosphate) were published by O'Connor *et al.* (1976b). Just as in the case of cytidine and uridine (O'Connor *et al.,* 1976a) the intensity variations of the bands were classified in both nucleotides into three classes depending on whether they were sensitive or insensitive to protonation.

In 5′-AMP the deprotonation occurred at the N − 1 position of the base (pK 3.3 – 3.9) and at the secondary phosphate (pK 6.1 – 6.5). The Raman spectra exhibited six diagnostic bands at 1253, 1378, 1407, 1483, 1560, and 1581 cm^{-1}, assigned to the deprotonation at the N − 1 position and two

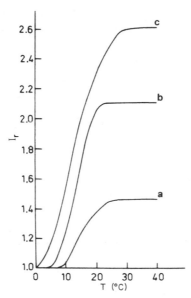

Fig. 23. Plot of the intensity of the bank at 1487 cm^{-1} in (a) 0.2 M 5'-GMP (pH-7.5), (b) 0.3 M 3'-GMP (pH-5.0), and (c) 0.03 M 5'-GMP (pH-5.0) versus temperature (ratio to intensity at 0°C) (from Gramlich *et al.,* 1976).

diagnostic bands at 978 and 1081 cm^{-1}, assigned to the secondary phosphate deprotonation.   The intensity of the adenine ring breathing mode at 722 cm^{-1} was pH-invariant in contrast with the bands at 630, 810, 1215, 1290–1353, and 1509 cm^{-1} which were pH-sensitive but not diagnostic.

For 5'-GMP, the deprotonation took place at the N − 7 position (pK 2.4), at the secondary phosphate (pK 6.1) and at the N − 1 position (pK 9.4). Three bands at 1412, 1488, and 1537 cm^{-1} appeared to be diagnostic for the deprotonation at the N − 7 position, one band at 980 cm^{-1} for the deprotonation at the secondary phosphate group and the two bands at 1178 and 1477 cm^{-1} were diagnostic for the proton dissociation at the N − 1 position.

In contrast with all other nucleotides studied, the spectrum of 5'-GMP showed no band of which the intensity was pH-invariant and only few of the observed bands which were pH-sensitive, can actually be considered as diagnostic according to the authors' definition.   As will be shown later the information obtained from the pH-profiles of the nucleotides and nucleosides has improved our understanding of pH-dependent cooperative conformational transitions in certain polynucleotides.

Base pairing and base stacking interactions of 5'-GMP are modified by the binding of Ca^{2+}, Mg^{2+} and some transition metal ions predominantly to the N − 7 position of the imidazole ring.   These GMP-metal interactions caused frequency and intensity changes of the guanine bands at 672, 1323, 1366, and 1488 cm^{-1}, as well as of the O—P—O band at 810 cm^{-1} and the PO$_3^{2-}$ band at 978 cm^{-1} (Makrigiannis *et al.*, 1980).

The hydrogen–deuterium (H–D) exchange in 5'-AMP adsorbed on electrochemically roughened silver surfaces was studied by Koglin *et al.* (1981). This modified Raman effect, called surface enhanced Raman scattering (SERS, cf. Chapter 1), led to an enormous intensity enhancement with only small frequency shifts in the 2000–3000 cm^{-1} range. Three sites of H–D exchange could be probed directly: The 2- and 8-CH in the adenine base, the CH in the ribose and the OH in the ribose. According to the authors the study of the kinetic parameters of the H–D exchange by SERS should provide more detailed information about structural fluctuations (opening–closing) in the more complex polynucleotides.

Ultraviolet resonance Raman spectra of cytidine monophosphate (CMP) and uridine monophosphate (UMP) were analyzed by Peticolas (1978) in detail. From the resonance intensity enhancement an estimate of the distortion of the geometry of these nucleotides in the excited electronic state has been made.

D. Transitions in Polynucleotides

1. Synthetic Polynucleotides

a. Poly (C)†

Poly (C) exhibits two pK$_a$ values of 5.7 and 3.0. In solutions at pH > 5.7 this homopolynucleotide exists as a single-stranded polymer with considerable base stacking and a partially ordered phosphodiester backbone. At pH values < 5.7 the formation of a double-stranded helix is observed. The protonation occurs at the N$_3$ position. In contrast with poly (A) the added proton is located in the interior of the poly (C) helix.

O'Connor and Scovell (1981) investigated the thermal melting profiles of poly (C) in the pH range 4.1–6.6 using the integrated intensities of three characteristic band envelopes which provided detailed information about the thermal conversion of the double-stranded helix to coil form and the effect of protonation:

(i)   The 780 cm^{-1} band of the vibrational envelope in the region 760–830 cm^{-1} has been assigned to the cytosine ring breathing mode. Its intensity did not vary with the protonation of cytidine but was sensitive to the temperature-induced denaturation process (hypochromic). The phospho-

---

† For an explanation of abbreviations, see Table III.

TABLE III

EXPLANATION OF ABBREVIATIONS

p	= phosphate
r	= ribo
d	= desoxy ribo
(A)	= (adenylic acid)
(G)	= (guanylic acid)
(C)	= (cytidylic acid)
(U)	= (uridylic acid)
(I)	= (inosinic acid)
poly (A)	≙ poly (dA)

diester backbone stretching mode at 805 cm^{-1} was not hypochromic and its intensity was directly affected only by base stacking interactions.

(ii)   The 1170–1310 cm^{-1} envelope consisted of two cytosine ring vibrations.   The intensity of both bands increased with the degree of protonation and was also temperature sensitive (hypochromic).

(iii)   The 1527 cm^{-1} band (assigned to the cytosine vibration) is a quantitative indicator of the extent of cytidine protonation.   In contrast with the above-mentioned 1170–1310 cm^{-1} envelope its intensity decreased with increasing protonation and temperature-dependent base stacking.   This band is probably the most sensitive monitor of the cooperative structural and conformational change involved in the single strand ⇌ double strand transition.

Figure 24 shows an example of the temperature-induced spectral changes of poly (C) at pH-5.37.   The pH dependence of the melting temperatures as revealed by the three envelopes is indicated in Table IV.   The T_m values derived from the 1170–1310 and 1527 cm^{-1} envelopes which were both pH-sensitive and hypochromic are in good agreement with those obtained from UV analyses (Langridge and Rich, 1963).

In summary, O'Connor and Scovell (1981) obtained the following results:

(i)   At neutral pH all band intensity profiles exhibited essentially the same noncooperative change during melting.

(ii)   In acid solutions these intensity profiles showed a cooperative melting behavior.

(iii)   As the pH decreased, the T_m of all three bands increased.

(iv)   The T_m values of the 1527 and 1170–1310 cm^{-1} envelopes were almost identical in the pH range studied.   However, the T_m values of the 760–830 cm^{-1} envelope were considerably lower at pH-5.37 to 4.24.

(v)   These ΔT_m values (up to 9°C at pH-4.78) reflected the sensitivity of

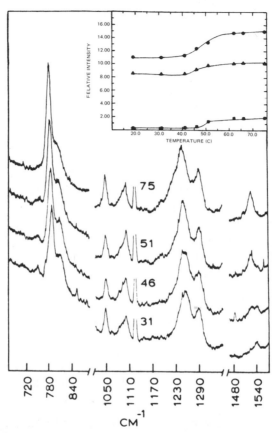

Fig. 24. Raman spectrum of poly (C) at pH-5.37 and at various temperatures. Insert: Raman thermal-melting profiles at pH-5.37. The monitored bands and the symbols are the same as in Fig. 3 (from O'Connor and Scovell, 1981).

each band concerning base stacking and/or protonation and they could be correlated with the extent to which the protons were dissociated from acidic poly (C) during thermal denaturation.

(vi)   During the thermal denaturation process a complete and coopera- tive loss of protons from acidic poly (C) at pH range 5.7 – 4.78 occurred while only incomplete dissociation was observed at lower pH values (4.43 – 4.10). In contrast with previous suggestions (Guschlbauer 1975, 1976) no increase in poly (C) protonation could be observed during thermal denaturation.

In contrast with other polynucleotides the PO_2-band at 1100 cm^{-1} broad- ened and became asymmetrical in poly (C) [and poly (A)] at low pH. Therefore, the intensity ratio 814 cm^{-1}/1100 cm^{-1} could not be taken as a monitor for the backbone geometry of poly (C).

TABLE IV
THERMAL MELTING TEMPERATURES FOR ACID POLY (C)[a]

Band (cm^{-1})	pH Dependence of T_m values (°C)							
	5.69	5.37	5.16	5.02	4.78	4.43	4.24	4.10
1527	32	50	58	62	68	76	80	83
1170–1310	32	49	57	61	67	75	80	82
760–830	(31)	46	54	56	59	71	78	82
ΔT_m[b]	—	4	4	6	9	5	2	—

  [a] from O'Connor and Scovell (1981).
  [b] ΔT_m is the difference between the T_m value obtained from the 780–805 cm^{-1} band and the T_m value obtained from either of the other two bands. The T_m values are considered reproducible to ± 1 °C.

b. Poly (rC)

Studies on aqueous polynucleotides and their complexes by Thomas and Hartman (1973) revealed that a strong, highly localized Raman band near 814 cm^{-1} (O—P—O symmetric stretching) occurred only in polyribonucleotides, e.g., polyribocytidilic acid [poly (rC)], which contained regions of ordered single-stranded structures [such as poly (rA), poly (rC) at low temperature] and/or regions of Watson–Crick base paired structures [such as poly (rA) · poly (rU), poly (rC) · poly rG), etc.]. After thermal denaturation, i.e., in their disordered structure, no band occurred at this frequency and only a very weak band near 795 cm^{-1} was detectable. The frequency shift from 814 to 795 cm^{-1} was correlated with conformational changes of the C—O—P—O—C linkages in the polynucleotide backbone.

The PO$_2$-symmetric stretching band at 1100 cm^{-1} was largely insensitive to the order–disorder transition in polynucleotides and was used for determining the intensity ratio 814 cm^{-1}/1100 cm^{-1}. This ratio was 1.64 ± 0.04 in completely ordered structures and approached zero in the disordered state; it was independent of the base sequence in paired regions and of the nature of Watson–Crick pairs.

In addition, the authors provided evidence that the conformation of the phosphodiester group (C—O—P—O—C) in ordered polyribonucleotides was very similar to that of the phosphomonoester group (C—O—P—O—H) in ordered mononucleotides such as 5-GMP and 5-AMP at pH-5.

Poly (rC) in the protonated and nonprotonated state in aqueous solutions has been extensively studied by Chou and Thomas (1977). Poly (rC) consists of a single-stranded ordered structure at neutral pH which is converted to a disordered double-stranded structure at pH range 5.5–3.7. When the pH is decreased below 3, polyribonucleotide precipitates and a random chain is generated.

The spectra of poly (rC) below 40°C revealed that the phosphate vibrations at 810 cm^{-1} (O—P—O symmetric stretching) and at 1098 cm^{-1} (PO$_2^-$ symmetric stretching) as well as the high intensity ratio (810 cm^{-1}/1100 cm^{-1}) strongly indicated an ordered single-stranded helical structure in which the backbone geometry of the C—O—P—O—C linkages was similar to that found in the "A-type" polynucleotide helices.

Several cytosine ring vibrations were noted which were characteristic of the protonated or neutral state; for example, the ring vibration at 1194 cm^{-1} clearly represented stacked neutral cytosine of the single stranded poly (rC) at pH-7, whereas a band at 1146 cm^{-1} was indicative of the protonated cytosine ring.

A noncooperative change in structure above 40°C was observed when the intensities of certain cytosine ring vibrations (1194, 1292, 1383, 1527 cm^{-1}, etc.) were plotted against temperature. The melting profiles above T_m were typical of an ordered backbone with unstacked bases.

The ordered double-stranded poly (rC) · poly (rC$^+$), which exists between pH-5.5 and 3.7, contained semi-protonated bases as a consequence of the uptake of $\frac{1}{2}$ mole H$^+$ per mole cytosine. As in the case of poly (rC) the backbone geometry was that of the "A-type." Denaturation occurred cooperatively above 80°C with the elimination of the semi-protonated base stacking, base pairing, and A-helical geometry. According to the melting behavior of several hypochromic and hyperchromic ring vibrations the thermal denaturation process was interpreted to yield two separated single strands containing a mixture of neutral and protonated cytosine rings in an alternating sequence poly (rC, rC$^+$). Such a distribution is thought to minimize the electrical repulsion between protonated residues and to maximize the entropy of the system.

Below pH-3 the poly (rC) · poly (rC$^+$) dissociates into 2 random chains of fully protonated poly (rC$^+$). In contrast with this poly (rA$^+$) · poly (rA$^+$) was found to be stable and the PO$_2^-$ and O—P—O stretching vibrations of poly (rC$^+$) were characteristic of a random chain at all temperatures.

A plot of the cytosine ring frequency near 1380 cm^{-1} as a function of pH at 32°C clearly demonstrated the stability of the poly (rC) · poly (rC$^+$) complex in the pH range 5.5–3.7 (Fig. 25).

c. Poly (A)

In neutral aqueous solutions poly (A) exists as a single-stranded structure. When the pH of the solution is decreased a cooperative transition at about pH-5.8 to a double-stranded helix is observed. This cooperative uptake of protons is, however, less expressed than in the case of poly (C).

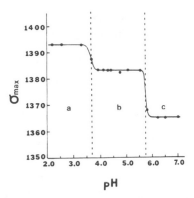

Fig. 25. Plot of the peak frequency of the Raman line near 1380 cm^{-1} as a function of solution pH; (a) poly (rC$^+$), (b) poly (rC) · poly (rC$^+$), (c) poly (rC) (from Chou and Thomas, 1977).

Raman spectra of poly (A) at different pH values were interpreted by O'Connor *et al.* (1976b) in the light of the diagnostic bands in 5′-AMP (cf. previous discussion). Several bands being characteristic of N − 1 protonation could be identified in the spectra at low pH. The increase in intensity of the shoulder at 705 cm^{-1} was interpreted as due to the formation of the double-stranded helix and the intensity decrease of the band at 1509 cm^{-1} was assigned to both protonation and conformational changes.

As mentioned earlier the PO$_2$-stretching mode at 1100 cm^{-1} broadened and became asymmetrical at low pH and was, therefore, in conjunction with the 814 cm^{-1} band, not a correct indicator of the backbone geometry of poly (A).

d. Poly (rA)

Raman spectra of polyriboadenylic acid [poly (rA)] have been studied in the pH range 7.2 – 5.2 and at different temperatures by Scovell (1978). The partially ordered single-stranded helix of poly (rA) at neutral pH converted to a double-stranded helix upon cooperative uptake of protons (pH range 6.0 – 5.7).

As already described for 5′-AMP in this section the intensity of the ring vibration at 1557 cm^{-1} increased with the degree of protonation and was found to be a good indicator of the acid form of poly (rA). At low temperatures and at pH-5.23 about 50 – 60% of the adenine residues were protonated at the N − 1 position which is located on the exterior of the double helix. If temperatures were raised above T_m a cooperative deprotonation accompanying the helix-to-coil transition was reflected in this band.

As in the case of poly (C), poly (rC), poly (A) and in contrast with all other single- or double-stranded polynucleotides the PO_2^- band at 1100 cm^{-1} was found to be sensitive to the degree of protonation via splitting into two bands at 1085 and 1100 cm^{-1}.

The adenine ring vibration at 725 cm^{-1} could be resolved into two bands: one at 725 cm^{-1} which was more prominent in neutral poly (rA) and one at 705 cm^{-1} which increased in intensity upon protonation.

The intensity ratio 725 cm^{-1}/705 cm^{-1} paralleled the noncooperative thermal denaturation of single-stranded poly (rA) as well as the cooperative melting of the double-stranded helix (Fig. 26). When the degree of protonation was increased, the electrostatic repulsion of the negatively charged phosphate units were reduced and thus the double helix was more stabilized. This higher rigidity was reflected in the higher T_m-values and the more cooperative melting.

e. Poly (G)

Several spectral forms of poly (G) as a function of the salt concentration were investigated by Delabar and Guschlbauer (1979). At low salt concentrations (Na$^+$/P $\sim$ 1) the spectrum of poly (G) was similar to that of guanosine or GMP at pH 7. The C=O vibration which was located between 1674

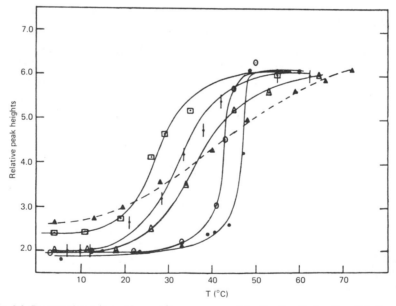

Fig. 26. Raman thermal melting profiles as expressed by the (I_{725}/I_{705}) ratio. Solution pH values and temperatures are (●) 5.23, 47; (◎) 5.35, 42; (△) 5.53, 36; (+) 5.61, 32; (□) 5.25, 26; (▲) 6.42, ~40 (from Scovel, 1978).

and 1680 cm^{-1}, was characteristic of a single-stranded structure (Rice *et al.*, 1973) and the intensity changes at 1390, 1580, and 1607 cm^{-1} indicated an interaction involving the pyrimidine ring.

The spectrum of poly (G) (in excess of NaCl) revealed similarities with that of the four-stranded gel of 5'-GMP. Two C=O vibrational bands were found above 1650 cm^{-1} and the interaction at the pyrimidine level were no more existent. As poly (G) consists of a multi-stranded stacked structure which is stable up to 100°C, it was not possible to study directly the melting behavior of this polynucleotide. Only minor intensity changes of several guanosine residues could be monitored. This observation extended earlier findings of Small and Peticolas (1971) who detected a number of frequency shifts in the spectra of poly (G) in 0.01 M sodium cacodylate when the temperature was raised to 90°C.

f. Poly (dG-dC)

Pohl *et al.* (1973) investigated neutral aqueous solutions (0.1–0.2 M) of poly (dG-dC)·poly (dC-dG), which is a synthetic DNA. Raman spectroscopy was used to monitor a salt-dependent, reversible and cooperative transition between two double-helical forms. This *order–order* conformational change of the double-stranded polynucleotides has been called R-L *transition*. In the present case the transition of the R-form (in 1 M NaCl) to the L-form was induced by raising the NaCl concentration above 2.4 M. As a consequence the following spectral differences between the two forms could be observed:

In the L-form the band at 682 cm^{-1} disappeared and a new band at 627 cm^{-1} evolved. These changes concerned the guanosine ring stretching or deformation modes. In addition the O—P—O stretching band at 832 cm^{-1} disappeared and the intensity of the PO$_2^-$ stretching band at 1094 cm^{-1} decreased significantly. As mentioned previously, these two bands were sensitive to the polymer conformation. A comparison of these two bands in poly (dG-dC)·poly (dC-dG) with other synthetic polynucleotides and natural RNA and DNA revealed that the low salt R-form could be assigned to the B-*conformation* of DNA while the high salt L-form could not be correlated with a known polynucleotide conformation. The kinetics of the R-L *interconversion* were followed by the time-dependent changes of the two ring vibrations at 625 and 680 cm^{-1}. At a final salt concentration of 4.4 M NaCl and a temperature of 16.7°C a relaxation time of 560 sec was measured. These results agree well with those previously obtained by UV absorbance (Pohl and Jovin, 1972).

Thamann *et al.* (1981) studied the Raman spectra of crystalline d(CpGpCpGpCpG) and of poly (dG-dC)·(dC-dG) in 0.1 and 4 M NaCl solutions. The comparison of these spectra showed that the high salt L-*form* of the polymer was identical to the left-handed Z-DNA structure of the crystalline oligomer. The authors suggested that the 625 cm^{-1} band in the high salt form or the intensity ratio 625 cm^{-1}/675 cm^{-1} could serve as an indicator of the relative amount of guanine residues in Z- or B-form present in synthetic or natural polynucleotides.

g. Poly (U)

Spectra of poly (U) solutions were found to exhibit no Raman hypochromism when the temperature was raised above 25°C and the absence of the O—P—O stretching band at 815 cm^{-1} which is indicative of an ordered backbone conformation revealed no structure formation under the conditions studied (Small and Peticolas, 1971). However, in the presence of Mg^{++} at low temperature, a band at 815 cm^{-1} appeared, reflecting the self-stacking of poly (U) and concomitantly, hypochromism was observed at the uracil bands at 791, 1236, and 1403 cm^{-1}.

h. Poly (C) · Poly (G)/Poly (C) · Poly (I)

Raman spectra of the double-helical complexes of poly (C)·poly (G) and poly (C)·poly (I) at neutral pH in the temperature range 0–100°C were analyzed by Brown et al. (1972).

Under conditions where a complete double-helical structure was existent, a strong band at 810–814 cm^{-1} could be observed in these polynucleotides. This O—P—O stretching band has been previously assigned to the A-type conformation of the sugar-phosphate backbone chain. An additional indicator of the formation of an A-type helical complex in poly (C)·poly (G) is the strong band at 669 cm^{-1} (guanosine–backbone interaction), which has been shown to occur in 5'-GMP upon helix formation (Small and Peticolas, 1971).

No change in the backbone structure of poly (C)·poly (G) was observed in the temperature range studied. Obviously the helix-coil transition temperature of this stable complex is too high. For this reason Brown et al. (1972) used poly (C)·poly (I) as a model for the poly (C)·poly (G) order–disorder transition.

Figure 27 illustrates the sharp melting characteristics of the poly (C)·poly (I) helix as derived from the hypochromic inosine ring vibration at 724 cm^{-1}. From this melting profile a T_m of 54°C was obtained.

The intensity ratio of the phosphate vibrations 810–814 cm^{-1}/1090–1100 cm^{-1} provides, in general, a good estimate of the fraction of the backbone chain in the A-type conformation for self-stacking single chains and for double-stranded helices (Table V). Except for poly (C)·poly (G) the fraction of A-type conformation decreases at high temperatures.

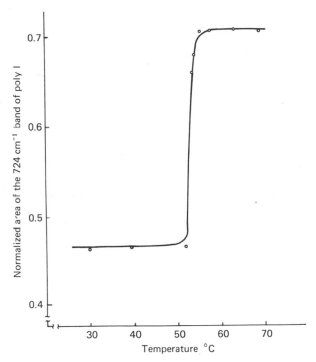

Fig. 27. Plot of the intensity of the 724 cm^{-1} band in poly I-poly C (relative to the intensity of the SO$_4^-$ band) (from Brown *et al.*, 1972).

i. Poly (A) · Poly (U)

The cooperative melting of double-stranded poly (A) · poly (U) in 0.14 M NaCl was studied by Small and Peticolas (1971). In principle the Raman spectra corresponded to the superposition spectra of the poly (A) and poly (U) components.

Several ring vibrations were found to decrease in intensity with increased stacking of the bases (Raman hypochromism) and it was possible to follow separately the stacking interactions of uracil and adenine in poly (A) · poly (U). The uracil band at 1236 cm^{-1} showed a sharp cooperative transition at 59°C when its intensity was plotted versus temperature. According to the melting profile, the poly (U) chain was completely disordered after separation from the double-helical strand. The stacking interactions in the poly (A) · poly (U) helix are therefore certainly larger than those found in the self-stacking single chain of poly (U).

The adenine band at 730 cm^{-1} showed a different melting behavior upon

TABLE V

RATIO OF PEAK HEIGHTS OF THE 810–815 CM^{-1} BAND TO THE 1098 CM^{-1}
BAND AS A MEASURE OF THE FRACTION OF THE BACKBONE BONDS IN THE
A-TYPE CONFORMATION[a]

Molecule	T (°C)	pH	I (810–815 cm^{-1}/I (1098)	Percentage A-type Conformation[b]
Poly A – poly U	15	7.0	1.7	100
Poly A – poly U	65	7.0	0	0
Poly G – poly C	95	7.0	1.4	82
Poly I – poly C	25	7.0	1.5	88
Poly C	18	6.4	1.7	100
Poly C	22	7.0	1.2	70
Poly C	75	7.0	0	0
Poly G	19	7.0	0.6	35
Poly I	9	7.0	1.2	70
Poly A	23	7.0	1.4	82
Poly A	80	7.0	0	0
Poly U (Mg^{++})	0	7.0	1.4	82
Poly U (Mg^{++})	20	7.0	0	0
t-RNA	—	7.0	1.6	94
DNA[c]	—	—	1.64	96

[a] After Brown et al. (1972).
[b] A-form as described in Erfurth et al. (1972).
[c] Fiber at low humidity of 75%.

thermal-induced unstacking with a T_m of 59°C. Above T_m the single chains of poly (A) were separated but not completely unstacked and this was reflected by an essentially noncooperative melting curve.

The totally polarized O—P—O stretching band at 814 cm^{-1}, which was found to be strong in the double-helical poly (A)·poly (U) complex and absent in the disordered separated chains, is a good indicator of the helical content of poly (A)·poly (U). A plot of the intensity of this band at 814 cm^{-1} versus temperature provided a sigmoidal curve with a T_m of 59°C.

Similar changes of the Raman spectra of poly (rA)·poly (rU) were described by Thomas (1975) upon formation of the double-helical complex. These changes concerned the Raman hypochromism of several adenine and uracil ring vibrations, frequently shifts of the uracil carbonyl group and the shift of the 814 cm^{-1} band to about 795 cm^{-1} when the double-helix dissociated.

Erfurth et al. (1975) investigated the double-helical complex of poly (A)·poly (T) and the hybrid double-helix of poly (rA)·poly (T). In the Raman spectra of poly (A)·poly (T) the authors assigned the band at 790 cm^{-1} to the backbone phosphate–sugar vibration indicative of the B-form double helix. In the poly (rA)·poly (T) spectra, however, a strong band at 814 cm^{-1} was found which is characteristic of the A-form of ribonucleotide structures. Based on their findings the authors concluded that the backbone sugar–phosphate vibration at 807–814 cm^{-1} exists only in nucleic acid polymers in the A-type conformation and that these frequencies are shifted to 790 cm^{-1} in the B-type conformation.

2. Native DNA and RNA

As mentioned previously the multiple functions of the nucleic acids are based upon their secondary structure, i.e., mainly on the extent and type of base pairing and stacking. Raman spectroscopy has shown that these secondary conformations or changes are reflected by the intensities and frequencies of the nucleotide subunit vibrations.

a. RNA

When the temperature of aqueous RNA solutions is raised above its melting point the secondary structure (A-type conformation)† is almost completely disrupted. The hydrogen bonds between the base pairs are split, sequences of stacked bases are melted and the highly ordered backbone geometry changes to a largely disordered one. These changes of the ordered structure are accompanied by Raman hypochromism and Raman hyperchromism of certain purine and pyrimidine stretching vibrations and a shift of the O—P—O stretching band near 812–795 cm^{-1} (Fig. 28).

The intensity of the 812 cm^{-1} band seems to be directly correlated with the number of nucleotides located in regions of ordered A-type structure and which participate in secondary interactions (Thomas and Hartman, 1973; Lafleur et al., 1972). In addition, intensity reversals of the external C=O stretching vibrations of uracil, guanine, and cytosine were observed.

Thomas et al. (1971) studied the conformational changes of 16 S- and 23 r-RNA during melting by monitoring the intensity decay of the O—P—O backbone band at 814 cm^{-1}. The intensity of the guanine band at 670 cm^{-1} decreased during melting of the r-RNA while that of the band at 785 cm^{-1} increased with increased temperature, thus reflecting the unstacking of cytosine and uridine residues. The intensity of the adenine band at 720 cm^{-1} did not change and revealed the stability of adenine stacking under the conditions used. In 1971 Small and Peticolas published a melting curve of yeast s-RNA based on the intensity decrease of the 814 cm^{-1} band upon raising the temperature. This plot clearly revealed a noncooperative melting behavior.

---

† The B-type conformation does not occur in RNA.

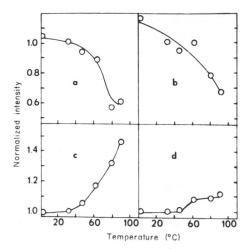

Fig. 28. Melting curves of tRNA[fMet] *E. coli* as shown by the intensity of the following Raman lines in the Raman spectra of D_2O solutions; (a) 670 cm^{-1} (G), (b) 812 cm^{-1} (OPO), (c) 1578 cm^{-1} (A + G), (d) 780 cm^{-1} (U + C) (from Thomas, 1975).

Transfer-RNAs, which code for different amino acids, were studied by Chen and Thomas (1974) and by Thomas *et al.* (1972). The O—P—O and PO_2^- stretching vibrations were all found to occur at the same frequency positions (814 and 1100 cm^{-1}) and give intensity ratios of about 1.38. From these spectral parameters the percentage of t-RNA nucleotide residues existing in regions of ordered secondary structure were calculated to amount to ~85%. The other nucleotides (~15%) could exist in random chain or highly strained backbone segments. Similar results were obtained by Thomas and Hartman (1973) who investigated the extent of ordered configuration in 23-s-RNA, R-17-RNA, and different t-RNAs.

Laser Raman studies of rat liver ribosomal RNA by Fabian *et al.* (1981) showed that the guanine base stacking in 5-s-RNA (as reflected by the 670 cm^{-1} band) is considerably higher than in yeast t-RNA[Phe], while the stacking of the adenine residues (725 cm^{-1} band) was lower. The fraction of paired quanine bases was calculated to be ~75%, while about 35% of the adenine residues should be paired in 5-s-RNA. These Raman data indicated a high regularity of the sugar–phosphate backbone in rat liver 5-s-RNA and support a base pairing pattern as proposed by Nishikawa and Takemura (1974).

b. DNA

In aqueous solutions at low temperature eucaryotic DNA exists as a double-stranded helix in which all bases are paired and stacked. In contrast with RNA, where the riboses exhibit C_3'-endo ring conformations in the A-helix geometry, the desoxyriboses of the DNA backbone show C_3'-exo ring conformations in the B-helix geometry under these conditions (Thomas and Hartman, 1973; Erfurth et al., 1975; Brown and Peticolas, 1975).

During thermal denaturation the double-stranded DNA was separated into two strands without distinct secondary structure ($T_m \sim 86°C$). The denaturation process was accompanied by typical frequency and intensity changes (Thomas, 1976). At low temperature a band near 830 cm^{-1} was observed which was assigned to the O—P—O stretching vibration, indicative of the B-helix geometry. No line near 812 cm^{-1} appeared which would have been indicative of the A-helix geometry.

In the denatured state nucleic acids generally show Raman bands near 795–798 cm^{-1} (O—P—O stretching).

When double helical DNA was completely alkylated at the N − 7 position of the guanine, the complex melted at about 52°C, i.e., about 35°C below the T_m of the native DNA and the alkylated guanine changed from the keto- to the zwitterionic-form upon melting (Mansy and Peticolas, 1976).

The reversible A $\leftrightharpoons$ B transition as a function of relative humidity (rh) can be observed in all DNAs in the fiber form. In contrast with thermal denaturation, the number and type of hydrogen bonds and the base stacking are essentially unaffected under these conditions.

As described by Peticolas (1975) and Erfurth et al. (1975), oriented fibers of calf thymus DNA showed in the presence of 3–4% NaCl below 65% rh, neither A-helix nor B-helix conformations. Above 65% rh the A-form successively appeared, reaching a maximum concentration at 82% rh. Above 85% rh the A-form disappeared and the B-type conformation abruptly started to appear, reaching its 100% maximum at 92% rh (Peticolas, 1975).

In agreement with the normal mode calculations of Brown and Peticolas (1975) the band at 807 cm^{-1} (O—P—O stretching) was used as an indicator of the extent of the A-type geometry in the nucleic acid chain. This band was shifted to 790 cm^{-1} in the B-type geometry and was hidden by the cytosine and thymine ring vibrations. Concomitantly at rh above 85% a band at 835 cm^{-1} appeared which is indicative of the B-type structure. However, this rh-induced A $\leftrightharpoons$ B transition is strictly dependent on the degree of orientation in the fiber sample and on the salt concentration.

Using the above-mentioned spectral parameters, we can say that DNA in neutral aqueous solutions at room temperature is always in the B-type conformation whereas RNA shows the A-type conformation.

Painter et al. (1981) reported on the low frequency Raman spectrum of lyophilized DNA in the B-type conformation at 50 and 100% rh. The spectra showed a strong Raman band at 30 cm^{-1} (50% rh) and a somewhat broader one at 29 cm^{-1} (100% rh) which were assigned to coupled torsional and bond-angle bending vibrations. As discussed by the authors, changes in these bands due to increased relative humidity and interactions with poly-*L*-lysine can be used to study the dynamics or conformational flexibility of the nucleic acids.

More recently Urabe *et al.* (1983) and Lindsay (1984) have observed Raman-active modes at 22, 33, ~60, and ~100 cm^{-1} in the *A*-form of lyophilized DNA. These lines appear when the scattering vector is parallel to the fiber axis, suggesting that they correspond to phonons propagating along the helical axis. The line at 22 cm^{-1} softens with the increase in relative humidity and comes down to 16 cm^{-1} at the critical point of the A $\rightarrow$ B transition. This is consistent with the suggestion of Eyster and Prohofsky (1977) that the A $\rightarrow$ B transition would involve an optical soft mode. Recent calculations by Devi Prasad and Prohofsky (1984) show that the vibration corresponding to the soft mode has an unsoftened frequency centered near 20 cm^{-1}, in agreement with experiment.

VI. SUMMARY AND CONCLUDING REMARKS

In this chapter we have initially covered details of the more conventional equilibrium order–disorder (cf. Chapter 1) transitions in lipids and bio-membranes and touched on the newly emerging ideas and results via Raman spectroscopy involving nonlinear processes in biological systems. In the last two major sections we have reviewed in some detail the somewhat more conventional studies (from a molecular biologist's point of view) of conformational transitions in model and natural protein and nucleic acid systems. These transitions which occur cooperatively in most instances play a critical role in biological processes and it is our hope that a review of this type may help focus attention on the universal dynamics of such transitions — much in the same way as has occurred in the study of the hierarchy of transitions in biomembranes. In biopolymeric systems such as proteins and nucleic acids, cooperative conformational and disordering effects occur as a function of subtle external stimuli such as pH, relative humidity, and inorganic salt concentration. For this reason studies of critical phenomena in such systems could provide new results with fundamental biological implications. One recent example is the exciting discovery of a soft mode associated with the A $\rightarrow$ B conformational transition in DNA.

REFERENCES

Akutsu, H., Kyogoku, Y., Nakahara, H., and Fukuda, K. (1975). *Chem. Phys. Lipids* **15**, 222.
Asher, I. M., and Levin, I. W. (1977). *Biochim. Biophys. Acta* **468**, 63.
Atkinson, G. H., Pallix, J. B., Freedman, T. B., Gilmore, D. A., and Wilbrandt, R. (1981). *J. Am. Chem. Soc.* **103**, 5069.

Bandekar, J., and Krimm, S. (1979). *Proc. Natl. Acad. Sci. USA* **76**, 774.
Baron, M. H., De Loze, G., Toniolo, C., and Fasman, G. D. (1979). *Biopolymers* **18**, 411.
Bellocq, A. M., Lord, R. C., and Mendelsohn, R. (1972). *Biochim. Biophys. Acta* **257**, 280.
Bonora, G. M., and Toniolo, C. (1981). *Gazz. Chim. Ital.* **111**, 239.
Bridoux, M., and Delhaye, M. (1970). *Nouv. Rev. Opt. Appl.* **1**, 23.
Brown, E. B., and Peticolas, W. L. (1975). *Biopolymers* **14**, 1259.
Brown, G. K., Kiser, E. J., and Peticolas, W. L. (1972). *Biopolymers* **11**, 1855.
Bunow, M., and Levin, I. W. (1977). *Biochim. Biophys. Acta* **489**, 191.
Burgess, A. W., and Scheraga, H. A. (1975). *J. Theor. Biol.* **53**, 403.
Callender, R. H., Doukas, A., Crouch, R., and Nakanishi, K. (1976). *Biochemistry* **15**, 1621.
Cantor C. R. (1981). *Cell* **25**, 293.
Cevc, G., Zeks, B., and Podgornik, R. (1981). *Chem. Phys. Lett.* **84**, 209.
Chantot, J. F., Haertlé, T., and Guschlbauer, W. (1974). *Biochimie* **56**, 501.
Chen, M. C., and Lord, R. C. (1976). *Biochemistry* **15**, 1889.
Chen, M. C., and Thomas, G. J., Jr. (1974). *Biopolymers* **13**, 615.
Chen, M. C., Lord, R. C., and Mendelsohn, R. (1973). *Biochim. Biophys. Acta* **328**, 252.
Chou, C. H., and Thomas, Jr. G. J., (1977). *Biopolymers* **16**, 765.
Chou, P. Y., and Fasman, G. D. (1977). *J. Mol. Biol.* **115**, 135.
Chu, G. Y. H., Duncan, R. E., and Tobias, R. S. (1977). *Inorg. Chem.* **16**, 2625.
Danielli, J. F., and Davson, H. (1935). *J. Cell. Physiol.* **5**, 495.
Delabar, J. M., and Guschlbauer, W. (1979). *Biopolymers* **18**, 2073.
De Voe, H., and Tinoco, I., Jr. (1962). *J. Mol. Biol.* **4**, 518.
Devi Prasad, K. V., and Prohofsky, E. W. (1984). *Biopolymers*, in press.
Drissler, F. (1980). *Phys. Lett.* **77A**, 207.
Drissler, F. (1981). *Collect. Phenom.* **3**, 147.
Drissler, F., and MacFarlane, R. M. (1979). *In* "Lasers in Photomedicine and Photobiology."
   Springer-Verlag, Berlin and New York.
Elliot, A., and Ambrose, E. J. (1950). *Nature* **165**, 921.
Erfurth, S. C., Kiser, E. J., and Peticolas, W. L. (1972). *Proc. Natl. Acad. Sci. USA* **69**, 938.
Erfurth, S. C., Bond, P. J., and Peticolas, W. L. (1975). *Biopolymers* **14**, 1245.
Eyster, J. M., and Prohofsky, E. W. (1977). *Biopolymers.* **21**, 2477.
Fabian, H., Böhm, S., Welfle, H., Reich, P., and Bielka, H. (1981). *FEBS Lett.* **123**, 19.
Fasman, G. D., Lindblow, C., and Bodenheimer, E. (1964). *Biochemistry* **3**, 155.
Fasman, G. D., Jtoh, K., Kiu, C. S., and Lord, R. C. (1978). *Biopolymers* **17**, 1729.
Fox, J. A., Tu, A. T., Hruby, V. J., and Mosberg, H. I. (1981). *Arch. Biochem. Biophys* **211**, 628.
Fringeli, U. P. (1977). *Z. Naturforsch.* **32C**, 20.
Fröhlich, H. (1968). *Int. J. Quantum Chem.* **2**, 641; *Phys. Lett.* **26A**, 402.
Fröhlich, H. (1968). *Collect. Phenom.* **3**, 139.
Frushour, B. G., and Koenig, J. L. (1974a). *Biopolymers* **13**, 455.
Frushour, B. G., and Koenig, J. L. (1974b). *Biopolymers* **13**, 1809.
Frushour, B. G., and Koenig, J. L. (1975). *Biopolymers* **14**, 2115.
Frushour, B. G., Painter, P. C., and Koenig, J. L. (1976). *J. Macromol. Sci.* **C15**, 29.
Gaber, B. P., and Peticolas, W. L. (1977). *Biochim. Biophys. Acta* **465**, 260.
Garel, J. R., and Baldwin, R. L. (1973). *Proc. Natl. Acad. Sci. USA* **70**, 3347.
Gellert, M., Lipsett, M. N., and Davies, D. R. (1962). *Proc. Natl. Acad. Sci. USA* **48**, 2013.
Govil, G., and Hosur, R. V. (1982). "Conformation of Biological Molecules." Springer-Ver-
   lag, Berlin and New York.
Gramlich, V., Klump, H., Herbeck, R., and Schmid, E. D. (1976). *FEBS Lett.* **69**, 15.
Guillot, J.-G., Pézolet, M., and Pallotta, D. (1977). *Biochim. Biophys. Acta* **491**, 423.

Gupta G., Bansal, M., and Sasisekharan, V. (1980). *Proc. Natl. Acad. Sci. USA* **77**, 6486.
Guschlbauer, W. (1967). *Proc. Natl. Acad. Sci. USA* **57**, 1441.
Guschlbauer, W. (1975). *Nucleic Acids Res.* **2**, 353.
Hsu, S. L., Moore, W. H., and Krimm, S. (1976). *Biopolymers* **15**, 1513.
Hui, S. W., Cowden, M., Papahadjopoulos, D., and Parsons, D. F. (1975). *Biochim. Biophys. Acta* **382**, 265.
Iqbal, Z., and Christoe, C. W. (1975). *J. Chem. Phys.* **62**, 3246.
Iqbal, Z., and Weidekamm, E. (1979). *Biochim. Biophys. Acta* **555**, 426.
Iqbal, Z., and Weidekamm, E. (1980). *Arch. Biochem. Biophys.* **202**, 639.
Iqbal, Z., Weidekamm, E., and Romero, O. (1979). *Helv. Phys. Acta* **52**, 386.
Johnson, J. H., Lewis, A., and Gogel, G. (1981). *Biochem. Biophys. Res. Comm.* **103**, 182.
Klug, T. L., and Applequist, J. (1974). *Biopolymers* **13**, 1317.
Koenig, J. L. (1972). *J. Polym. Sci. Part D*, 59.
Koenig, J. L. (1973). *Macromol. Rev.* **6**, 59.
Koenig, J. L., and Frushour, B. G. (1972). *Biopolymers* **11**, 1871.
Koglin, E., Séquaris, J. M., and Valenta, P. (1981). *Z. Naturforsch.* **36C**, 809.
Lafleur, L., Rice, J., and Thomas, Jr., G. J., (1972). *Biopolymers* **11**, 2423.
Langridge, R., and Rich, A. (1963). *Nature* **198**, 725.
Levin, I. (1980). *In* "Proceedings of the International Conference on Raman Spectoscopy, Ottawa" (W. Murphy, ed.), p. 528. North-Holland, Amsterdam.
Lewis, A. (1976). *Spex Speaker* **21**, 1.
Lindsay, S. M. (1984). *Bull. Amer. Phys. Soc.* **29**, 376.
Lord, R. C., and Thomas, Jr., G. J., (1967). *Spectrochim. Acta* **23A**, 2551.
Lowey, S. (1965). *J. Biol. Chem.* **240**, 2421.
Makrigiannis, G., Papagiannakopoulos, P., and Theophanides, T. (1980). *Inorg. Chim. Acta* **46**, 263.
Mansy, S., and Peticolas, W. L. (1976). *Biochemistry* **15**, 2650.
Mansy, S., Peticolas, W. L., and Tobias, R. S. (1979). *Spectrochim. Acta* **35A**, 315.
Marcelja, S. (1974). *Biochim. Biophys. Acta* **367**, 162.
Marcus, M. A., and Lewis, A. (1977). *Science* **195**, 1328.
Mendelsohn, R., Dluhy, R., Curatolo, W., and Sears, B. (1982). *Chem. Phys. Lipids* **30**, 287.
Miyazawa, T. (1960). *J. Chem. Phys.* **32**, 1647.
Miles, H. T., and Frazier, J. (1972). *Biochem. Biophys. Res. Commun.* **49**, 199.
Moore, W. H., and Krimm, S. (1976). *Biopolymers* **15**, 2465.
Nagle, J. F., and Scott, H. L. (1978). *Physics Today* February, 38.
Narva, D. L., Callender, R. H., and Ebrey, T. G. (1981). *Photochem. Photobiol.* **33**, 567.
Nibler, J. W., and Knighten, G. V. (1977). *In* "Raman Spectroscopy of Gases and Liquids" (A. Weber, eds.). Springer-Verlag, Berlin and New York.
Nishikawa, K., and Takemura, S. (1974). *J. Biochem.* **76**, 935.
O'Connor, T., and Scovell, W. M. (1981). *Biopolymers* **20**, 2351.
O'Connor, T., Johnson, C., and Scovell, W. M. (1976a). *Biochim. Biophys. Acta* **447**, 484.
O'Connor, T., Johnson, C., and Scovell, W. M. (1976b). *Biochim. Biophys. Acta* **447**, 495.
Painter, P. C., and Coleman, M. M. (1978). *Biopolymers* **17**, 2475.
Painter, P. C., and Koenig, J. L. (1976a). *Biopolymers* **15**, 241.
Painter, P. C., and Koenig, J. L. (1976b). *Biopolymers* **15**, 2155.
Painter, C. P., Mosher, L., and Rhoads, C. (1981). *Biopolymers* **20**, 243.
Papahadjopoulos, D., Jakobson, K., Nir, S., and Isac, T. (1973). *Biochim. Biophys. Acta* **311**, 330.
Pearce, P. A., and Scott, H. L. (1982). *J. Chem. Phys.* **77**, 951.
Peticolas, W. L. (1975). *Biochemie* **57**, 417.

Peticolas, W. L. (1978). *Proc. Intl. Conf. Raman Spectrosc. 6th* **1**, 131.
Pézolet, M., Yu, T.-J., and Peticolas, W. (1975). *J. Raman Spectrosc.* **3**, 55.
Pézolet, M., Pigeon-Gosselin, M., and Coulombe, L. (1976). *Biochim. Biophys. Acta* **453**, 502.
Pohl, F. M., and Jovin, T. M. (1972). *J. Mol. Biol.* **67**, 375.
Pohl, F. M., Ranade, A., and Stockburger, M. (1973). *Biochim. Biophys. Acta* **335**, 85.
Prescott, B., Thomas, Jr., G. J., Beress, L., Wunderer, G., and Tu, A. T. (1976). *FEBS Lett.* **64**, 144.
Rice, J., Lafleur, L., Mederos, G. C., and Thomas, G. J. (1973). *J. Raman Spectrosc.* **1**, 207.
Robson, B. (1977). *Nature* **267**, 577.
Schröder, H. (1977). *J. Chem. Phys.* **67**, 1617.
Scovell, W. M. (1978). *Biopolymers* **17**, 969.
Sederel, W. L., Bantjes, A., Feijen, J., and Anderson, J. M. (1980). *Biopolymers* **19**, 1603.
Shelnutt, J. A., Rousseau, D. L., Dethmers, J. K., and Margoliash, E. (1981). *Biochemistry*, **20**, 6485.
Small, E. W., and Peticolas, W. L. (1971). *Biopolymers* **10**, 1377.
Snyder, R. G., Hsu, F. L., and Krimm, S. (1978) *Spectrochim. Acta* **34A**, 395.
Sugawara, Y., Harada, J., Matsuura, H., and Shimanouchi, T. (1978). *Biopolymers* **17**, 1405.
Sugeta, H., Go, A., and Miyazawa, T. (1972). *Chem. Lett.* **1**, 83.
Sugeta, H., Go, A., and Miyazawa, T. (1973). *Bull. Chem. Soc. Japan* **46**, 3407.
Takamatsu, T., Harada, J., Shimanouchi, T., Ohta, M., and Yayashi, K. (1976). *FEBS Lett.* **72**, 291.
Tang, J., and Albrecht, A. C. (1974). *In* "Raman Spectroscopy" Vol. 2. (H.A. Symanski, ed.), Plenum, New York.
Tardieu, A., Luzatti, V., and Reman, F. C. (1973). *J. Mol. Biol.* **75**, 311.
Thamann, T. J., Lord, R. C., Wang, A. H. J., and Rich, A. (1981). *Nucleic Acid Res.* **20**, 5443.
Thomas, G. J., Jr. (1975). *In* "Structure and Conformation of Nucleic Acids and Protein — Nucleic Interactions" (M. Sundaralingam and S. T. Rao, eds.), pp. 253. University Park Press, Baltimore.
Thomas, G. J., Jr. (1976). *The Spex Speaker* **21**, 1.
Thomas, G. J., Jr., and Hartmann, K. A. (1973). *Biochim. Biophys. Acta* **312**, 311.
Thomas, G. J., Jr., Medeiros, G. C., and Hartmann, K. A. (1971). *Biochem. Biophys. Res. Commun.* **44**, 587.
Thomas, G. J., Jr., Madeiros G. C., and Hartmann, K. A. (1972). *Biochim. Biophys. Acta* **277**, 71.
Tomlinson, B. L., and Peticolas, W. L. (1970). *J. Chem. Phys.* **52**, 2154.
Tredgold, R. H. (1977). *Adv. Phys.* **26**, 79.
Tsuboi, M. (1974). *In* "Basic Principles in Nucleic Acid Chemistry" (P.O.P. Tso, ed.), Vol. 1, pp. 399. Academic Press, New York.
Tsuboi, M., Takahashi, S., Muaraishi, S., and Kajiura, T. (1971). *Bull. Chem. Soc. Jpn.* **44**, 2921.
Tu, A. T., Jo, B. H., and Yu, N.-T. (1976). *Int. J. Peptide Protein Res.* **8**, 337.
Urabe, H., Tominaga, Y., and Kubata, K. (1983). *J. Chem. Phys.* **78**, 5937.
Verma, S. P., and Wallach, D. F. H. (1976). *Proc. Natl. Acad. Sci USA* **73**, 3558.
Wallach, D. F. H., Graham, J. M., and Oseroff, A. R. (1970). *FEBS Lett.* **7**, 330.
Wallach, D. F. H., Verma, S. P., and Fookson, J. (1979). *Biochim. Biophys. Acta* **559**, 153.
Webb, S. T., and Stoneham, M. E. (1977). *Phys. Lett.* **60A**, 267.
Webb, S. T., Stoneham, M. E., and Fröhlich, M. (1977). *Phys. Lett.* **63A**, 407.
Weidekamm, E. *et al.* (1977). *Biochim. Biophys. Acta* **464**, 442.
Williams, R. W., and Dunker, A. K. (1981). *J. Mol. Biol.* **152**, 783.
Wilser, W. T., and Fitchen, D. B. (1974). *Biopolymers* **13**, 1435.

Winchester, B. G., Mathias, A. P., and Rabin, B. R. (1970). *Biochem. J.* **117,** 299.

Yacoby, Y., and Linz, A. (1974). *Phys. Rev.* **139,** 23.

Yellin, N., and Levin, I. W. (1977). *Biochim. Biophys. Acta* **489,** 177.

Yu, N.-T., and East, E. J. (1975). *J. Biol. Chem.* **250,** 2196.

Yu, N.-T., and Jo, B. H. (1973). *Arch. Biochem. Biophys.* **156,** 469.

Yu, N.-T., Lin, C. S., and O'Shea, D. C. (1972). *J. Mol. Biol.* **70,** 117.

Yu, N.-T., Lippert, J., and Peticolas, W. L. (1973). *Biopolymers* **12,** 2161.

5

Neutron Scattering Studies of Structural Phase Transitions

W. Bührer

Institut für Reaktortechnik
Swiss Federal Institute of Technology (ETH)
Zürich, CH-5303 Würenlingen
Switzerland

Z. Iqbal*

Institute of Inorganic Chemistry
University of Zürich
CH-8057 Zürich, Switzerland

I. INTRODUCTORY REMARKS

Neutron inelastic scattering spectroscopy provides complete information about the vibrational spectra of solids by virtue of the fact that slow neutrons

* Present address: Allied Corporation, Corporate Research Center, Morristown, New Jersey 07960.

TABLE I

Physical Constants and Characteristic Data for the Neutron

Mass (m_n)	$= 1.675 \times 10^{-27}$ kg
Charge	$= 0$
Spin	$= \frac{1}{2}$

Standard dynamical parameters for (conventional) thermal neutrons

Energy (E_0)	$= \frac{1}{2} m_n \cdot v^2 = \hbar^2/2m_n\lambda^2 = \hbar^2 k^2/2m_n$
v (velocity)	$= 2200$ m/sec
E_0	$= 25.3$ meV $\approx$ 6THz $\approx 40 \times 10^{12}$ s$^{-1} \approx 200$ cm^{-1}
T	$= 293$ K
λ (wavelength)	$= 1.798$Å
k (wavevector)	$= 3.49$Å^{-1}

have energies and wavelengths (cf. Table I) that match those of phonon and collective excitations in solids. It is, therefore, a unique tool for probing the lattice dynamics of structural phase transitions (SPTs) in solids. In addition, quasi-elastic and elastic neutron scattering experiments provide crucial information regarding the evolution of the order parameter in such transitions. Neutron scattering studies of SPTs particularly in ferroelectrics and ionic crystals were pioneered in the 1970s by Shirane and his group at Brookhaven (cf. Shirane, 1971 and references therein). More recently this work has been extended by groups in Europe, Japan, and elsewhere in the U.S. to more complex systems such as molecular crystals undergoing incommensurate (cf. Chapter 1) phase transitions. The recent work has been reviewed by Dorner (1981), Currat and Pynn (1979), and Dorner and Comes (1977).

In this chapter we first attempt a description of the neutron scattering method as applied to SPT research at a fairly general level and the proceed to review results involving the three main types of SPTs under current investigation; namely, displacive, order–disorder, and incommensurate. Although we will consider some of the more conventional ionic and metallic materials, an attempt will be made to focus on the recently investigated molecular-type systems. The overall aim of this chapter is to provide a selective review of recent SPT research by neutron scattering methods with a view to pointing out evolving areas of activity and new problems in this field.

II. BASIC PRINCIPLES OF NEUTRON SCATTERING

Experiments with thermal neutrons are most useful in the study of condensed matter. The advantage stems from the fundamental nature of the neutron (see Table I, where some of the physical constants of the neutron are summarized). The de Broglie wavelength of a thermal neutron is of the same order of magnitude as the interatomic distances in crystals, and the energy of a thermal neutron is of the same order as the energy of a normal lattice excitation.   Therefore, in a scattering process, the neutron matches the lattice vibrations with respect to energy and wavevector, and there exist pronounced interference effects which allow the determination of the complete dispersion relations, $\omega_j(\mathbf{q})$, over the whole Brillouin zone.   Because the neutron is uncharged, it penetrates deeply into the target and allows the bulk properties of the material to be studied without limitations with respect to the surfaces.   The neutron interacts with the target via nuclear forces, and hence there are no restrictions as regards the type of interatomic binding forces.   Metallic, ionic, covalent, molecular, and hydrogen-bonded crystals can all be readily investigated.   The neutron probes directly the motion of the nucleus, whereas in optical measurements the nuclear motions are observed through the coupling of the photon with the electrons.   In contrast with Raman scattering which measures both the one- and two-phonon response close to T_c, neutron scattering experiments allow an unambiguous determination of the soft-mode energy and damping because neutrons always couple linearly to the soft mode (Satija and Cowley, 1982).   One disadvantage of neutron scattering is the relatively poor energy and wavevector resolution, which is of the order of 1 percent for a normal experiment, as a result of the low intensity of available neutron beams.   This necessitates having a large experimental facility, for example, a nuclear reactor or a spallation source, thus making the method somewhat exclusive.

In this section we describe those aspects of the basic theoretical principles and experimental techniques of inelastic neutron scattering which are mostly used for investigations of the lattice dynamical aspects of SPTs. Hence we restrict ourselves to nuclear scattering, and magnetic scattering is not discussed at all.   In what follows the relevant scattering cross sections are given at first without derivation.   For a thorough discussion the interested reader is referred to the books of Squires (1978) and Marshall and Lovesey (1971).   This is then followed by a discussion of the coherent scattering cross sections in crystals and the selection rules involved.   In the experimental section we focus primarily on the presently most versatile neutron scattering instrument — the triple axis spectrometer.   More details of the experimental techniques and additional references are given by Dolling (1974).

A. Theoretical Aspects

1. Scattering Cross Section

Suppose a beam of neutrons is incident on a crystalline sample as shown in Fig. 1.   The neutron may either be scattered or absorbed, or it can pass without interaction.   The absorption process is only restrictive for a few

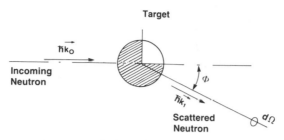

Fig. 1. Neutron scattering process: k_0, incoming neutron; k_1, scattered neutron; T, target; Φ, scattering angle; and $d\Omega$, element of solid angle.

isotopes such as, ^{3}He, ^{10}B, or ^{113}Cd, which show a resonance in the thermal region. In the process of scattering, the neutron changes its momentum, and if the interaction is not elastic, the energy of the neutron is also changed. The incident and the scattered neutron waves are characterized by the momentum vectors $\hbar\mathbf{k}_0$ and $\hbar\mathbf{k}_1$, respectively, where $\mathbf{k} = 2\pi/\lambda$, and λ is the neutron wavelength. Every nucleus in the sample is a scattering center, and the scattered neutrons combine and interfere within a total field. If in this field neutrons are found with their momentum changed by

$$\hbar\mathbf{Q} = \hbar(\mathbf{k}_0 - \mathbf{k}_1) \tag{1}$$

and their energy changed by

$$\hbar\omega = \hbar^2/2m_n(\mathbf{k}_0^2 - \mathbf{k}_1^2) = E_0 - E_1, \tag{2}$$

then the crystalline sample must be able to change its dynamical properties by the same quantities. The scattering process is then characterized by the differential cross section $d^2\sigma/d\Omega dE_1$, which gives the probability that an incident neutron of energy E_0 is scattered by an angle ϕ into the solid angle element $d\Omega$, and in the final energy interval $(E_1, E_1 + dE_1)$. The cross section has the dimension of an area and is usually given in barns (1 barn = 10^{-24} cm^2). Quantum mechanically the cross section is evaluated in the Born approximation (Schiff, 1968). The incoming neutrons are represented by plane wave functions $|k_0\rangle$, impinging on the sample in the state $|i\rangle$. In the scattering process the neutron changes to state $|k_1\rangle$ and leaves the sample in the state $|f\rangle$. The transition probability is given by Fermi's golden rule

$$\sum_{\substack{\mathbf{k}_1 \\ in\ d\Omega}} w_{\mathbf{k}_0,\ i\to\mathbf{k}_1,\ f} \cong \rho_{k_1} |\langle\mathbf{k}_1\ f|V|\mathbf{k}_0\ i\rangle|^2, \tag{3}$$

Here ρk_1 is the density of final scattering states per unit energy, and V is the interaction potential neutron-nucleus. The cross section for the change of the system from state $|i>$ to $|f>$ is

$$\left(\frac{d\sigma}{d\Omega}\right)_{i\to f} = \frac{1}{d\Omega} \sum_{\substack{\mathbf{k}_1 \\ \text{in } d\Omega}} w_{\mathbf{k}_0, \, i\to\mathbf{k}_1, \, f}, \qquad \text{incident flux.} \qquad (4)$$

In an experiment, we actually measure $d^2\sigma/d\Omega\, dE_1$, and the partial differential cross section for for all transitions from $|\mathbf{k}_0>$ to $|\mathbf{k}_1>$ is then given by the sum over all final states $|f>$ and averaging over all initial states $|i>$ as

$$\left(\frac{d^2\sigma}{d\Omega\, dE_i}\right) = \frac{k_1}{k_0}\left(\frac{m_n}{2\pi\hbar^2}\right)^2 \sum_i p_i \sum_f |<\mathbf{k}_1 f|V|\mathbf{k}_0\, i>|^2$$
$$\times \delta(E_i - E_f - \hbar\omega), \qquad (5)$$

where the δ function represents the conservation of the energy in the neutron-target system during the scattering process, and the p give the probability that the sample is in the initial state $|i>$, given by Boltzmann statistics, and $\sum_i p_i = 1$.

The potential V of the neutron–nucleus interaction is of short range order, but actually unknown. Because the wavelength of thermal neutrons is much larger than the range of interaction and the radius of the nucleus, neutron–nucleus scattering is isotropic and characterized by a single parameter. For purely nuclear scattering the true potential of interaction is replaced by the Fermi pseudopotential

$$V = \frac{2\pi\hbar^2}{m_n} \sum_1 b_1 \delta[\mathbf{r} - \mathbf{R}_1(t)], \qquad (6)$$

where b_1 is the scattering length of the nucleus at position $\mathbf{R}_1$. The neutron interacts with the target atom via nuclear forces, and the strength of interaction and hence b_1 will depend on the isotope and, if the nuclear spin is nonzero, it will depend on whether the spins of the neutron and the nucleus are parallel or antiparallel; the index 1 is therefore in general necessary even for a sample of one chemical element. The scattering length is an empirical quantity, and some characteristic values are given in Table II. By substituting Eq. (6) into Eq. (5), the cross section can be evaluated. The result is (expressed in terms of time-dependent Heisenberg operators, Squires, 1978) as

$$\frac{d^2\sigma}{d\Omega\, dE_1} = \frac{k_1}{k_0}\frac{1}{2\pi\hbar} \sum_{11'} b_1 b_{1'} \int_{-\infty}^{+\infty} \langle e^{-i\mathbf{Q}\hat{\mathbf{R}}_l(0)}\, e^{i\mathbf{Q}\hat{\mathbf{R}}_l(t)}\rangle$$
$$\times e^{-i\omega t}\, dt, \qquad (7)$$

showing clearly the correlation between spatial and time-dependent behavior. Equation (7) includes products of two functions, one depending on the

TABLE II

Some Representative Scattering Lengths b_1^a

Isotope	$b_1 (10^{-14} \text{ m})$
H	−0.3741
D	0.6674
^{16}O	0.5805
^{51}V	−0.0414
^{58}Ni	1.44
^{60}Ni	0.28
^{62}Ni	−0.87
^{64}Ni	−0.38
^{197}Au	0.736
^{278}U	0.855

^{a} From Koester et al., 1981.

nuclear interaction, while the other is determined by the structural and dynamical properties of the atoms in the undisturbed sample. The properties of the scattering system are described by the thermal averages of the operators, $\hat{\mathbf{R}}_l(t)$.

The scattering length b_1 may not be the same for all nuclei in the actual scattering system, and generally the nuclei having different scattering lengths will be statistically distributed in the crystal. The neutron sees a crystal in which the scattering length varies from one point to the other, and only the system with an average scattering length can give interference effects   This coherent scattering is proportional to the average value $\bar{b}^2$. Incoherent scattering arises from the random distribution of the deviations from $\bar{b}$, it shows no interference effects and is given by $b^2 - \bar{b}^2$. Coherent scattering is of most interest in the study of SPTs and we will discuss it here in more detail. The coherent part of the cross section [Eq. (7)] is given by

$$\left(\frac{d^2\sigma}{d\Omega \, dE_1} \right)_{\text{coh}} \simeq \bar{b}^2 \, \mathbf{k}_1/\mathbf{k}_0 \sum_{ll'} \int_{-\infty}^{\infty} \langle e^{-i\mathbf{Q}\hat{\mathbf{R}}_{l'}(0)} \, e^{i\mathbf{Q}\hat{\mathbf{R}}_l(t)} \rangle \, e^{-i\omega t} \, dt. \quad (8)$$

Coherent scattering is determined by the correlation between the positions of the same atom at different times and by the correlation between the positions of different atoms at different times, and it arises only if the geometrical conditions are satisfied.

2. Scattering by a Crystal

The instantaneous position of a nucleus in a crystal is given by

$$\mathbf{R}\begin{pmatrix} \ell \\ \kappa \end{pmatrix} = \mathbf{r}\begin{pmatrix} \ell \\ \kappa \end{pmatrix} + \mathbf{u}\begin{pmatrix} \ell \\ \kappa \end{pmatrix} \quad (9)$$

where ℓ is the cell index and κ $(1, \ldots, r)$ gives the position within the unit cell. $\mathbf{r}(^{\ell}_{\kappa})$ is the equilibrium position and the displacements $\mathbf{u}(^{\ell}_{\kappa})$ are the result of the thermal fluctuations. In the harmonic approximation the displacements can be expressed by the set of normal coordinates (Maradudin, 1974)

$$\mathbf{u}\begin{pmatrix} \ell \\ \kappa \end{pmatrix} = \sqrt{\hbar/2Nm_\kappa} \sum_{\mathbf{q}j} \frac{1}{\sqrt{\omega_j(\mathbf{q})}} \mathbf{e}\left(\kappa \middle| \begin{matrix} \mathbf{q} \\ j \end{matrix}\right) \exp \; i\mathbf{q}\mathbf{r} \begin{pmatrix} \ell \\ \kappa \end{pmatrix}$$
$$\times \left[a^+\begin{pmatrix} -\mathbf{q} \\ j \end{pmatrix} + a\begin{pmatrix} \mathbf{q} \\ j \end{pmatrix} \right]. \tag{10}$$

Here m_κ is the mass of the atom at position $\mathbf{R}(^{\ell}_{\kappa})$, a^+ and a are the phonon creation and annihilation operators N is the number of unit cells in the macrocrystal, and $\omega_j(\mathbf{q})$ and $\mathbf{e}(\kappa|^{\mathbf{q}}_{j})$ are the frequencies and orthonormalized eigenvectors of the normal mode with wavevector $\mathbf{q}$, respectively, obtained by solving the dynamical matrix equation (Maradudin, 1974)

$$D(\mathbf{q})\cdot\mathbf{e}\begin{pmatrix} \mathbf{q} \\ j \end{pmatrix} = \omega_j^2(\mathbf{q})\cdot\mathbf{e}\begin{pmatrix} \mathbf{q} \\ j \end{pmatrix}. \tag{11}$$

$D(\mathbf{q})$ can be expressed in terms of the interatomic forces in the crystal.

The initial state $|i>$ of the crystal is given by the quantum numbers of the $3vN$ oscillators corresponding to the normal modes. In the scattering process the crystal can change to the state $|f>$ characterized by another set of quantum numbers. Expressions (9) and (10) can be inserted into (8) and the exponent can be expanded in a power series involving different changes in occupation numbers,

$$\frac{d^2\sigma}{d\Omega dE_1} \approx 0\text{ph} + 1\text{ph} + 2\text{ph} + \cdots. \tag{12}$$

In this multi-phonon expansion the first term corresponds to a zero-phonon process, the second to the one-phonon process (change of only one state $n_j \rightarrow n_j \pm 1$), the third term to the two-phonon process, and so on. For coherent scattering the zero-phonon term corresponds to the well-known elastic Bragg scattering with cross section

$$\left(\frac{d\sigma}{d\Omega}\right)^{\text{coh}} \approx \sum_{\tau} \delta(\mathbf{Q} - 2\pi\tau) |F(\tau)|^2, \tag{13}$$

where the static structure factor F is given by

$$F(\tau) = \sum_{\kappa} \bar{b}_\kappa e^{i2\pi\tau\kappa} e^{-W_\kappa}. \tag{14}$$

The evaluation of the one-phonon term leads for the coherent part to

$$
\left(\frac{d^2\sigma}{d\Omega dE_1}\right)^{\mathrm{coh}}_{\mathrm{1ph}} \approx \frac{k_1}{k_0} \sum_{\mathbf{q},j} \delta[E_1 - E_0 - \hbar\omega_j(\mathbf{q})] \sum_{\tau} \delta(\mathbf{Q} \pm \mathbf{q} - 2\pi\tau)
$$
$$
\times [\hbar/w_j(\mathbf{q})] \, (n + \tfrac{1}{2} \pm \tfrac{1}{2})|G_j(\mathbf{Q})|^2,
$$

(15)

where n is the population factor

$$
n = 1/\exp[\hbar\omega_j(\mathbf{q})/k_B T]^{-1}
$$

(16)

and the dynamical structure factor G is given by

$$
G_j(\mathbf{Q}) = \sum_{\kappa} \frac{\bar{b}_\kappa}{\sqrt{m_\kappa}} \, e^{i\mathbf{Q}\mathbf{r}_H} \cdot \mathbf{Q}e(\kappa|^{\mathbf{q}}_j)e^{-W_\kappa}.
$$

(17)

Two-phonon and higher order processes are usually regarded as background but can be important at higher temperatures. Equations (13) and (15) contain δ functions for energy- and crystal-momentum conservation, and these conditions allow the determination of crystal structure and phonon dispersion curves. Exp$(-W_H)$ is the Debye–Waller factor originating in the harmonic motion of the ions, W depends on temperature and momentum $\hbar\mathbf{Q}$ and is a measure of the mean square ionic displacements. The upper and lower sign in Eq. (15) refer to phonon annihilation and creation, respectively.

The scattering cross sections (Eqs. (13), (15)) are written for δ functions, i.e., perfect translational symmetry and harmonic behavior of the crystal are assumed. These conditions are probably satisfied at low temperatures and far from phase transitions. It can be used in SPT studies to specify the state and structure of the phases in question, but in the transition regime strong corrections are generally necessary. Interference processes are only perfect if long range order exists. The short range deviation from the long range average structure gives rise to diffuse scattering, and the correlation length or the range of order can be determined from the width of the observed peaks.

If in an order–disorder transition, dynamic clusters of the new phase are formed, the neutron intensity profiles will be broadened in energy and the scattering is called quasi-elastic. Investigations of quasi-elastic scattering gives information on the geometry and relaxation time of the clusters. Analysis of the broadening of the inelastic phonon line yields information on the lifetime of the excitation and on anharmonic terms in the interatomic potential.

3. Selection Rules in Coherent Inelastic Scattering

Infrared and Raman experiments are governed by selection rules which on the one hand can help identify the normal modes, but on the other hand limit the experimental information. In the case of neutron scattering no such restrictive selection rules exist. The relative intensity of a particular phonon mode $(\mathbf{q}, j)$ measured at the general point $\mathbf{Q}$ in reciprocal space, is given by

$$|G_j|^2 = \left| \sum_\kappa \frac{\overline{b}_\kappa e^{-W_H}}{\sqrt{m_\kappa}} \mathbf{Q} \mathbf{e} \left(\kappa \middle| \begin{matrix} \mathbf{q} \\ j \end{matrix} \right) e^{-i\mathbf{Q}\tau_H} \right|^2, \tag{18}$$

where the summation extends over all atoms in the unit cell and G_j is periodic in reciprocal space and need only be evaluated in the structure zone defined by vectors τ' such that

$$\exp(i\, 2\pi\tau'\mathbf{r}) = 1 \tag{19}$$

for all atoms in the unit cell (Elliott and Thorpe, 1967). If the structure zone is f times larger than the Brillouin zone, then a phonon may be measured at f inequivalent points.

Phonons with wavevector $\mathbf{q}$ belong to an irreducible representation of a subgroup of the crystal lattice that leaves $\mathbf{q}$ invariant. The symmetry types and the corresponding representations can be determined by standard procedures (Elliott and Thorpe, 1967; Worlton and Warren, 1974). Multidimensional representations show symmetry-related degeneracies, and compatibility relations can be deduced from the characters of the representations. If a representation occurs only once at $\mathbf{q}$, then the polarization vectors are completely determined by symmetry, and the structure factor of this mode can readily be calculated. If a representation occurs many times, then the polarization vectors are determined by the interatomic forces in the crystal and only the sum of structure factors for modes of the same symmetry can be group-theoretically calculated. Within the structure zone, points and directions of high symmetry can usually be found where the structure factor is high for a given representation, but small for all the others. Together with the scalar product $(\mathbf{Q} \cdot \mathbf{e}(\begin{smallmatrix} \mathbf{q} \\ j \end{smallmatrix}))$, which allows distinction between modes of longitudinal and transverse polarization, it is then generally possible to assign an experimentally observed peak to a specific mode j, and phonons in a complicated system with many branches can be clearly separated despite the relative poor energy resolution in the scattering experiment. Besides measuring the phonon frequencies $\omega_j(\mathbf{q})$, the polarization vectors $\mathbf{e}(\begin{smallmatrix} \mathbf{q} \\ j \end{smallmatrix})$ of a mode can also be determined. By measuring the intensity of the one-phonon peaks at different points in the structure zone, the components of $\mathbf{e}(\begin{smallmatrix} \mathbf{q} \\ j \end{smallmatrix})$ can be evaluated from Eq. (15) by a least-squares routine and fitting of the theoretical values to the experimental intensities. This, however, is not an easy matter and is usually performed for a few selected, basically important modes.

B. Experimental Methods

The neutron scattering experiment is a measurement of the differential cross section. The principle is very simple: An incoming neutron beam of well-defined energy E_0 and momentum $\hbar k_0$ is produced, and after scattering from the target, a detector counts the number of neutrons with energy E_1, scattered into the solid angle $d\Omega$ in a given direction. Furthermore, it is necessary to normalize the scattered intensity with respect to the incoming neutron flux.

The source of neutrons is the most important part of the experimental set-up. The scattering cross sections are rather weak and therefore a high incoming neutron flux is necessary. Nuclear reactors and the recently developed spallation sources can give the required flux of $10^{14} - 10^{15}$ n/cm²/ sec. The fast fission or spallation neutrons are slowed down in a moderator. The thermal neutrons have a Maxwellian distribution, and the energy of the peak flux is given by the moderator temperature. Thermal neutrons are classified according to the respective moderator temperature as: *cold* ($E_0 \lesssim 5$ meV), *thermal,* or *hot* ($E_0 \gtrsim 100$ meV); and experiments can be performed with an energy which matches best the excitation energies and momentum transfers being studied.

Basically, there are two ways of defining the energy of thermal neutrons to the order of 1%:

(i) by Bragg scattering from a single crystal and
(ii) by the chopping of the incident neutron beam in pulses and time-of-flight analysis of the scattered neutrons. We only discuss the first method which is best suited for steady-state operation of the source and has been primarily used in SPT studies. Time-of-flight techniques will become increasingly important when spallation sources are operational.

Conventional crystal structure analysis is an elastic experiment, i.e., the energy of the scattered neutrons is not analyzed. However, near-phase transitions are not only the crystal structures monitored, but also the evolving order parameters. Hence elastic, quasi-elastic and inelastic scattering have to be investigated.

The most versatile crystal instrument is the *triple axis spectrometer* originally due to Brockhouse (1961). Figure 2 illustrates the schematic layout. Neutrons can pass along a beam tube through the biological shielding of the source. A $(2\theta)_M$-Bragg reflection at the monochromator single crystal (graphite, beryllium, copper) selects a well-defined energy E_0 out of the incoming neutron beam spectrum. The monochromator system is surrounded by shielding material of approximately 1 m radius to suppress fast neutron and gamma radiation emerging from the source. The flux of the

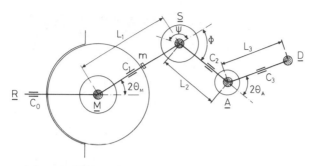

Fig. 2. Schematic layout of triple axis spectrometer. M, first axis, monochromator system; S, second axis, sample with orientation ψ, scattering angle Φ; A, third axis, analyzer system; R, neutron source (reactor); D, detector; C_i, collimators or diaphragms for beam definition; L_i, variable lengths of arms (especially in conjunction with curved monochromator–analyzer systems); and m, neutron beam monitor.

monochromatic neutron beam is usually monitored with a fission chamber of low efficiency. The monochromatic beam hits the sample crystal which can be oriented at any desired angle ψ with respect to the incoming neutrons of momentum $\mathbf{k}_0$. The scattered neutrons, deflected by the angle ϕ, arrive at the analyzer crystal, those with the selected energy E_1 are reflected at the second Bragg system $(2\theta)_A$ and are finally counted with a ^{3}He detector, again shielded to suppress unwanted background. Present day spectrometers are equipped with curved monochromator and analyzer crystal systems to focus the neutrons and at the sample position and to increase the flux in the detector. Collimators or slits can be inserted in the neutron beam to define the angular divergences.

In addition, the length of the arms between monochromator, sample table, analyzer, and counter can be varied. This makes it possible to adapt the $(\mathbf{Q},\omega)$-resolution of the spectrometer to the requirements of the experiment. The spectrometer is computer-controlled, and during a measurement the energy (wavevectors) of the incident and scattered neutrons, the scattering angle, and the sample orientation can be varied.

The equations for conservation of energy and quasi-momentum are

$$\pm \hbar \omega = E_0 - E_1 \quad \text{and} \quad \mathbf{k}_0 - \mathbf{k}_1 = \mathbf{Q} = 2\pi\boldsymbol{\tau} + \mathbf{q}, \tag{20}$$

the energy–wavevector relation of the unknown excitation is

$$\omega = \omega_j(\mathbf{q}), \tag{21}$$

and if these three conditions are simultaneously fulfilled, a peak in the scattered intensity is expected. The experimental scan consists of a sequence of intensity measurements at points in $(\mathbf{Q},\omega)$ space.

In a triple axis spectrometer the number of instrumental parameters

$(\mathbf{k}_0,\mathbf{k}_1\,\psi,\phi)$ is larger than the number of parameters characterizing the dynamical process $(Q_x,Q_y,\hbar\,\omega)$. This gives the possibility of specifying additional parameters in the experiment, and the most common type of scan is the const.-$\mathbf{Q}$ mode of operation with fixed analyzer energy. The scattering diagram for a set of consecutives points is shown in Fig. 3a. For a selected wavevector $\mathbf{q}$, with momentum transfer $\hbar\mathbf{Q}$, the scattered neutron intensity is mapped as a function of energy transfer, and the observed peak position is assigned to the energy of the excitation. The fact that the measurement can be performed at preselected $\mathbf{q}$ values is very advantageous, particularly in SPT studies where the anomalous behavior or the temperature dependence of a phonon mode for special $\mathbf{q}$ vectors have to be investigated. Furthermore, the const.-$\mathbf{Q}$ mode is best suited for excitations with weak dispersion, whereas for a strong dispersion the const.-ω techniques (see Fig. 3b) give the best results.

The experimentally measured intensity does not give the cross section directly. Several corrections have to be applied, such as, resolution or background effects, multiple scattering, or multi-phonon scattering. The resolution function of a triple axis spectrometer has been given in detail by Cooper and Nathans (1967), and is represented by a four-dimensional function in $(\mathbf{Q},\omega)$-space. The extensions are determined by the energies of the neutrons $E_0(E_1)$, by the lattice spacings and the mosaic spreads of the monochromator

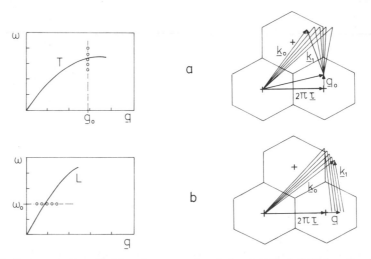

Fig. 3. Representations of triple axis scans; points in $(\mathbf{q},\omega)$-space (left side); and scattering diagrams (right side). (a) Constant $-\mathbf{Q}$ measurement of a transverse phonon with fixed analyzer energy and (b) constant $-\omega$ measurement of a longitudinal phonon.

and analyzer crystals, and by the vertical and horizontal angular divergences of the neutron beam along its path from reactor to counter.

The typical energy resolution is on the order of $\sim 0.5 - 0.05$ meV for quasi-elastic scattering. In observing fluctuations this corresponds to a time scale of $\sim 10^{-11}$ sec. For larger times to be investigated the energy resolution can be improved with the back-scattering technique, such as at the neutron beam facilities at the HFR, Grenoble (see ILL information for users, 1981). Basically the principle is not changed. We still have monochromator and analyzer crystals, but now in a very sophisticated arrangement. The resolution of approximately ~ 1 μeV allows studies in the time scale up to $\sim 10^{-8}$ sec.

Corrections of the observed intensities are essential if the resolution function embraces a region of strongly varying cross section. Necessary corrections can always be reduced by improving the resolution, which, however, is at the expense of intensity, and consequently in the experiment a compromise between accuracy and overall measuring time has to be achieved.

III. RECENT STUDIES OF SELECTED MATERIALS AND TRANSITION TYPES

The materials selected for discussion in this section represent basically the two limiting situations in SPTs:

(i) the displacive transitions where the structural change involves a displacement which is an extremely small fraction of the interatomic distance and

(ii) order – disorder transitions where the displacement approaches that of an interatomic distance. Propagating soft modes are observed in case (i), whereas relaxational or diffusive motions leading, in a second-order phase transition, to a critical slowing down of the relaxational time τ, are evident in the case of order – disorder transitions. A special situation exists in the case of incommensurate transitions, which are also considered in this section. Here an atomic modulation wave is triggered and the entire crystal loses its rigorous translational symmetry.

In real systems it is customary to find that due to coupling effects both displacive and order – disorder components in the phase transition process occur, particularly in molecular crystals. In the following discussion we have classified the examples considered based on the primary displacement involved. In molecular – ionic crystals such as KCN, however, the situation is complicated because the transition is essentially order – disorder in nature but has a sizable displacive component due to strong reorientational–translational coupling.

A. Displacive Transitions

1. Chloranil

The molecular crystal chloranil ($C_6Cl_4O_2$) undergoes a cell-doubling phase transition similar to $SrTiO_3$. The eigenvector representing this transition is shown in Fig. 4. The transition in chloranil is almost ideally second order and hence, like $SrTiO_3$, can be used as a model SPT system for detailed investigation. Neutron scattering studies of chloranil have been reported by Ellenson and Kjems (1977), complementing extensive light scattering measurements (Ecolivet, 1981; Wada et al., 1980; Hanson, 1975), heat capacity and NQR measurements (Chihara et al., 1973; Chihara and Nakamura, 1973; and Chihara and Masukane, 1973), and diffuse x-ray diffraction (Terauchi et al., 1975) measurements.

Three important and crucial aspects of the SPT in chloranil were elucidated via the neutron scattering study of Ellenson and Kjems (1977), demonstrating the unique power of this method. The first involved a careful measurement of the Bragg intensities of the superlattice reflections ($\bar{1}, 0, 3.5$) and $\bar{1}, 0, 2.5$) — representing the order parameter of the transition — which evolve with temperature in the 4–100 K temperature range of the low temperature phase. The intensity data for the two reflections shown in a log–log plot as a function of the reduced temperature $1-T/T_c$ is displayed in Fig. 5. The value of the critical exponent β extracted from both sets of data is

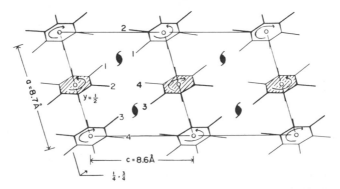

Fig. 4. Projection of the structure of chloranil on the $a-c$ plane and the symmetry-breaking rotations below T_c as indicated by the arrows. The shaded molecules lie at one-half of the b axis parameter above the plane (from Ellenson and Kjems, 1977).

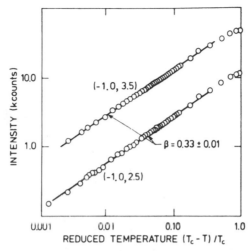

Fig. 5. Log–log plot of corrected intensity data at the indicated reciprocal lattice points as a function of $1 - T/T_c$, for chloranil ($C_6Cl_4O_2$). The value of the exponent β is the result of a least squares fit with $T_c = 90.25$ K (from Ellenson and Kjems, 1977).

0.33 ± 0.02 in the reduced temperature range 0.005 and 0.05. The value of the exponent β obtained thus agrees with that predicted for the three-dimensional Ising model (cf. Chapter 1).

The second important aspect of the SPT in chloranil investigated by Ellenson and Kjems (1977) was a detailed investigation of the librational mode at the $(0, 0, \frac{1}{2})$ zone boundary which crosses over to the zone center below the cell-doubling transition at T_c. This mode shows the typical behavior of a soft mode as evident from the data plotted in Fig. 6. Below T_c the neutron data overlap nicely with the Raman data of Hanson (1975), also indicated schematically in the figure. Due to rapidly increasing phonon energy and the decreasing Bose population factor, the neutron scattering experiment could not follow the soft mode to temperatures much below 80 K. The dispersion of the soft mode in the principal directions about the $(0, 0, \frac{1}{2})$ zone boundary point showed that the mode softening was generally confined to the region about the zone boundary and did not extend back to the zone center. The shape of the dispersion surface about the zone boundary point was quite anisotropic, but the anisotropy appears not to have lowered the dimensionality of the critical behavior as reflected by the observed value of the critical exponent. From 95–270 K the soft-mode frequency was found to follow the linear relationship $\omega_s^2 = A(T - Tc)$, consistent with a similar functional dependence found via Raman scattering measurements for the soft mode below T_c (Wada *et al.*, 1980). This behavior is in contrast with observations in $SrTiO_3$, where both the order parame-

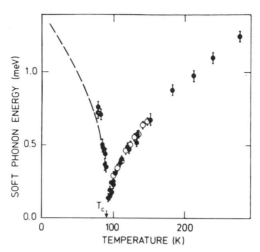

Fig. 6. Soft-mode energy versus temperature for chloranil ($C_6Cl_4O_2$). Measurements in the $(h,0,l)$ zone (●), $(0,k,l)$ zone (○), the Raman data taken from Hanson (1975) (———) (from Ellenson and Kjems, 1977).

ter η and the soft-mode frequency ω_s evolved with an exponent $\simeq 0.3$ around T_c, indicating that η and ω_s are proportional to one another (Steigmeier and Auderset, 1973). Microscopically, ω_s represents the response of the system to a modulating field and hence should be directly proportional to the electric susceptibility and *not* to the order parameter. Further theoretical and experimental work is, therefore, needed to clarify the relationship between ω_s and η in the critical regime of SPTs.

A third, interesting aspect of the neutron scattering study of chloranil is the discovery of critical scattering or a central peak in the vicinity of T_c. As evident in the spectra shown in Fig. 7, the intensity of this scattering centered at zero energy transfer, increases dramatically as T_c is approached and masks the phonons from about 89–95 K. The energy width of the peak is probably infinitely small since no broadening was found even with an instrumental resolution of 0.9×10^{-3} meV (Ellenson and Kjems, 1977). Zero energy transfer scans indicated that the central peak scattering had considerable extent and anisotropy in **q** space. The half-width K_1 in **q** space of this scattering can be written as $K_1 = 1/\xi$, where ξ can be interpreted as a correlation length. It was found that K_1 in the c^* direction evolved with the inverse of the reduced temperature with an exponent of 0.62 ± 0.4. It is notable that this corresponds closely to the exponent ν of the correlation length for a three-dimensional Ising model (cf. Chapter 1) consistent with the measurements of the order parameter. This very interesting experimental result

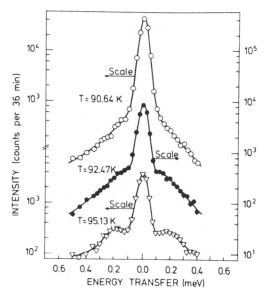

Fig. 7. Inelastic scans for chloranil ($C_6Cl_4O_2$) at the zone boundary ($\bar{1}$,0,2.5) in the critical region where the central peak dominates. The intensity scale is logarithmic and the curves are displaced corresponding to a factor of 10 (from Ellenson and Kjems, 1977).

needs further confirmation via other experimental techniques. Girard *et al.* (1982) has also observed a central component around T_c in a light scattering experiment, while the Brillouin scattering measurements of Ecolivet (1981) indicate an anomaly in the longitudinal acoustic mode propagating along the *a*-crystallographic axis near T_c, suggesting that the SPT in chloranil may be more complicated than originally perceived, and that it may involve a three-phonon nonlinear coupling process.

2. Sym-Triazine

The molecular crystal sym-triazine ($C_3N_3H_3$) undergoes an interesting type of strain-induced elastic phase transition which has been widely studied now by a variety of techniques. The transition occurs at $T_c \approx 200$ K under ambient pressure from a trigonal structure (space group $R\bar{3}c$) to a monoclinic structure of space group $C2/c$ (Rae, 1978). Hydrostatic pressure was found to increase the transition temperature according to the relation $T_c(p) = 198.8 + 18.2p$, where the temperature T is given in degrees K and the pressure p in Kbar (Zussman and Oron, 1977). A neutron scattering study of the transition at ambient pressure was reported by Heilman *et al.* (1979) and at pressures up to 5 Kbar by Eckert *et al.* (1982). A more complete neutron scattering study of a fully deuterated single crystal has been recently reported by Dove *et al.* (1983).

The eigenvector of the SPT shown in Fig. 8 suggests that the primary displacement would be a zone-center transverse acoustic shearing mode while a secondary displacement would correspond to rotational motions. The first light scattering study of the transition by Elliott and Iqbal (1975) indicated the basic correctness of this picture. There was no soft librational mode as in chloranil but appreciable softening of some of the modes indicating a librational–translational coupling mechanism. A theoretical study of this coupled-mode picture by Rae (1982) extended the earlier models applied to chloranil by Chihara and coworkers and to the nearly analogous transition in the molecular–ionic NaN_3 crystal by Iqbal and Christoe (1975).

Heilman *et al.* (1979) measured the [ζ00] TA modes in the vicinity of the intense ($\bar{1}$02) Bragg reflection. The data with $\mathbf{q} = 0.1 \, a_h^*$ as a function of temperature shown in Fig. 9 indicate a dramatic softening as T_c is approached from above and, interestingly enough, this extends considerably out into the Brillouin zone. The soft mode remains underdamped down to energies of at least 0.07 meV and no central peak or critical scattering is observed. The soft-mode energy remains finite at T_c consistent with the

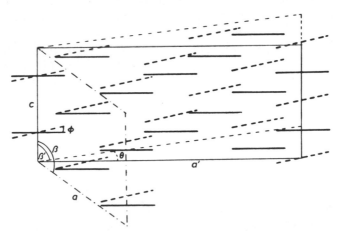

Fig. 8. The displacements involved in the phase change in sym-triazine viewed along the *a* axis of the high-temperature hexagonal cell which is identical to the unique *b* axis of the low temperature monoclinic cell. High (—) and low temperature unit cells (---), the reduced low temperature cell (· – ·), the molecular planes (————) (————), and θ and ϕ, the shear and molecular rotation angles, respectively, are indicated (after Smith and Rae, 1978).

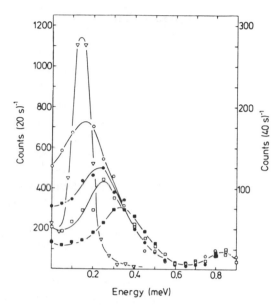

Fig. 9. Neutron inelastic scattering spectra showing the transverse acoustic modes in symtriazine with $q = 0.1\ a_h^*$ at 205 K (∇) (right-hand axis) and 215 ($\bigcirc$), 230 ($\bullet$), 250 ($\square$), and 295 K ($\blacksquare$) (left-hand axis). The weak peak at 0.8 meV is the *Bragg tail* (from Heilman *et al.*, 1979).

weakly first-order character of the transition. Measurements at pressures up to ~5 Kbar indicate a similar softening of the $[\zeta 00]$ transverse acoustic phonon branch. This suggests that the effect of pressure on the transition can be described primarily by its effect on the T_c of the transition — supporting the qualitative applicability of the so-called modified *law of corresponding states* (Benedek and Kushida, 1960; Heller, 1966) in the case of SPTs. Furthermore, NQR studies indicate that the transition is clearly second order at higher pressures — hence suggesting the existence of a tricritical point (cf. Chapter 1).

The absence of central peak scattering, an underdamped soft mode close to T_c, and an order parameter, which according to x-ray diffraction measurements (Rae, 1978) evolves with a mean-field exponent, support the theoretical study of Folk *et al.* (1979) which indicates the absence of dynamic fluctuations in the neighborhood of such elastic phase transitions. Further support of this comes from Raman scattering studies of the analogous transition in the molecular–ionic crystal NaN_3, where the order parameter also evolves through the critical regime with a mean-field exponent (Iqbal, 1973; Simonis and Hathaway, 1974). Brillouin scattering measurements (Kushida and Terhune, 1984) also show an underdamped soft acoustic mode and the absence of central peak scattering in NaN_3.

B. Transitions in the Order–Disorder Limit

1. Polyphenyls

Polyphenyls are nonrigid molecules (see Fig. 10) with respect to the torsional angle between the planes of the phenyl rings. The *intra*molecular conjugation energy between the phenyl rings is not sufficient to overcome the ortho-hydrogen atom repulsion, and this situation induces the existence of a double-well intramolecular potential as illustrated in Fig. 9 (cf. Cailleau *et al.*, 1980a). In the crystalline phase, the double-well potential is a result of the competition between the ortho-hydrogen repulsion and the crystal packing forces. The barrier height of this potential increases with increasing number of phenyl groups. Disorder consists of an equal orientational distribution involving the two wells—the jump from one well to another being an activated single molecule relaxation process. An SPT in such a system, approached from above, involves the ordering of the molecular orientations in one well and pretransitional effects appear with the growth of ordered clusters in the disordered phase. In *p*-terphenyl the order–disorder transition occurs at $T_c = 180$ K. A triple-axis neutron scattering experiment shows the presence of a quasi-elastic component which diverges at T_c, but no soft mode is observed (Cailleau, *et al.* 1979 and 1980a). These data are illustrated in Fig. 11, providing a clear-cut signature of an SPT in the order–disorder limit. The observed relaxation times T_c range from 2×10^{-11} sec at 300 K to 1.15×10^{-8} sec close to T_c. Another interesting observation is that the superlattice reflection intensity evolves with an exponent β (corre-

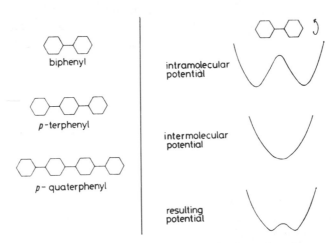

Fig. 10. Schematic drawing of intramolecular, intermolecular, and resulting torsional potential in the polyphenyls (from Cailleau *et al.*, 1980a).

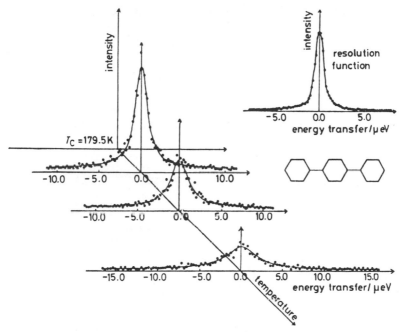

Fig. 11. Energy spectra of neutron scattering in deuterated p-terphenyl at the superlattice point ($\frac{3}{2},\frac{1}{2},0$). The full curves represent a fit of a convolution of a single Lorentzian scattering equation with the resolution function of the spectrometer. The fitted values of the half-widths at half maximum obtained are 0.36, 0.73, and 1.67 eV at respectively $T_c + 0.3$, $T_c + 0.8$, and $T_c + 1.6$ °K, which yield the cluster lifetimes discussed in the text (from Cailleau *et al.*, 1980a).

sponding to the order parameter) which is rather low (≈ 0.15, Cailleau *et al.*, 1976). This indicates that the fluctuations in this system may be quasi-one-dimensional in character.

With decreasing chain length, SPTs in polyphenyls such as biphenyl cross over to the *nearly* displacive SPT regime, due to the relative low barrier of the double-well potential. A soft mode is observed in biphenyl by neutron scattering (Cailleau *et al.*, 1980b), but the transition is complicated by the occurrence of an intermediate incommensurate phase (see discussion below). SPTs involving incommensurate phases will be considered in the next subsection.

2. Potassium Cyanide (KCN)

Molecular–ionic crystals like KCN undergo order–disorder phase transitions which are modulated by the molecular ion (here CN^-) flipping or reorientational rate that in turn leads to reorientational–translational coupling and a primarily displacive elastic transition component. In KCN, which is cubic at high temperature, an SPT with a sizable first-order character occurs at 168 K, in which the elastic constant C_{44} (corresponding to shear strains along the cube faces tending to distort the cubic cell to an orthorhombic one) decreases markedly and extrapolates to zero at about 14 K below the observed T_c. The transition is also accompanied by the ordering of the CN$^-$ ions. Inelastic neutron scattering measurements (Rowe *et al.*, 1978) showed that the transverse acoustic branch corresponding to C_{44} softens far into the

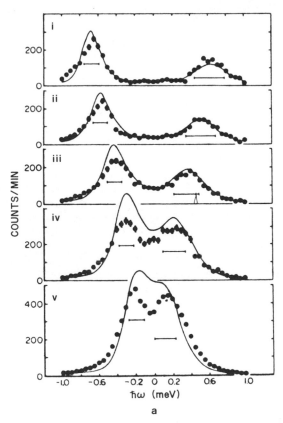

a

Fig. 12. (a) Comparison of neutron inelastic scattering lineshapes for the transverse acoustic mode in KCN with q = 0.1 in the [100] direction: full lines are calculated on the basis of a rotational–translational coupling model. (i) $\hbar\Omega = 0.656$ meV, 296 K, (ii) $\hbar\Omega = 0.557$ meV, 239 K, (iii) $\hbar\Omega = 0.432$, 190 K, (iv) $\hbar\Omega = 0.324$ meV, (v) $\hbar\Omega = 0.249$ meV, 169 K; Q = (1.9,2.0,0.0). (b) Similar data to (a) except that q = 0.5. The horizontal bars represent calculated resolution widths for a planar dispersion surface. (i) $\hbar\Omega = 3.56$ meV, 239 K, (ii) $\Omega = 2.28$ meV, 190 K, (iii) $\hbar\Omega = 2.12$ meV, 169 K, Q = (−0.5,2.0,0.0) (from Rowe *et al.*, 1978).

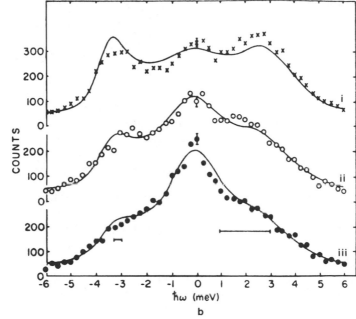

Figure 12 – Continued

Brillouin zone, similar to the behavior of the softening acoustic mode in *s*-triazine. However, the data of Rowe *et al.* shown in Figs. 12a and b indicate both the displacive and order–disorder character of the transition. The data in Fig. 12a, scanned at a fixed q of $\frac{1}{10}$ of the Brillouin zone, shows an essentially undamped soft mode and no scattering at $\hbar\omega = 0$. However, the same mode, shown in Fig. 12b, scanned at a q of $\frac{1}{2}$ of the Brillouin zone, indicates increased damping as T_c is approached and, more interestingly, the onset of scattering at $\hbar\omega = 0$. These results can be explained in terms of a relaxation-type reorientational–translational coupling model (Michel and Naudts, 1977a,b), which can be described as follows: At a $q \simeq 0.1$, the $\hbar\omega_j$ of the phonon is much smaller than the CN^- ion flipping parameter γ and we have a two-peak soft-mode response, involving no critical slowing down of the CN^- ion fluctuations. However, when we sample at $q = 0.5$, the phonon $\hbar\omega$ approaches that of γ and we can then monitor the three-peak response characteristic of an order–disorder system, which includes the central peak arising from the critical slowing down of the CN^- ion reorientations corresponding to $q = 0.5$. More recently Loidl *et al.* (1980) have invoked an alternative interpretation of the data involving the coupling of finite energy librational modes of CN^- ions with translational phonons.

3. Superionic Conductors

Superionic conductors (SIC) or solid electrolytes constitute a particularly interesting class of partially disordered systems (for an introduction, see Mahan and Roth, 1976). They consist of an ordered scaffold structure and a disordered sublattice of mobile ions, and thus phenomena observed in solids and liquids come together in an interesting manner. Each of the mobile ions disposes, in general, of more than one equivalent site, and the probability of a diffusional jump depends on the kinetic energy (temperature) of the mobile ion, of the configuration of the cage of the neighboring scaffold ions, and on the short range interaction within the sublattice of the mobile ions. Different kinds of phase transitions are observed in SIC:

(i) the crystal undergoes a reconstructive first-order transition in which the scaffold lattice transforms to a more *open* structure and the mobile ions can easily change places; examples are AgI, CuI, CuBr;

(ii) the scaffold lattice remains unchanged, but the mobile ion shows increasing disorder. The change of the order parameter may occur

(a) very abruptly (first order); an example is Ag_2HgI_4;
(b) diffuse (second order); examples are CaF_2, PbF_2, Na_2S, where the spread in temperature is typically 100 K;
(c) gradually without a transition; an example is Ag-β-alumina.

Elastic neutron scattering provides information on the crystal structures of the phases in question. The major advantage stems from the fact that neutrons are sensitive to light elements in the neighborhood of heavy ones (Ag in AgI, F in PbF_2). Quasi-elastic scattering gives information on the time scale and type of motion in the diffusion process.

Inelastic scattering, which is very powerful in investigating second-order displacive transitions as discussed previously, is less successful in studies of first-order transformations. In SIC the ionic conductivity is determined by the dynamics of the lattice. The instantaneous position of the conducting ion relative to its neighbors is of interest in the diffusion process. It represents a suitable reaction coordinate for ionic jumps which can be expressed in terms of the phonon structure (eigenvectors, density of states). Therefore it is necessary, in general, to study large parts of the phonon spectrum and not only a particular mode of wavevector $\mathbf{q}_c$.

a. AgI

Silver iodide is the prototype and most well-known solid electrolyte which shows a number of phase transitions as a function of temperature and pressure. The phase diagram is displayed in Fig. 13. At room temperature the β (wurtzite) and γ (sphalerite) modifications coexist. At high pressure AgI has

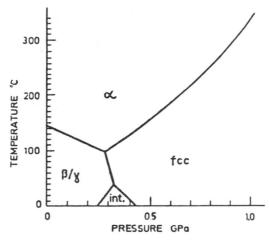

Fig. 13. Phase diagram of AgI (from Mellander *et al.*, 1981).

the rocksalt structure like the other silver halides AgBr and AgCl. Of particular interest is the $\beta \rightleftharpoons \alpha$ first-order transition at 147 °C from the moderately conducting β phase to the superionic conducting α phase.

The structure of β-AgI is hexagonal wurtzite (space group C_{6v}^4) with 2 molecular units in the cell, as determined by x-ray and neutron experiments on single crystals (Burley, 1963; Cava *et al.*, 1977). However, despite the good experimental data, the agreement between the observed and calculated structure factors is not satisfactory, and there remain uncertainties about the detailed atomic positions. The phonon dispersion relation has been investigated by inelastic neutron scattering by Bührer *et al.* (1978). The dispersion curves, shown in Fig. 14, show a large energy spread between the optic modes. It is interesting to note the low energy band near 2 meV with almost no dispersion. It is also noteworthy that low energy modes involving Ag-ion motion have been observed in $RbAg_4I_5$ (Shapiro and Salamon, 1979) and $AgCrS_2$ (Brüesch *et al.*, 1983). The phonon frequencies of AgI have been fitted with a nine parameter valence shell model, the calculation agrees satisfactorily with the experiment. The model has been used to compute the eigenvector weighted densities-of-states for silver and iodine ions in AgI. It turns out that the silver ions move predominantly in the lower energy modes despite the fact that they are lighter than the iodine ions. In the high temperature α-AgI phase the iodine ions form a *bcc*-lattice.

The 2 silver ions are statistically distributed in the 12 (d) tetrahedral pockets of the iodine scaffold lattice and perform strong anisotropic thermal vibrations. The Fourier synthesis of the silver scattering density is presented in Fig. 15. The density is rather high and well localized around $(\frac{1}{4},\frac{1}{2},0)$. The

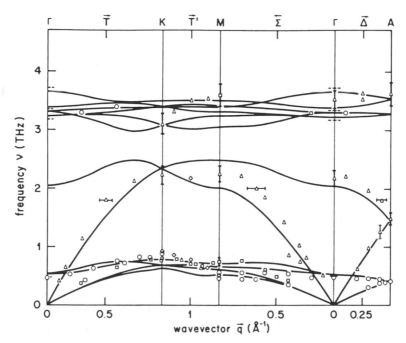

Fig. 14. Observed and calculated phonon dispersion in β-AgI at 160 K (from Bührer *et al.*, 1978) transverse $\perp c$ (O), transverse $\parallel c$ ($\square$), unknown ($\diamond$), longitudinal mode ($\triangle$), valence shell model calculation (————).

smaller contributions near $(x,x,0)$, $x \sim 0.4$, suggest a diffusion path of silver ions between neighboring tetrahedral sites. The dynamics of the Ag ions has been studied by quasielastic neutron scattering by Eckold *et al.* (1976). According to their results, the local random motion takes place on a time scale on the order of 10^{-12} sec, while the translational motion with a correlation time of $\sim 10^{-11}$ sec is composed of a residual and a flight time of comparable magnitude. Acoustic phonon modes have been measured by neutron scattering (Brüesch *et al.* 1980). The longitudinal modes are well defined with frequencies and line-widths similar to those observed in β-AgI. The transverse modes on the other hand show a lower energy and very large line broadening due to configurational disorder. The elastic and inelastic neutron experiments suggest that the state of the Ag ions in β-AgI is far from liquid-like, and that the diffusive and vibrational motions are correlated.

The mechanism of the β–α phase transition is still a matter of controversy. The low energy modes contain displacements of the iodine sublattice which correspond to the reorganization of the hexagonal to the cubic structure (Bührer and Brüesch, 1975). One of the modes could, therefore, be considered a *soft mode* which drives the transition, but no temperature

Fig. 15. Section ρ $(xy0)$ of Fourier synthesis of the silver scattering density in α-AgI at 160°C (from Cava *et al.*, 1977).

dependence except anharmonic broadening has been observed in the phonon spectrum between 40 and 290 K by neutron experiments (Bührer *et al.*, 1978), and the Raman-active zone-center mode is stable up to the transition point (Hanson *et al.*, 1975).   In the theory of Rice *et al.* (1974), the interaction of interstitial cation defects with the strain field they induce, is considered as the driving force.   However, even near the transition temperature the occupation of the largest interstitial positions (the octahedral sites) is lower than 0.04 (Cava *et al.*, 1977).   The thermal motion of the ions in β-AgI is very large; the mean-square displacement of the silver ion near the $\beta - \alpha$ transition, as determined from experimental Debye–Waller factors and shell model calculations, is even larger than the corresponding values in AgCl and AgBr near their respective melting temperatures (Fig. 16).   Lindemann's formula suggests melting for displacements larger than a critical value, but due to the very special interatomic forces in AgI, the crystal lattice finds a new equilibrium configuration in a partially disordered state.   With a suitably chosen potential and a new molecular dynamics procedure, where the shape and volume of the repeating cell are allowed to vary dynamically with time; Parinello *et al.* (1983) were indeed able to reproduce the phase diagram of AgI.

b. Fluorites (PbF$_2$)

Many compounds with the fluorite structure exhibit a specific heat anomaly at a temperature T_f a few hundred degress below the melting tempera-

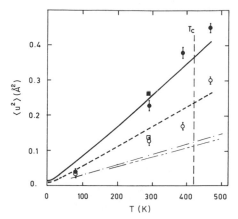

Fig. 16. Mean-square ionic displacements for Ag and I in β-AgI. Experimental (neutron scattering) ($\bullet$, $\bigcirc$), experimental (x-ray scattering) ($\blacksquare$, $\square$), calculation (shell model, harmonic approximation): Ag in AgI (———), I in AgI (---), Ag in AgBr ($\cdot - \cdot -$), Ag in AgCl (----------).

ture T_m. The transition is spread out in temperature and is accompanied by a smooth increase in ionic conductivity due to dynamical disorder in the anion sublattice. In the transition region no change in the scaffold structure and no discontinuity of the lattice constants have been observed.

PbF$_2$ is the compound with the lowest T_f and a large difference between T_f and T_m ($T_f = 711$ K, $T_m = 1128$ K) and, therefore, has been more extensively investigated. The unit cell is cubic and consists of three interpenetrating fcc-lattices, the cations are at (000), and the anions are displaced by $\pm(\frac{1}{4},\frac{1}{4},\frac{1}{4})$ (see Fig. 17). With increasing temperature, the anions start moving, and in the first stage of disorder they create Frenkel pairs occupying the cube centers $(\frac{1}{2},\frac{1}{2},\frac{1}{2})$. The concentration of interstitial ions increases rapidly with temperature in the region of the transition, and the attractive interaction between the defects lowers the Frenkel energy. At higher defect concentrations the nearest-neighbor interaction becomes important and suppresses further generation of interstitial defects. Complex defects are formed, and the diffraction data cannot be satisfactorily explained with simple models based on the occupation of high symmetry crystallographic sites.

The diffuse scattering, originating from the anion disorder, was studied by quasi-elastic neutron scattering (Clausen *et al.*, 1981). The measured intensity contours show a very asymmetrical distribution. The intensities could be explained by clusters involving Frenkel pairs plus relaxed neighboring ions. The clusters are dynamical aggregates and, from the energy width, the lifetime was determined to be $\sim 10^{-12}$ sec, which is longer than the typical phonon frequencies. The coherent elastic scattering data were then analyzed with a model allowing for both types of defects. Satisfactory results

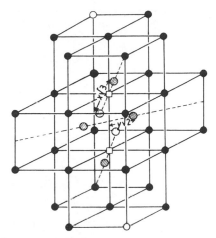

Fig. 17. Disordered structure of PbF$_2$ [cation (O), anion (●)] with Frenkel pair [anion vacancy (O), "I" site interstitial (◐)] and relaxed anion site [anion vacany (□), "R" site interstitial (◑)] (from Dickens *et al.*, 1982).

were obtained and Fig. 18 illustrates the percentage of fluorine ions leaving their regular sites as a function of temperature.

Phonon dispersion curves of PbF$_2$ have been measured by Dickens and Hutchings (1978), the results are displayed in Fig. 19. They exhibit no peculiar behavior except anharmonic broadening at high temperatures.

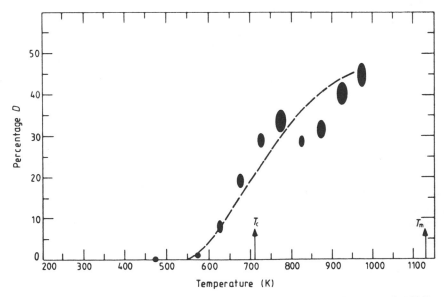

Fig. 18. Percentage of fluorine ions leaving their regular sites (from Dickens *et al.*, 1982).

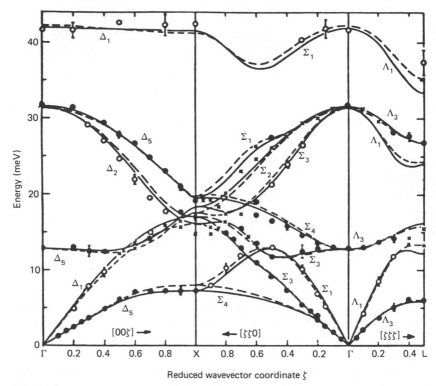

Fig. 19. Observed and calculated phonon dispersion in PbF$_2$ at 10 K (from Dickens and Hutchings, 1978).

The curves have been fitted to various shell models [cf. (---) and (———) in Fig. 19]. However, the model parameters show no clear relation to fast-ion conduction and unusual anharmonic properties.

C. Incommensurate Phase Transitions

Incommensurate phase transitions can generally be described in terms of a displacive process in which the distortion wavevector is an irrational fraction of the underlying lattice. Generally, in these materials the periodicity is restored at a transition point where the incommensurate phase locks into a new commensurate structure. The incommensurate phase is characterized by the occurrence of satellite Bragg reflections, of indices, for example $(h, k \pm n\delta, \ell)$, where h, k, and ℓ are the Miller indices, n is an integer, and δ (which is both temperature- and pressure-dependent) is the distance in reduced coordinates between the main Bragg reflections and the first-order satellite in reciprocal space. The excitations of the incommensurate phase are expected to display a number of novel features. For example, two modes corresponding to fluctuations in the amplitude (amplitudons) and the phase (phasons) of the frozen in modulation wave, respectively, are expected to occur.

Historically, incommensurate phases were first observed and studied in low-dimensional metallic systems such as $K_2Pt(CN)_4Br_{0.30}\cdot3H_2O$ (KCP) (Renker *et al.*, 1973), tetrathiofulvalene-tetracyanoquinodimethane (TTF–TCNQ) (Comes *et al.*, 1975; Shirane *et al.*, 1976; Mook and Watson, 1976; Ellenson *et al.*, 1976) and layered compounds (Moncton *et al.*, 1975). In the following discussions these materials and the recently discovered organic charge transfer superconductors will be considered first, and this will be followed by discussions of selected examples of more conventional three-dimensional insulating materials.

1. Low-Dimensional Metals

In ionic metals (such as the low-dimensional synthetic metals discovered and studied over the past decade), the motion of the ions is screened by the conduction electrons. This screening leads to anomalies in the longitudinal phonon dispersion surface, which can be studied by inelastic neutron scattering. In 1D-metallic systems the Fermi surface consists of two planes at $+K_F$ and $-K_F$; energy conserving scattering can then take place exclusively between these two planes with a momentum change of $2K_F$ which leads to a pronounced singularity [the well-known Kohn anomaly (Kohn, 1959)] in the susceptibility $\chi(\mathbf{q})$ at $\mathbf{q} = 2K_F$. If Ω_q represents the unrenormalized phonon frequency and λ the strength of the electron–phonon coupling, then the renormalized phonon frequency $[\omega(\mathbf{q})]$ can be written as

$$\omega^2(\mathbf{q}) = \Omega_q^2[1 - \lambda\chi(\mathbf{q})]. \tag{22}$$

Since the Kohn anomaly involves a divergence of $\chi(\mathbf{q})$, satellite Bragg peaks characteristic of an incommensurate or modulated structure appear at $\mathbf{q} = \pm 2K_F$ and a gap in the conduction band opens up (Peierls, 1964) below a critical temperature T_c. In an ideal 1D-metallic system the transition should theoretically occur at $T = 0$, but real systems are at best only quasi-one-dimensional (see Barisic and Saub, 1973; Horowitz *et al.*, 1974) and hence a phase transition is expected at finite temperatures. The overall situation then is similar to an SPT in which the giant $2K_F$ Kohn anomaly gives rise to a high temperature soft mode in the metallic state which then condenses to form a low temperature modulated structure that is insulating.

Two real systems of this type; namely, KCP and TTF–TCNQ have been investigated in some detail and will be discussed below. The recently discovered salts, analogous in structure to KCP and TTF–TCNQ, consisting of tetramethyltetraselenafulvalene (TMTSF) and (usually) non-centrosymmetric anions, undergo stepwise increments of dimensionality with decreasing temperature (see Proceedings of CNRS Conference on Low Dimensional Synthetic Conductors and Superconductors, 1982) and achieve a superconducting state under high pressure conditions (except for the perchlorate salt). These materials have yet to be investigated in detail by neutron scattering, although extensive x-ray diffuse scattering and neutron diffraction results (Moret *et al.*, 1983) are already available.

KCP is built up of Pt chains separated by ~10Å. The 1D-metallic properties along the Pt chains arise from the addition in nonstoichiometric proportion of the halogen which removes electrons from the d_{z^2} Pt orbitals of the insulating $K_2Pt(CN)_4$ salt—thus giving a (commensurate) $2K_F$ value of $0.30c^*$ (where c^* represents the reciprocal lattice constant) for the composition $K_2Pt(CN)_4Br_{0.30}\text{-}3H_2O$. Incommensurate values of the expected modulation would be achieved by small changes of stoichiometry around the commensurate value. Diffuse x-ray scattering provided the first evidence of a modulated structure, in the form of streaks of diffuse scattering perpendicular to the c axis and $\mathbf{q} = 0.30c^*$ (Comes *et al.*, 1973a,b). Neutron inelastic scattering studies of the acoustic phonon dispersion at 300 K (see Fig. 20) show the predicted dip in the dispersion — the so-called Kohn anomaly — perpendicular to the c axis at $\mathbf{q} = 0.30 = 2K_F$ (Renker *et al.*, 1975). The *giant* Kohn anomaly in the longitudinal dispersion parallel to the chain

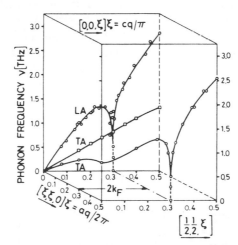

Fig. 20. Phonon dispersion in KCP at 300 K. The dip in the dispersion corresponds to a giant Kohn anomaly which appears in planes perpendicular to the z axis and at a distance of $2K_F$ from the origin (from Renker *et al.*, 1975).

direction reflects the 1D character of the electronic system. At low temperature, KCP becomes an insulator via a Peierls-like transition in which the Pt chains are sinusoidally modulated in such a way that neighboring chains are of opposite phase. Some aspects of this coupling and the absence of long range lateral coupling of the chains emerges from a detailed temperature-dependent study of the neutron inelastic scattering dispersion around $2K_F$ in which intensity contours of the scattering were also measured (Carneiro et al., 1976).

Neutron inelastic scattering studies on TTF–TCNQ similarly showed the precursor Kohn anomaly in the metallic phase (Mook and Watson, 1976; Shirane et al., 1976). Below 38 K a modulated structure, which is in this case incommensurate with the underlying lattice because $2K_F = 0.295b^*$, is observed. There are two interesting features: One is the observation of a modulation which varies with temperature in the range of 38–49 K in one specific direction and the other is the pressure-induced decrease of the incommensurability revealed by neutron elastic scattering measurements at high pressure (Megtert et al., 1981). The incommensurability vanishes at 35 K and 15 Kbar and is also associated with a further drop in the dc conductivity of the salt in its semiconducting phase due to a *locking* of the charge density waves to the lattice.

2. Three-Dimensional Insulators

The first detailed study of an incommensurate SPT in an insulator crystal was published by Iizumi et al. (1977), involving potassium selenate (K_2SeO_4), which undergoes a transition to an incommensurate phase at 129.5 K with a wavevector $\mathbf{q} = (1 - \delta)a^*/3$. The value of δ decreases with decreasing temperature until the lattice locks discontinuously to a commensurate, ferroelectric structure at $T_c = 93$ K. Neutron inelastic scattering measurements disclose the existence of a strongly temperature-dependent excitation of $\mathbf{q} \sim \frac{1}{3}a^*$ which goes to nearly zero frequency at $T_i = 130$ K. The dispersion surfaces for modes propagating in the [100] direction are depicted in Fig. 21. In addition, a central peak with no detectable energy width at $\omega = 0$ was observed. The soft mode corresponds to the amplitudon in the incommensurate phase but no evidence of the phason component, which is expected to correspond to a Goldstone mode involving a continuous broken phase symmetry, was observed in the relatively low resolution neutron inelastic scattering data.

Neutron inelastic scattering studies of the compound Rb_2ZnBr_4, which has an incommensurably modulated structure between 200 and 355 K that is related to K_2SeO_4, clearly show dynamical behavior that is dramatically different (de Pater et al., 1979). The soft mode in contrast with that in

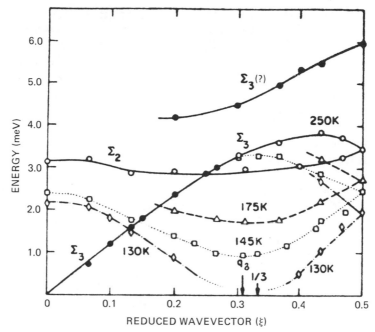

Fig. 21. Dispersion curves of transverse modes propagating in the [100] direction K_2SeO_4 [$\mathbf{q} = (\xi a^*, 0, 0)$] (from Iizumi *et al.*, 1977).

K_2SeO_4, is overdamped above T_i and so are both the amplitude and phase fluctuations below T_i. However, diffuse quasi-inelastic scattering corresponding to order parameter fluctuations are observed both in the commensurate and incommensurate phases. The scattering intensity distribution is ellipsoidal in shape with the principal axis along the modulation wavevector (de Pater *et al.*, 1979).

More recently very high resolution measurements using a triple-axis spectrometer installed with a neutron cold source, allowed the observation of a new excitation in the incommensurate phase of biphenyl (see Section III.B) which exists between $T_{i(I)} = 21$ K and $T_{i(II)} = 38$ K with wavevector $\mathbf{q} = \pm \delta_a a^* \pm \frac{1}{2}(1 - \delta_b)b^*$ (Cailleau *et al.*, 1980b). The observed relatively sharp excitation is superimposed on the overdamped amplitudon mode as shown by the constant $\mathbf{q}$ scans in Fig. 22. Various experimental checks such as measurement of both the energy loss and energy gain spectra, the measurement of the dispersion of the mode and its comparison with that of the acoustic mode, ruled out interpretations other than that of a *pinned* phason mode for the observed excitation. In K_2SeO_4, Quilichini and Currat (1983) were able to resolve a heavily damped response near the strong $(1 + q_\delta, 0, 2)$

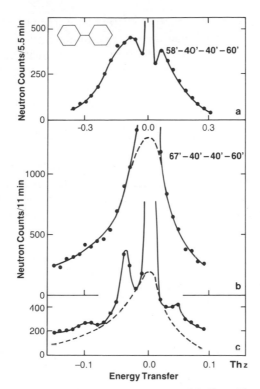

Fig. 22. Constant **q** scans at different temperatures and indicated beam collimations, in biphenyl; $q_{a^*} = 2$ and $q_{b^*} = 0.542$. (a) At T $= 49$ K, the soft mode is well resolved ($\lambda_i = 4.83\text{Å}$), (b) at T $= 38$ K near the transition it is overdamped ($\lambda_i = 5.6\text{Å}$), and (c) at T $= 23$ K in the incommensurate phase ($\lambda_i = 5.6$ Å) a new excitation appears. The small peak at -0.1 THz is identified as an acoustic phonon. The overdamped mode is roughly indicated by (———) (from Cailleau *et al.*, 1980b).

satellite reflection in the incommensurate phase, which was identified as the phase mode.

One such preliminary observation of an acoustic-like phason mode was made in deuterated thiourea, $SC(NH_2)_2$ (Denoyer *et al.*, 1980), in which two incommensurably modulated phases exist between $T_i = 213$ K and $T_c = 185$ K. In addition, a softening phonon was detected, in contrast with the earlier neutron inelastic scattering measurements of MacKenzie (1975), which became overdamped near T_i.

3. NiTi Alloys and Compounds

Transition metal alloys and compounds show a variety of effects in their phonon dispersion and structural phase transitions, which are related to electron–phonon interactions (Sinha, 1980). The equiatomic intermetallic compound NiTi exhibits a thermoelastic phase transition associated with a reversible shape change when the temperature is cycled around the transition temperature T_m. Above this martensitic transition, anomalies have been observed by electrical resistivity measurements (Sandrock *et al.*, 1971), x-ray and electron diffraction (Dautovich and Purdy, 1965), ultrasonic measurements (Mercier *et al.*, 1980), and elastic neutron scattering experiments (Salamon *et al.*, 1979). All the observations are characterized as premartensitic effects, but due to different samples the results cannot be correlated easily.

Acoustic phonon dispersion curves of NiTi have been measured at 420 K (150 K above the transition temperature) by Bührer *et al.* (1980) and the results are displayed in Fig. 23. As compared to the isostructural β-brass, the curves exhibit a peculiar behavior near the zone center Γ and along the Σ direction.

(i)   For small wavevectors, the transverse mode (elastic constant C_{44}) has an unusual convex curvature. Ultrasonic experiments (Mercier *et al.*, 1980) revealed a temperature-dependent softening of C_{44}, however, C_{44} remains at a finite value down to T_m, and it does not lead to an acoustic zone-center

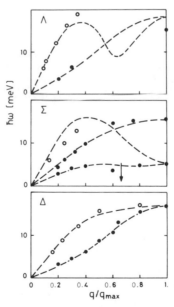

Fig. 23. Phonon dispersion curves in NiTi at 430 K. Experimental data for longitudinal (O) and transverse modes (●) (from Bührer *et al.*, 1981). Theoretical calculation (————) (from Bruinsma, 1982), vertical arrow represents the soft-mode region.

instability as observed in the A15 compound, Nb_3Sn (Axe and Shirane, 1973), where the shear modulus $(C_{11} - C_{12})$ tends to zero.

(ii) The transverse acoustic mode along Σ with polarization [110] has a low frequency and a pronounced dip near $q \cong \frac{2}{3} q_{max}$. If the temperature is lowered, the neutron intensity is shifted to lower energies and merges with the growing central component of the spectrum.

By alloying NiTi with Fe, the martensitic transition can be suppressed more strongly than the onset of the soft-phonon behavior, and thus a well-separated phase is realized (Salamon et al., 1979), which is not interrupted by the martensitic transition. Detailed studies of NiTi(Fe) have been performed by Satija et al. (1983). The inelastic intensities measured as a function of temperature near $q = (\frac{2}{3},\frac{2}{3},0)$ exhibit very broad features similar to the scattering observed in TTF–TCNQ. Superlattice peaks of the new phase do not appear exactly at the commensurate q vector $(\frac{2}{3},\frac{2}{3},0)$ but slightly displaced by a value δ which in direction and magnitude, does not repeat from one Brillouin zone to another (Shapiro et al., 1984).

A theoretical account for the phonon dispersion in NiTi has been given by Bruinsma (1982). The contribution of the electron–phonon interaction to the dispersion has been computed starting from a self-consistent band structure calculation. The dispersion curves and the anomalies can qualitatively be reproduced as shown by the solid lines in Fig. 23. The dip along Σ is associated with areas of the Fermi surface having large electron–phonon matrix elements. The calculation provides an understanding of the soft-phonon regime; however, the relation between the premartensitic phenomena and the martensite, as well as the martensitic transition, are still not understood.

IV. CONCLUSIONS AND NEW DIRECTIONS

In this chapter we have reviewed selected studies of structural phase transitions using neutron scattering methods. The emphasis has been on new results involving relatively complex materials ranging from molecular and molecular–ionic insulators and super-ionic conductors to molecular metals of quasi-one-dimensional character and the more conventional transition metal alloy systems. We have covered the whole spectrum of phase transition regimes from the nearly ideal displacive to the order–disorder limit. Also considered were the special cases of incommensurate phase transitions in conventional materials and the more exotic low-dimensional molecular metals, where electron–phonon interactions create *giant* anomalies in the phonon dispersion surface.

The soft-mode picture, clearly established in the case of ferroelectric insulators, now appears to apply also to molecular systems of increasing complexity. Two limiting dynamic regimes have emerged represented by the displacive and the order–disorder descriptions of structural phase transitions. Although evident already in the earlier studies of ferroelectric systems, the examination of molecular and molecular–ionic crystals, where librational motions (which concurrently also lead to dynamic disorder) play a crucial role, has underlined the importance of the subtle interplay between disorder and symmetry-breaking distortion in the critical regime. A central peak has also been shown to exist in molecular crystals. It appears with unresolvable linewidth in the near-condensation regime of a soft mode in the displacive limit. In the order–disorder limit, at least one component with finite lifetime appears, reflecting the relaxation of clusters of the *new* in the *old* phase. However, situations exist (in, e.g, elastic transitions) where the central peak is clearly missing. In such situations renormalization group theory predicts the absence of fluctuations and hence the lack of a central component. Further work in this area should focus on *doped* or intentionally disordered systems in an attempt to sort the intrinsic from extrinsic contributions to the central peak.

Studies of incommensurate structures have already provided evidence for the existence of a new phase-like excitation — the phason — in three-dimensional systems. In low-dimensional metallic systems, *giant* Kohn anomalies at twice the Fermi wavevector, have been established. Neutron inelastic scattering studies at high pressure and low temperature, in and around the superconducting regimes of the more recently investigated quasi-one-dimensional organic conductors, should provide new and exciting results. Moreover, further experimental work is necessary to characterize the incommensurate phase excitations, in both three- and low-dimensional solids.

REFERENCES

Axe, J. D., and Shirane, G. (1973). *Phys. Rev.* **138,** 1965.
Barisic, S., and Saub, K. (1973). *J. Phys. C: Solid State Phys.* **6,** L367.
Benedek, G. B., and Kushida, T. (1960). *Phys. Rev.* **118,** 46.
Brockhouse, B. N. (1961). *In* "Inelastic Scattering of Neutrons in Solids and Liquids." IAEA, Vienna.
Brüesch, P., Bührer, W., and Smeets, H. J. M. (1980). *Phys. Rev.* **B22,** 970.
Brüesch, P., Hibma, T., and Bührer, W. (1983). *Phys. Rev.* **B27,** 5052.
Bruinsma, R. (1982). *Phys. Rev.* **B25,** 2951.
Bührer, W., and Brüesch, P. (1975). *Solid State Commun.* **16,** 155.
Bührer, W., and Nicklow, R. M., and Brüesch, P. (1978). *Phys. Rev.* **B17,** 3362.
Bührer, W., Mercier, O., Brüesch, P., and Gotthardt, R. (1981). Prog. Rep. 1980, ETH, AF-SSP-Zurich.

Burley, G. (1963). *J. Chem. Phys.* **38**, 2807.
Cailleau, H., Baudour, J. L., and Girard, A. (1976). *Solid State Commun.* **20**, 577.
Cailleau, H., Heidemann, A., and Zeyen, C. M. E. (1979). *J. Phys. C: Solid State Phys.* **12**, L411.
Cailleau, H. *et al.* (1980a). *Faraday Discuss. Chem. Soc.* **69**, 7.
Cailleau, H., Moussa, F., Zeyen, C. M. E., and Bouillot, J. (1980b). *Solid State Commun.* **33**, 407.
Carneiro, K., Shirane, G., Werner, S. A., and Kaiser, S. (1976). *Phys. Rev.* **B13**, 4258.
Cava, R. J., Reidinger, F., and Wuensch, B. J. (1977). *Solid State Commun.* **24**, 411.
Chihara, H., and Nakamura, N. (1973). *J. Chem. Phys.* **59**, 5392.
Chihara, H., and Masukane, K. (1973). *J. Chem. Phys.* **59**, 5397.
Chihara, H., Nakamura, N., and Tachiki, M. (1973). *J. Chem. Phys.* **59**, 5387.
Clausen, K. *et al.* (1981). *Solid State Ionics* **5**, 589.
Comes, R., Lambert, M., and Zeller, H. R. (1973a). *Phys. Status Solidi b* **58**, 587.
Comes, R., Lambert, M., Launois, H., and Zeller, H.R. (1973b). *Phys. Rev.* **138**, 571.
Comes, R., Shapiro, S. M., Shirane, G., Garito, A. F., and Heeger, A. J. (1975). *Phys. Rev. Lett.* **35**, 1518.
Cooper, M. J., and Nathans, R. (1967). *Acta Cryst.* **23**, 357.
Currat, R. and Pynn, R. (1979). *In* "Neutron Scattering in Materials Science" (G. Kostorz, ed.), p. 131. Academic Press, New York.
Dautovich, D. P., and Purdy, G. R. (1965). *Can. Metall. Q.* **2**, 129.
Denoyer, F., Moudden, A. H., and Lambert, M. (1980). *Ferroelectrics* **24**, 43.
Dickens, M. H., and Hutchings, M. T. (1978). *J. Phys.* **C11**, 461.
Dickens, M. H., Hayes, W., Hutchings, M. T., and Smith, C. (1982). *J. Phys.* **C15**, 4043.
Dolling, G. (1974). *In* "Dynamical Properties of Solids" (G. K. Horton and A. A. Maradudin eds.). North-Holland, Amsterdam.
Dorner, B. (1981). *In* "Structural Phase Transitions I" (K. A. Muller and H. Thomas, eds.), p. 93. Springer-Verlag, Berlin and New York.
Dorner, B., and Comes, R. (1977). *In* "Dynamics of Solids and Liquids by Neutron Scattering" (S. W. Lovesey and T. Springer, eds.), p. 127. Springer-Verlag, Berlin and New York.
Dove, M. T., Heilman, I. V., Kjems, J. K., Kurittu, J., and Pawley, G. S. (1983). *Phys. Status Solid. b* **120**, 173.
Eckert, J., Fincher, C. R., and Heilman, I. U. (1982). *Solid State Commun.* **41**, 839.
Eckold, G., Funke, K., Kalus, J., and Lechner, R. E. (1976). *J. Phys. Chem. Solids* **37**, 1097.
Ecolivet, C. (1981). *Solid State Commun.* **40**, 503.
Ellenson, W. D., and Kjems, J. K. (1977). *J. Chem. Phys.* **67**, 3619.
Ellenson, W. D., Comes, R., Shapiro, S. M., Garito, A. F., and Heeger, A. J. (1976). *Solid State Commun.* **20**, 53.
Elliott, G. R., and Iqbal, Z. (1975). *J. Chem. Phys.* **63**, 1914.
Elliott, R. J., and Thorpe, M. F. (1967). *Proc. Phys. Soc.* **91**, 903.
Folk, R., Iro, H., and Schwabl, F. (1979). *Phys. Rev.* **B20**, 1229.
Girard, A., Delugeard, Y., Ecolivet, C., and Cailleau, H. (1982). *J. Phys. C: Solid State Phys.* **15**, 2127.
Hanson, D. M. (1975). *J. Chem. Phys.* **63**, 5046.
Hanson, R. C., Fjeldly, T. A., and Hochheimer, H. D. (1975). *Phys. Status Solidi B* **70**, 567.
Heilman, I. U., Ellenson, W. D., and Eckert, J. (1979). *J. Phys. C: Solid State Phys.* **12**, L185.
Heller, P. (1966). *Phys. Rev.* **146**, 403.
Horowitz, B., Gutfreund, H., and Weger, M. (1974). *Phys. Rev.* **B9**, 1246.
Iizumi, M., Axe, J. D., Shirane, G., and Shimaoka, K. (1977). *Phys. Rev.* **B15**, 4392.
Iqbal, Z. (1973). *J. Chem. Phys.* **59**, 1769.

Iqbal, Z., and Christoe, C. W. (1975). *Solid State Commun.* **17**, 71.

Koester, L., Rauch, H., Herker, M., and Schroder, K. (1981). *Ber. Kernforschungsanlage Jeulich* **1755.**

Kohn, W. (1959). *Phys. Rev. Lett.* **2**, 393.

Kushida, T., and Terhune, R. W. (1984). *Phys. Rev. B,* in press.

Loidl, A., Knorr, K., Daubert, J., Dultz, W., and Fitzgerald, W. J. (1980). *Z. Phys.* **B38**, 153.

MacKenzie, D. R. (1975). *J. Phys. C: Solid State Phys.* **8**, 2003.

Mahan, G. D., and Roth, W. L. (1976). *In* "Superionic Conductors." Plenum, New York.

Maradudin, A. A. (1974). *In* "Dynamical Properties of Solids" (G. K. Horton and A. A. Maradudin, eds.). North-Holland, Amsterdam.

Marshall, W., and Lovesey, S. W. (1971) "Theory of Thermal Neutron Scattering." Oxford Univ. Press (Clarendon), London and New York.

Megtert, S., Comes, R., Vettier, C., Pynn, R., and Garito, A. F. (1981). *Solid State Commun.* **37**, 875.

Mellander, B. E., Lunden, A., and Friesel, M. (1981). *Solid State Ionics* **5**, 477.

Mercier, O., Melton, K. N., Gremaud, G., and Hagi, J. (1980). *J. Appl. Phys.* **51**, 1833.

Michel, K. H., and Naudts, J. (1977a). *Phys. Rev. Lett.* **39**, 212.

Michel, K. H., and Naudts, J. (1977b). *J. Chem. Phys.* **67**, 547.

Moncton, D. E., Axe, J. D. and DiSalvo, F. J. (1975). *Phys. Rev. Lett.* **34**, 634.

Mook, H. A., and Watson, C. R. (1976). *Phys. Rev. Lett.* **36**, 801.

Moret, R., Pouget, J. P., Comes, R., and Bechgaard, K. (1983). *J. Phys.* **44**, C3–957.

Neutron Beam Facilities at the HFR (1981). ILL Information for Users, F-38042, Grenoble, France.

Parinello, M., Rahman, A., and Vashista, P. (1983). *Phys. Rev. Lett.* **50**, 1073.

de Pater, C. J., Axe, J. D., and Currat, R. (1979). *Phys. Rev.* **B19**, 4684.

Peierls, R. E. (1964). "Quantum Theory of Solids." Oxford Univ. Press (Clarendon), London and New York.

Proceedings CNRS Conference on Low Dimensional Synthetic Conductors and Superconductors, Les Arcs. (1982) *J. Phys. (Colloq.,* No. 3).

Quilichini, M., and Currat, R. (1983). *Solid State Commun.* **48**, 1011.

Rae, A. I. M., (1978). *J. Phys. C: Solid State Phys.* **11**, 1779.

Rae, A. I. M., (1982). *J. Phys. C: Solid State Phys.* **15**, 1883.

Renker, B. *et al.* (1973). *Phys. Rev. Lett.* **30**, 1144.

Renker, B., Pintschovius, L., Glaser, W., Rietschel, H., and Comes, R. (1975). *In* "Lecture Notes in Physics," Vol. 34, p. 53. Springer-Verlag Berlin and New York.

Rice, M. J., Strassler, S., and Toombs, G. A. (1974). *Phys. Rev. Lett.* **32**, 596.

Rowe, J. M., Rush, J. J., Chesser, N. J., Michel, K. H., and Naudts, J. (1978). *Phys. Rev. Lett.* **40**, 455.

Salamon, M. B., Meichle, M., Wayman, C. M., and Shapiro, S. M. (1979). AIP Conf. Proc. No. 53, American Inst. of Physics, New York.

Sandrock, G. D., Perkins, A. J., and Heheman, R. F. (1971). *Metall. Trans.* **2**, 2769.

Satija, S. K. and Cowley, R. A. (1982). *Phys. Rev.* **B25**, 6765.

Satija, S. K., Shapiro, S. M., Salamon, M. B., and Wayman, C. M. (1983). Rep. BNL-33712, Brookhaven, New York.

Schiff, L. I. (1968). "Quantum Mechanics," 3rd. Ed. McGraw-Hill, New York.

Shapiro, S. M., and Salomon, M. B. (1979). *In* "Fast Ion Transport in Solids" (P., Vashista, J. N., Mundy, and G. K., Shenoy, eds.). North-Holland, New York.

Shapiro, S. M., Noda, Y., Fujii, Y., and Yamada, Y. (1984). Rep. BNL-34749, Brookhaven National Laboratory, New York.

Shirane, G. (1971). *Rev. Mod. Phys.* **46,** 437.
Shirane, G., Shapiro, S., Comes, R., Garito, A. F., and Herger, A. J. (1976). *Phys. Rev.* **B14,** 2325.
Sinha, S. K., (1980). *In* "Dynamic Properties of Solids" (G. K. Horton and A. A. Maradudin, eds.). North-Holland, Amsterdam.
Simonis, G. J., and Hathaway, C. E. (1974). *Phys. Rev.* **B10,** 4419.
Smith, J. H., and Rae, A. I. M. (1978). *J. Phys. C. Solid State Phys.* **11,** 1761.
Squires, G. L. (1978). "Thermal Neutron Scattering." Cambridge Univ. Press, London and New York.
Steigmeier, E. F., and Auderset, E. F. (1973). *Solid State Commun.* **12,** 565.
Terauchi, H., Sakai, T., and Chihara, H. (1975). *J. Chem. Phys.* **62,** 3832.
Wada, M., Shichi, H., Sawada, A., and Ishibashi, Y. (1980). *J. Phys. Soc. Jpn.* **49,** 1892.
Worlton, T. G., and Warren, J. L. (1974). *Comput. Phys. Commun.* **8,** 71.
Zussman, A., and Oron, M. (1977). *J. Chem. Phys.* **66,** 743.

Index